D1030670

Holden-Day Series in Psychology
Robert Bush, Editor

MACH BANDS: *Quantitative studies on neural networks in the retina*

Ernst Mach

FLOYD RATLIFF
The Rockefeller Institute, New York

MACH BANDS: *Quantitative studies on neural networks in the retina*

HOLDEN-DAY, INC. 1965
San Francisco, London, Amsterdam

Frontispiece. *Ernst Mach in his later years. Reproduced from H. Henning,* Ernst Mach als Philosoph, Physiker und Psycholog, *Leipzig, Johann Ambrosius Barth, 1915.*

Printed in the United States of America

Library of Congress Catalog Card Number: 65-10436

Preface

One hundred years ago Ernst Mach published the first of his several quantitative studies on the interdependence of neighboring elements in the retina. However, Mach's application of mathematical modes of thought to the study of the nervous system was so far ahead of the times that his papers attracted little attention when they first appeared.

Within recent years considerable interest has developed in the mathematical analysis of the properties of complex neural networks. The main reason for this seemingly belated development of interest is that only within the last quarter-century or so have the techniques of electrophysiology finally become sufficiently advanced to provide a sound empirical foundation for such studies. The interplay of the fundamental neural processes of excitation and inhibition, about which Mach could only speculate, can now be observed directly and with relative ease in practically all parts of the nervous system.

Of lesser importance, but nevertheless significant, is the recent development of a computer technology which has made the reduction of large amounts of neurophysiological data and the numerical solution of complex mathematical problems much less formidable than in years past. Furthermore, the ease with which mathematical models of neural processes can now be manipulated, both by means of computers and by special electrical analogs, makes these models useful as investigative tools in neurophysiology as well as mere descriptive devices. Once the fundamental properties of a neural network are known, exploratory work on more complex properties can be carried out on simulated networks prior to the technically more difficult physiological experiments on the real nervous system.

Finally, work in other fields has stimulated further interest in the properties of neural networks. The mathematical problems in the development of electro-mechanical sensing and pattern recognition devices, for example, are quite similar to those encountered in the quantitative study of neural networks; advances in each field are frequently relevant to the investigations being carried out in the other.

Nearly fifteen years ago I first became acquainted with Ernst Mach's psychophysical investigations in the field of vision, and saw their relevance to my own electrophysiological research on inhibitory interaction in the retina. Since that time a large number of experimental and theoretical papers by other investigators have appeared on this and closely related subjects. This recent upsurge of interest and activity in the investigation of the quantitative properties of neural networks further intensified my own interest in the subject. What started out to be a translation of a few of Mach's papers and a small collection of miscellaneous notes for my own use gradually evolved into an extensive and systematic study of a topic that cuts across the boundaries of many interrelated disciplines—including some aspects of history of science, theory of knowledge, psychophysics of vision, mathematical theories of inhibitory interaction, and neurophysiological investigations of the function and significance of inhibitory interaction in the retina. (The Introduction gives a brief summary of, and guide to, the material covered.)

It is my hope that the separate treatments of the diverse topics covered in this book will be of interest to students and investigators in each of the several special fields touched upon. But the book is not primarily intended for the specialist in any particular field, even though it includes some details that may be of interest to him only. I hope instead, in this age of increasing specialization and increasing difficulty of communication among different disciplines, that this attempt to integrate many diverse studies will help to break down some of the barriers that have been erected around the various special disciplines and, in some measure, to attain the genuine unity of science which Mach foresaw. To achieve this end, one of the major aims of the book is to examine some of the foundations of the empirical knowledge on which all of science is based.

The following brief account of how the book came into being illustrates the one aspect of the theory of knowledge with which the book is mainly concerned: the basis for, and meaning of, the common distinction that we make between the subjective and the objective.

The whole story begins with a star seen over Budapest, Hungary, in the year 1924. To the casual observer this was an ordinary star, but to an astronomer at the University of Budapest it appeared to be something out of the ordinary. An apparent doubling of lines in photographs of its spectrum indicated that it might be not one star, but two—a so-called *binary* star. Such double lines, previously observed in the single spectra of visibly separate binary stars, were attributed to the Doppler effect. As the two stars rotate about their common center of gravity the light waves emitted from the one approaching the earth appear to be shortened, while the light waves emitted from the one receding from the earth appear to be lengthened. Thus the spectral lines of any elements that the two stars have in common may be slightly displaced with respect to one another in the spectrogram. If the pair of stars is revolving in a plane that passes near the solar system, the Doppler effect may be so pronounced that, twice during each complete revolution of the pair, single spectral lines become clearly separated into two.

Using the Doppler effect as an indicator, astronomers had been able to detect many close binary stars which appeared to be single by ordinary telescopic means of observation. In this particular case, however, the evidence was inconclusive. Everyone who saw the spectrogram could clearly see two thin parallel lines at a certain spot, but physical measurements with a slit photometer showed only a single thick line. The astronomer who made these observations was very much disappointed because he could not prove the existence of the double lines—and thus the existence of a Doppler effect—by physical measurements, and he finally abandoned the work.

However, Georg von Békésy, a student at the University of Budapest who was among those to whom the astronomer had shown the photograph, was very much intrigued by the apparent contradiction between the visual appearance of the spectrum and its physical measurements, and he could not put the whole affair out of his mind. Von Békésy had long been interested in art and in the various optical and psychological techniques used by artists, and his familiarity with these techniques led him to believe that the effect observed in the spectrogram might be one of the optical illusions already known to artists and to sensory psychologists. But an examination of a large number of optical illusions described in the literature revealed none to explain the effect in question.

At that time von Békésy was using a Jamin interference refractometer in his research for his doctoral thesis. This instrument had been improved by Ludwig Mach, and the improvements had been described in the Proceedings of the Royal Academy, Vienna. While looking up this work von Békésy discovered quite by accident that in 1865 Ernst Mach (Ludwig Mach's father) had described in these same Proceedings "subjective" visual phenomena, which seemed to explain fully the apparent doubling of the single broad lines in the spectrogram. (These phenomena are now known as "Mach bands" and are the main subject of this book.) By that time, however, several years had gone by, the astronomer had moved to another laboratory, and the whole problem was forgotten for the time being.

In the years of inflation after World War I von Békésy was unable to continue his research in optics because of the high cost of the necessary instruments. He turned to the field of communications and through this work became interested in the function of the ear. Von Békésy's physical measurements of the mechanical properties of the basilar membrane (work for which he later won the Nobel prize) convinced him that some sort of neural "sharpening" mechanism must be required, in addition to the physical sound analyzing mechanisms of the ear, to account adequately for the remarkable sharpness of frequency discrimination by the auditory system. Remembering the incident described above, it occurred to him that some form of neural interaction similar to that which supposedly caused the Mach bands in vision might be the neural basis for a sharpening mechanism in the ear. He therefore advanced this hypothesis in a paper on the theory of hearing which he published in 1928.

In this paper he illustrated, by means of a visual analogy, how the sharpening mechanism might work; the mechanical displacement of the basilar membrane was represented by variations in photographic density —the lighter the region on the photograph, the greater the displacement represented. Using this visual analog of the auditory process he showed how a broad stimulus distribution along the basilar membrane, with a single flat maximum such as that produced by the combination of two resonance curves, could produce a sensation distribution with two fairly distinct and rather sharp maxima.

The bands in the photograph that von Békésy published were quite distinct. They were so distinct, in fact, that several of his colleagues reproached him for using the figure in his article, insinuating that the photograph might have been retouched in order to show the bands. Also, a few days after the article appeared, von Békésy received a letter from E. von Hornbostel who was an expert in the field of hearing and who regularly reviewed papers on sensory physiology for the *Berichte der allgemeinen Physiologie*. In this letter he stated that when he saw the published photograph he was immediately convinced that it had been retouched. Von Békésy was greatly disturbed by all this criticism and now began to doubt the validity of the phenomenon himself. Although he knew that *he* had not retouched the photograph, there was the possibility that the publisher had done so in order to make its appearance conform to that indicated in the accompanying graphs in the article.

After a sleepless night he gathered together all the leftover photographs and negatives to send to von Hornbostel in order to prove that the phenomenon was not an artifact—either intentional or unintentional. But it turned out not to be necessary. Von Békésy had neglected to read von Hornbostel's letter carefully in its entirety because of his great concern about the possibility that someone—unknown to him—might have actually retouched the photographs. On rereading the letter, he discovered that von Hornbostel himself had furnished the necessary proof. He had carefully scanned the published photograph under the microscope and found that the diameters of the black dots produced by the halftone process (the size of which determined the darkness of a given region) were uniform throughout the critical area. Evidently, as Mach had already concluded in 1865, the bands were produced by some process of interaction in the nervous system of the observer rather than by a physical process that occurred at some stage of the reproduction and publication of the photograph.

Following World War II, von Békésy was unable to continue his research under the conditions then prevailing, so he left Hungary, going first to The Royal Institute of Technology in Stockholm and later to Harvard University. It was there, in 1951, that our paths crossed and that my part in this story began. For some time previously I had been interested in the visual mechanisms that underlie the detection and enhancement of lines and contours. My initial work in this field, which was carried out under the direction of Lorrin A. Riggs at Brown University, had been to consider the possible role of minute involuntary eye movements in these mechanisms. Subsequently, I had worked under the direction of H. K. Hartline at the Johns Hopkins University on electrophysiological studies of inhibitory interaction in the retina of the marine arthropod, *Limulus.*

In our discussions of this and other work of mutual interest, von Békésy pointed out the formal similarity between the quantitative account of the inhibitory interaction in the eye of *Limulus* given by H. K. Hartline, Henry G. Wagner and myself, and Ernst Mach's quantitative theory of inhibitory interaction in the human retina. At the same time von Békésy introduced me to the other work of Mach—in particular, Mach's views on the theory of knowledge that were presented in his *Mechanics* and *The Analysis of Sensations.* My latent interest in the theory of knowledge, which had led me to the study of vision in the first place, was aroused once again, and I began a serious study of Mach and his work, mainly for my own entertainment and edification. But the study soon outgrew my original plans and gradually developed into this book.

In any attempt to integrate many diverse approaches to a particular problem, as in this book, one must cross the artificial boundaries that we have marked out around the various areas of knowledge and disciplines of science. The course of action is determined by the problem to be investigated rather than the particular discipline to which one belongs; where the problem leads one must follow. In following such a course one inevitably, and in most cases quickly, reaches the limits of his own knowledge and experience and must turn to others for help. I therefore wish to take this opportunity to express my gratitude to the many individuals who have been of assistance to me in the preparation of this book—in particular to my colleagues Alan R. Adolph, Frederick A. Dodge, Jr., Bruce Knight, Jr., G. David Lange, William H. Miller, Conrad G. Mueller, Jr., Richard L. Purple Robert L. Schoenfeld, and Charles F. Stevens—all of whom helped me with various and sundry problems which I could not solve alone and which are too numerous to mention here. It is inevitable, however, that there will be some errors of interpretation and errors of omission in this book. The responsibility for these, of course, is my own.

I am very grateful to many individuals and organizations for permission to reproduce figures and to quote passages from published material. (A specific acknowledgment appears in the text along with each figure reproduced and with each passage quoted.) I wish also to express my thanks to the American public at large for the continued and generous (if unknowing) support it has given to my experimental research and study in this area by means of grants and other aid from public funds administered by the Office of Naval Research and the National Institute of Neurological Diseases and Blindness.

Acknowledgments are due to Miss Jun Uramatsu who translated some articles from the French for me, and to Miss Christine Rosner and Mrs. Maria Lipski who translated some articles from the German. I should also like to express my gratitude to Mrs. Lipski for the typing of the manuscript. Finally, I am most grateful for the apparently unlimited patience and understanding exhibited by the editors and publishers and by my wife Orma and my daughter Merry during the several years that I worked on the translations of Mach's papers and the writing of this book.

Floyd Ratliff

The Rockefeller Institute
New York
January 1965

Table of Contents

Contents

To Georg von Békésy

and H. Keffer Hartline

tions were in themselves a vindication of his belief in the essential unity of science—indeed, of all human knowledge. This belief rested on the premise that all knowledge is based on experience and that no fact or truth may be established independently of experience. How Mach came to adopt this point of view, how it shaped his theory of knowledge, and how this theory interprets several fundamental problems, including the problem of objectivity—these are the main points discussed in Chapter 1 of this book.

Quite early in Mach's scientific career, more or less by accident, he discovered the visual phenomenon which now bears his name. During one of his excursions into sensory psychophysiology, while experimenting with rotating discs used to produce various spatial distributions of light and shade, Mach found bright and dark bands appearing where, according to physical calculations, none were expected. Formerly, such phenomena had generally been attributed to "unconscious inferences" or "errors of judgment" on the part of the observer or had been dismissed as "mere optical illusions" unworthy of study. But for Mach, these were not explanations; they were merely various ways of expressing the still unexplained facts. Through psychophysical experiments, Mach sought to find an explanation in the mutual dependence of neighboring retinal points on one another, a dependence which he believed could be accounted for in terms of the function of the neural network which was known to exist in the retina. Mach's original psychophysical investigations of the Mach bands and related phenomena as well as the more recent psychophysical studies which have grown out of his early work are surveyed in Chapter 2.

Mach's analysis of the probable physiological bases of the Mach bands and related contrast phenomena, which he began one hundred years ago, was probably the first attempt to express the integrative action of the nervous system in precise mathematical terms. The basic neural process postulated in Mach's mathematical formulation was a reciprocal inhibitory interaction among neighboring elements of the retina. The integration of opposed excitatory and inhibitory influences is the basic process utilized in practically all of the quantitative models of neural networks that have since been proposed to explain the Mach bands and similar contrast effects. Chapter 3 is devoted to a survey and comparison of six of these models, including the one proposed by Mach.

Mach's formulation, which was based almost entirely on psychophysical evidence, anticipated the much later discovery, by modern electrophysiological techniques, of inhibitory interaction in the retina and in other parts of the nervous system. The nature of inhibitory interaction in the retina and its functional significance, as revealed by research within the past quarter of a century, are discussed in Chapter 4. First, there is a consideration of the rather obvious possibility, first pointed out by Mach, that inhibition among neighboring elements of the retina may serve to enhance the appearance of borders and contours and, in so doing, to compensate for blurring of the retinal image by imperfections in the lens and other dioptric apparatus of the eye. Following this, there is an examination of the more subtle, and possibly more important, roles that inhibition may play in vision, such as the generation of highly specialized patterns of optic nerve activity in response to particular spatial, spectral, and temporal patterns of illumination on the retina.

Chapters 3 and 4 both focus on one of the most fundamental, and yet most neglected, problems facing modern biological science: how unitary structures and elementary processes are organized into the complex functional systems that make up organs and organisms. This elaborate organization is one of the things—perhaps the only one—which distinguishes living things from the non-living. And yet this problem is not presently of first importance in biological research; instead, biology seems to be becoming more and more analytic, more and more confined to the study of the structure and behavior of single cells and of the molecular and submolecular events within them. Indeed, in recent years, the application of methods and concepts developed in the physical and chemical sciences to the study of living organisms has been so thoroughgoing that it is sometimes difficult to tell where the physical sciences end and the biological sciences begin.

But there are no grounds for asserting, a priori, that there must be a conflict between the analytic and the organic or holistic approaches to biology. Indeed, the assertion that the whole is "something more" than the sum of its constituent parts is more dogma than established fact. And it is more fitting, perhaps, to view such an assertion as nothing more than a statement of a problem. The fact that the properties of the whole may not always be implicit in the known properties of the parts may be only an indication of our state of knowledge (or ignorance) of the properties of the parts and the laws that govern their integration. It is a major aim of this book to show that in the special case of the retina, where a considerable amount of the essential evidence is available, the properties of the network of interconnected receptors and retinal neurons, acting as a whole, do appear to be derived ultimately from the properties of the individual components which interact with one another in accordance with definite laws.

The changes in perceived brightness, color, or contour that may be produced by the interdependence of neighboring retinal elements are not easy to distinguish from effects which may depend somewhat more directly on the intensity, spectral composition, and spatial and temporal distribution of the light falling on the retina. For example, Mach bands are ever present but are rarely noted. They are likely to be discovered, as by Mach, only when they come as a surprise. When some "objective" phenomenon resembling them is expected, then these "subjective" phenomena are not always immediately recognized for what they really are, and properties of the observer's senses may be mistaken for properties of the object observed. Among those diverse errors which have arisen from such confusion of observer and object, three are discussed in Chapter 5: one that occurred in the measurement of the wavelength of X-rays, another which arose in the determination of the size of the earth's shadow on the moon, and a third which came up during the selection of dyestuffs at the Gobelin tapestry works. Some similar errors that may arise in the use of instrumental aids to observation are also treated. Using these several specific practical problems as a point of departure, Part One of the book concludes with a general discussion of the meaning of objectivity.

Mach's papers on the interdependence of retinal points were published mainly in the Proceedings of the Royal Academy, Vienna. They are now difficult to obtain, and, although often cited, they are seldom seen. The collected papers, translated into English, are presented as Part Two of this book. They are of value to students of the history of science and of epistemology, as well as to students of psychophysiology, for in them one can see the origin and early development of some of Mach's major views on the theory of knowledge.

PART ONE

On neural networks in the retina and the problem of objectivity

I see Mach's true greatness in his incorruptible skepticism and independence. Albert Einstein

CHAPTER ONE *Ernst Mach (1838-1916)*

This account of Mach's life emphasizes the origin, development, and eventual influence of his view of science and epistemology. His alternate occupation with physics and the psychophysiology of the senses and his study of the historical development of the physical sciences gave him an unusual breadth of firsthand experience on which to base his theory of knowledge. Thus firmly grounded, his positivistic views had a profound and lasting influence upon the course of modern science and philosophy. Perhaps best known is his criticism of Newtonian mechanics, for it, and his suggestion of a new relativistic mechanics, provided the basis of Einstein's theory of gravitation and general relativity. Other contributions, though less well known, were equally important in their respective fields. Of particular interest here are his theoretical and experimental contributions to the analysis of visual sensations, and his views on the relation between the physical and the psychical.

It would be difficult today to determine with any certainty what events guided Mach's life and thought had he himself not been interested in this very problem. His autobiographical notes reflect this interest and provide us with a firsthand account of the events that he thought were most significant. The sketch of Mach's life presented here draws mainly upon these notes* and upon his original accounts of his scientific and philosophical work.

For the most part, this brief sketch indicates only the general lines followed in the one hundred or so experimental researches reported by Mach and his associates. A few details of one psychophysical experiment (on the sensation of movement) and one physical investigation (on supersonic projectiles) are given, however, to illustrate his method of work and his experimental talent. Also discussed are some of the major ideas in his theory of knowledge—which had a more far-reaching and continuing influence than his experimental work. In order to present Mach's own views, rather than an interpretation of them, the leading thoughts in his theory of knowledge are outlined by a number of direct quotations from his own writings.

A SKETCH OF MACH'S LIFE AND WORK

Ernst Mach was born February 18, 1838, in Turas, Moravia, not far from Vienna. His father, Johann Mach, at that time a tutor for the family of Baron Breton, had studied philosophy at Prague and was also much interested in animal psychology and agriculture. Mach's mother, Josephine Mach née Lanhaus, was artistic, having a gift for music, drawing, and poetry. Both parents were rather idealistic and solitary people. Because of the father's interest in agriculture the family always lived in the country, generally in the neighborhood of Vienna.

Ernst Mach was the only son. He had two sisters, both younger than he. The youngest sister wrote *Recollections of a Governess,* which gives many details of the Mach family's life. According to her account, although the father's teaching and farming were never quite sufficient to keep the family free from want, they lived contentedly.

Mach described himself as a "weak pitiful child who developed very

* The following accounts contain sketches of Mach's life—all mainly autobiographical (for complete references see Bibliography): "Professor Mach and His Work," Paul Carus (1911); *Ernst Mach als Philosoph, Physiker und Psycholog,* Hans Henning (1915); "Die Leitgedanken meiner naturwissenschaftlichen Erkenntnislehre und ihre Aufnahme durch die Zeitgenossen" (Mach, 1910a); *Die Grundgedanken der Machschen Philosophie,* Hugo Dingler (1924); and "Über eine unveröffentliche Selbstbiographie Ernst Machs," Friedrich Herneck (1956). (Henning's book contains a nearly complete list of Mach's publications—approximately 150, in all.)

Throughout the remainder of this book references are generally cited in the text by name of author and date of publication alone. This provides the key to the Bibliography where the citation is given in full.

slowly." Yet, if his later recollections are correct, his mental development must have been very rapid. For example, in his fifth year Mach had an experience in a flour mill which seemed to presage his later critical, empirical, anti-metaphysical views. About this he wrote as follows:

> We had to bring a message to the miller. Upon our arrival the mill had just begun to work. The terrible noise frightened me, but did not hinder me from watching the teeth of the shaft which meshed with the gear of the grinding mechanism and moved on one tooth after another. This sight remained until I reached a more mature level, and, in my opinion, raised my child-like thinking from the level of the wonder-believing savage to causal thinking: from now on, in order to understand the unintelligible, I no longer imagined magic things in the background, but traced in a broken toy the cord or lever which had caused the effect (Herneck, 1956, p. 210).

While Mach and his sisters were young, they were taught by their father. Mach received much intellectual stimulation from his father who, although he had had no thorough scientific education, was a keen observer of nature and had a clear understanding of many of the fundamental principles of science. He introduced his son to experimental physics, for example, by using a simple apparatus—a flower pot and a tumbler in a rainbarrel full of water—to demonstrate the principles of atmospheric pressure. Furthermore, he told him about the lives and studies of Archimedes and other scholars and scientists of antiquity—all in Latin and Greek. But at that time Mach was little attracted by the study of history and ancient languages. Machines and parts of machines occupied his mind.

At the age of ten Mach entered the lowest class of a Gymnasium directed by Benedictine monks at Seitenstetten in lower Austria. But his intellect and temperament were not well suited to the education they offered. He had not the slightest taste for pious proverbs, such as "The beginning of wisdom lies in the fear of the Lord," and the clerical teachers found the boy to be "very much without talent." They advised his father to let him learn a trade or business, because in their view he was "unfit for study." In retrospect, Mach felt that this was a just decision; like many original thinkers, he found no interest in the meaningless parroting of facts and maxims. He preferred to try to discover for himself the origins and causes of things and events.

Disappointed with his son's failure, Mach's father resumed teaching him Latin, Greek, history, and the elements of algebra and geometry at home. His interest in mathematics and natural sciences allowed him to be left to himself with these subjects. But he still had little enthusiasm for the ancient languages until at last he achieved some fluency in understanding and translating the texts. Then the works of the classical authors began to be more interesting to him. Later, the ability to read these languages proved very useful to him in his studies of the origin and development of scientific concepts.

After the suppression of the revolution in 1848, Austria entered a reactionary clerical period. Having grown up in a liberal family, Mach asked permission to learn a trade so that he might be able to emigrate to America. His father agreed, and for two years Mach was apprenticed to a cabinet maker in a neighboring village. This was a pleasant time for Mach, who always enjoyed making things with his own hands. These experiences as a manual laborer also led him to value greatly the help of the skilled worker in his later scientific researches. Most important, probably, was the influence of these practical experiences on his later views of science, and particularly on his views of the origin and development of scientific concepts. In his *Kultur und Mechanik,* he attempted to show how, early in the development of our culture, the systematic study of mechanical principles arose directly from practical experience, especially that involving manual labor.

When he was 15, Mach entered the sixth grade of the Gymnasium at Kremsier in Moravia, which was under the direction of Piarist monks. At first he made a poor impression. Mach's appraisal of the situation was that he lacked the "smartness and cunning" necessary for success in such a school. He again did very poorly in history where rote memorization was so important, but he did learn much from the subject. Long readings from source material taught him, for example, that the secular and clerical leaders of mankind were by no means thinking only of the welfare of their subjects "that was supposedly entrusted to them by God." Mach's skeptical view of organized religion was not tempered by the religious atmosphere at the Gymnasium. For him, at least, the seemingly endless religious rituals and exercises defeated their own purpose.

While at the Gymnasium, he was inspired to some extent by a teacher of natural history and another of physics, and his work gradually improved. But his greatest inspiration came from a book which he found in his father's library. It was Kant's *Prolegomena to Any Future Metaphysics.* Mach was only 15 at the time, and the book had a profound influence on him; it destroyed the naïve realism of his youth and, in so doing, stimulated his interest in the theory of knowledge. He soon turned away from Kant's critical idealism, however. While still a boy, he recognized Kant's "thing in itself" as an unnecessary metaphysical invention. Concerning this episode he later wrote:

> The book made at the time a powerful and ineffaceable impression upon me, the like of which I never afterwards experienced in any of my philosophical reading. Some two or three years later the superfluity of the role played by "the thing in itself" abruptly dawned upon me. On a bright summer day in the open air, the world with my ego suddenly appeared to me as *one* coherent mass of sensations, only more strongly coherent in the ego. Although the actual working out of this thought did not occur until a later period, yet this moment was decisive for my whole view (Mach, 1914, p. 30).

By the time Mach entered the University of Vienna at the age of 17 to study mathematics and physics, the anti-metaphysical direction his thoughts were to take in his lifelong study of physics, psychophysiology, and epistemology had probably already been determined.

At the university, mathematics and natural sciences were rather poorly represented on the faculty, while in such fields as philology and history the teachers were excellent. The beginning students were somewhat neglected. In his first years Mach had to gain by private study the vital knowledge of differential and integral calculus in order to understand the advanced lectures on mathematical physics, where this knowledge was presupposed. Among his many teachers at the university Mach speaks well of the mathematician and physicist von Ettingshausen, who was also director of the Physical Institute at the university. He also mentions that Petzval, well-known for his work in photographic optics, was a highly talented teacher of mathematics—although somewhat indolent and almost unapproachable.

Mach's first experimental work at the Physical Institute was in the field of acoustics. He constructed his own apparatus and succeeded in proving the existence of the Doppler effect, which had not previously been demonstrated under laboratory conditions. In fact, its existence was still denied by some mathematicians and physicists, and Doppler and Petzval had engaged in a spirited controversy on the subject at one time.

In January, 1860, at the age of 22, Mach took the degree of Doctor of Philosophy. The examinations were conducted in the medieval manner. The candidate had to pass three separate examinations, each lasting two hours, chosen from a wide variety of fields. In these examinations everything except the candidate's special studies was discussed. Mach remarked later that this procedure encouraged a diversified smattering of knowledge which, at the same time, was compatible with great ignorance.

Mach planned to go to Königsberg to continue his studies under F. Neumann, but was unable to do so because of his financial situation. He found it necessary to qualify as a private docent in physics so that he could earn a living by giving private lectures. He lectured on mathematics, Fechner's psychophysics, and Helmholtz's theory of hearing. At first he regretted the time spent on these lectures; he would have preferred to use it in furthering his own studies. Nevertheless, the time was not lost; he gained a select circle of listeners, some of whom were later famous, and he broadened his own interests. In addition, by his communication with the two well-known physiologists at Vienna, E. Brücke and C. Ludwig, Mach gained an insight into the scientific life of Germany and became better acquainted with the current work on the physiology of the senses.

Mach's first experience as a teacher led him to believe that a critical and historical presentation of fundamental concepts was the most instructive method to use, and once he had adopted this approach he followed it throughout his life. (Practically all his major writings were of a critical-historical nature.) Also early in his career, he formulated his well-known principle of economy of thought in science. In it he stated that the contest of scientific ideas could be interpreted as a vital struggle, as a survival of the fittest, and that any such furtherance of knowledge could be regarded as a special case of a biologically advantageous process. For the behavior and survival of man, and possibly of other higher animals, seemed to him to depend as much upon thought and upon the evolution of knowledge as upon the evolution of physical characteristics.

Concerning his view of the economical nature of science, Mach said:

> When in the beginning of my educational work as a private docent of physics in 1861 I began to pay attention to the labors of investigators to whom I had occasion to refer, I recognized that the salient characteristic of their procedure lay in the choice of the simplest, most economical, most direct means to attain the end desired. Through my intercourse in 1864 with the political economist E. Hermann, who, according to his specialty, sought to trace out the economical element in every kind of occupation, I became accustomed to designate the intellectual activity of the investigator as economical. This becomes apparent in the simplest instances. Every abstract comprehensive expression of the behavior of facts, every substitution of a numerical table by a formula or rule of construction, the law by which it was compiled, every explanation of a new fact by one that is better known, may be regarded as rendering an economical service. The farther we analyze in detail scientific method —its systematic, organizing, simplifying and logico-mathematical arrangements—the more we recognize scientific procedure as economical (Carus, 1911, pp. 30-31).

Mach's theory of knowledge developed rapidly during this period of his life. No longer able to accept Kant's ideas, he turned to Berkeley's idealism, latent in Kant. But Berkeley's point of view, Mach found, was not entirely compatible with his physical studies. Mach's acquaintance with Herbart's mathematical psychology and Fechner's psychophysics increased his dissatisfaction with the theories of knowledge with which he was then familiar and his studies on the psychophysiology of the senses finally led to his own critical empiricism, which he believed to be entirely free of metaphysics. His ultimate standpoint was close to that of Hume, but unfamiliar with Hume's work at that time, he was not directly influenced by him. Hume's influence, Mach says, probably came to him indirectly through Hume's younger contemporary, Lichtenberg. In anv event, Mach's theory of knowledge was almost completely formulated while he was still a young man; all later developments in it were largely elaborations of his early anti-metaphysical point of view which had arisen as a reaction to Kant's ideas. (Even though he did not follow Kant, Mach says that the *Prolegomena* nevertheless provided the stimulus that led him to his critical-historical treatment of mechanics.)

Mach's early research was supported by a grant from the Vienna Academy. He accepted the grant with some hesitation, not knowing whether he would be able to make a discovery significant enough to merit the award. But a chance observation during a train trip called his attention to the problems of the labyrinth of the internal ear. He noticed that trees, houses, chimneys, and other fixed objects seemed to swerve from the vertical when he rounded a sharp curve. His knowledge of mechanics gave him a clue to the physical forces that were at work in sensations of angular acceleration and rotation. Several years of extensive study subsequently bore out his initial insight into this problem.

To test his ideas he constructed an enclosed chair that could be rotated (Fig. 1.1), not unlike the modern devices for training astronauts. In this chair all visual signs of movement could be eliminated by a light weight paper box (not shown) that enclosed the subject and moved with him and the chair. With visual cues thus removed, impressions of motion depend largely upon changes in acceleration. The observer might feel that he is at rest during uniform rotation; or, when uniform rotation is suddenly stopped, he might feel that he is rapidly rotating in the opposite direction.

These and other experiments led Mach to conclude that excitation of the nerves leading from the labyrinth of the internal ear was produced by the inertia of the fluid contents of the semicircular canals. Motion of fluid with respect to the canal containing it, or vice versa, produces a sensation of motion; in the absence of other cues, the observer may not know whether the sensation of motion is produced by the acceleration of his own body or its deceleration and stopping.* For some reason, it is

* Independently, Breuer in Vienna and Brown in Edinburgh later reached similar conclusions. See Mach's *Bewegungsempfindungen,* 1875.

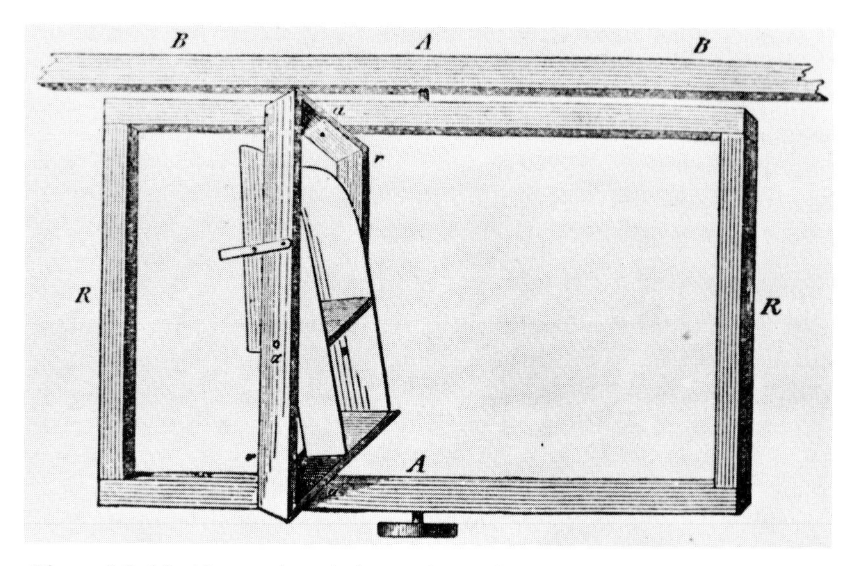

Figure 1.1. *Mach's rotating chair for the study of sensations of movement and orientation. From Mach (1875).*

not now generally known that Mach first made this important discovery.

In 1864, at the age of 26, Mach was appointed to the chair of mathematics at the University of Graz. There he lectured on differential and integral calculus and on analytical geometry. He also continued his private study in order to add to what he called "the still threadbare mathematical knowledge" which he had gained at the University of Vienna. At this time he began to publish some of his research on vision and the retina. These early investigations (see Part Two) and the later work they stimulated are the main subject of this book. He also continued his research on the ear, studying especially hearing and the physics of sound waves.

Three years later, in 1867, Mach became professor of experimental physics at the German University of Prague. This subject suited him better and gave him the opportunity to invest in much-needed equipment and to experiment more intensively. He continued his research on vision and hearing and resumed study on various physical aspects of wave motion. At this time also, Mach's important note "On the Definition of Mass" was finally published in Carl's *Repertorium,* after having been held for about a year and then rejected by Poggendorf, who was then the editor of the *Annalen der Physik und der Chemie.*

At Prague Mach married Luise Marussig, an orphan whom he had met earlier in Graz. From 1868 to 1881 four sons and one daughter were born to them. (In later years Mach's son Ludwig collaborated with him in his experimental research.) In his writings, Mach frequently mentions that the early speech of his children and their naïve questions about such things as, "Where does the light go when it is put out?" stimulated him to think about many fundamental problems that he otherwise might not have considered. He once remarked, "Such childlike questions in the mouths of mature men shape the character of a century." He believed that any student of the theory of knowledge would gain much by observing children whose mental activity had not yet been shaped or prematurely developed into a socially acceptable adult form by special training at home or in school.

Mach's mother died in 1868 and his father in 1880. One of his sons took his own life soon after obtaining his doctor's degree with excellence at Göttingen. The cause of this tragic event is not known.

During a break in Mach's experimental work, caused by an illness he had contracted in the summer of 1870, he resumed his historical studies. In 1872 he published the first of his several major works in this area, *History and Root of the Principle of the Conservation of Energy*.* In this study he first expressed in some detail his thoughts on a scientific theory of knowledge with reference to mechanics and the science of heat. His view of the economy of science is also presented here, but in a condensed form. In fact, the essence of his whole theory of knowledge is in this short work, and Mach refers to this period in his life as the time of his greatest intellectual activity. About this time the emphasis in Mach's experimental work shifted to physical optics and various aspects of electricity, but he did not abandon entirely his research on the psychophysiology of the senses.

In 1880 attendance at the German University in Prague fell off because of the establishment of the Bohemian University there. Mach's income was diminished and he found it necessary to do special technical work to make up the loss. In a few weeks he earned almost as much as a year's salary at the university. He realized that this way of earning a living could not be combined with scientific work, but the extra money did benefit his scientific career. It enabled him to attend a congress of electricians in Paris in 1881 which gave him new inspiration for his work and broadened his circle of acquaintances. The additional employment he obtained through them eased his financial problems in the following years.

By this time, Mach had gained considerable renown, and his ability was recognized by various important figures. For example the American

* The term "energy" was not fully accepted at that time and the title of the German edition uses the word *Arbeit* (work).

philosopher and psychologist William James, who visited Mach in Prague in 1882, remarked of him in a letter:

> I don't think anyone ever gave me so strong an impression of pure intellectual genius. He apparently has read everything and thought about everything, and has an absolute simplicity of manner . . . (Frank, 1949, p. 79).

Mach now had sufficient leisure time to work more intensively on his critical studies in the theory of knowledge. He published the *Science of Mechanics* in 1883 and the *Analysis of Sensations* two years later. His interest in these studies was so great that he turned down a financially advantageous offer from Munich and remained at Prague so that the work would not be interrupted. In retrospect, one can see that this was a wise decision, for these two studies turned out to be the most significant and most influential of all his major works. Mach's experimental work never slackened; he continued to devote much of his own time to it, even though he was assisted by an increasing number of students and young colleagues. Indeed, it was in this busy period that he initiated one of his better known physical investigations—his studies on flying projectiles.

During his visit to Paris, in 1881, Mach chanced to hear a lecture by the Belgian artillerist, Melsens. In this lecture Melsens suggested that projectiles traveling at high velocities might carry ahead of them masses of compressed air, which, if so, might account for the explosive effects produced on impact. To test this theory and others which had been advanced previously, Mach and his colleagues took so-called *schlieren* photographs of projectiles in flight. This method utilizes the optical effects produced by turbulence of the air. ("Heat waves" arising from hot pavement are a familiar example of such effects.) To avoid blur, however, the schlieren photograph must be taken with an extremely short exposure. With the equipment then available, it was no mean accomplishment to take photographs of high velocity projectiles fired from rifles and cannons.

In an early version of Mach's apparatus the flying projectile cut two wires in its path and thus directly shorted an electrical circuit, causing a Leyden jar to discharge across a spark gap to provide the illumination. (The photograph shown in Fig. 1.2a was obtained by this method.) This apparatus had the disadvantage that the wires in the path of the projectile interfered with the phenomena under observation. To circumvent this problem Mach designed an improved version of the apparatus (Fig. 1.2b) in which the projectile, passing through a ring, forced air through a small tube; the escaping air caused a candle flame at the end of the tube to waver. The flame in turn shorted a circuit, causing a Leyden jar to

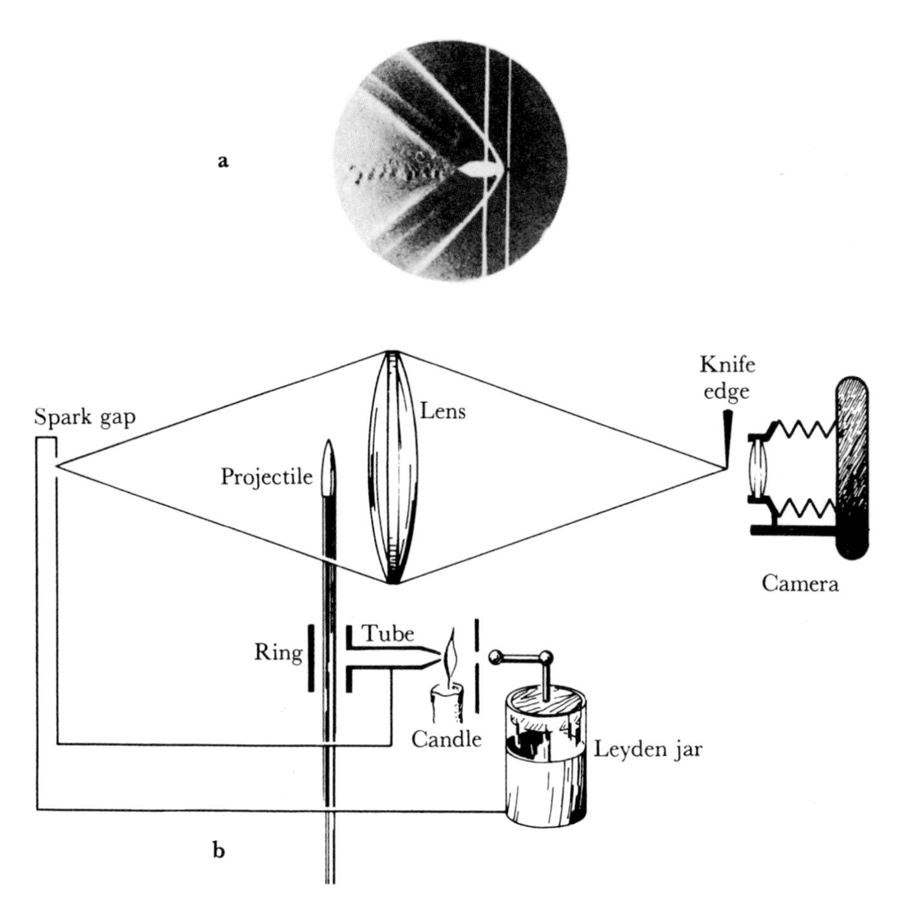

Figure 1.2. (a) *Schlieren photograph of a flying projectile traveling at 520 meters per second. Circuit providing spark illumination is closed when projectile cuts the two vertical wires. From Mach and Mach (1889).* (b) *Schema of apparatus for photographing flying projectiles with no wires in the path of the projectile. Redrawn after Mach (1910b).*

discharge and produce a brief spark for illumination of the projectile. By an adjustment in the length of the tube, the discharge could be set off at the moment the projectile reached the center of the field covered by the camera.

Mach found that a projectile moving more slowly than the velocity of sound produces no unusual effects. When the projectile reaches and exceeds the velocity of sound, however, a head wave, or "shock wave," is set up which is heard as a sharp report. This shock wave is distinct from the sound wave produced by the firing of the gun itself and travels ahead of and along with the projectile. The photographs show clearly that this is a true wave, superficially similar to the bow wave produced by a boat, not compressed air being carried bodily with the projectile, as Melsens had surmised. These waves are now familiar to everyone as the sonic booms occasionally produced by high-speed jet aircraft.

Because the work was done so long before the advent of modern jet propulsion and supersonic planes and rockets, some of its important practical and theoretical aspects were overlooked and nearly forgotten until attention was again drawn to them by von Neuman (Courant and Friedrichs, 1948). However, the work is now well known to scientists and engineers in the field, and Mach numbers, Mach reflections, Mach cones, Mach shock lines, and Mach shock discs are common terms in modern works on supersonic phenomena.

Mach was not very sympathetic to the possible military uses of his research, as is shown by his opening remarks in a popular lecture on the subject of the flight of projectiles:

> To shoot, in the shortest time possible, as many holes as possible in one another's bodies, and not always for exactly pardonable objects and ideals, seems to have risen to the dignity of a duty with modern men, who, by a singular inconsistency, and in subservience to a diametrically contrary ideal, are bound by the equally holy obligation of making these holes as small as possible, and, when made, of stopping them up and of healing them as speedily as possible. Since, then, shooting and all that appertains thereto, is a very important, if not the most important, affair of modern life, you will doubtless not be averse to giving your attention for an hour to some experiments which have been undertaken, not for the advancing of the ends of war, but for promoting the ends of science, and which throw some light on the phenomena attending the flight of projectiles (Mach, 1910b, pp. 309-310).

He did, however, have some hope for the future which he expressed in his closing remarks:

> Very, very gradually, however, as civilization progresses, the intercourse of men takes on gentler forms, and no one who really knows the good old times will ever honestly wish them back again, however beautifully they may be painted and rhymed about.
>
> In the intercourse of the nations, however, the old club law still reigns supreme. But since its rule is taxing the intellectual, the moral, and the material resources of the nations to the utmost and constitutes scarcely less a burden in peace than in war, scarcely less a yoke for the victor than for the vanquished, it must necessarily grow more and more unendurable. Reason, fortunately, is no longer the

exclusive possession of those who modestly call themselves the upper ten thousand. Here, as everywhere, the evil itself will awaken the intellectual and ethical forces which are destined to mitigate it. Let the hate of races and of nationalities run riot as it may, the intercourse of nations will still increase and grow more intimate. By the side of the problems which separate nations, the great and common ideals which claim the exclusive powers of the men of the future appear one after another in greater distinctness and in greater might (Mach, 1910b, pp. 336-337).

Toward the end of the 19th century Mach was well known throughout the scientific world. The greatest impact that he made on science, however, resulted not from his experimental studies, but from his critical analyses of the foundations of science and his theory of knowledge. His own University of Vienna recognized the importance of these contributions when, in 1895, it appointed Mach to a chair, instituted for him, in "Philosophy, especially the History and Theory of the Inductive Sciences." In the following year he published *Principles of Heat,* a critical-historical account of the development of the science of heat, somewhat along the lines of his earlier *Mechanics.* He ended his active academic career in 1901 when he became professor emeritus. In that same year Mach became a member of the Austrian House of Lords. (Once, during a serious illness, Mach went to the House in an ambulance in order to be present to cast a much needed vote in favor of a law limiting the working day to nine hours.) For some time, he had been a member of the Academy of Sciences in Vienna to which he had submitted a number of his works. Following his retirement from active work at the university, Mach changed his residence to Haar, near Munich, where his son Ludwig lived, and spent the rest of his life there.

In 1898 Mach had suffered a paralytic stroke which affected his right side. Fortunately he remained mentally alert and even made use of his disability in various studies on the sensory and motor deficiencies resulting from his paralysis. His capacity for work was much diminished, however, and for a few years he published little except new editions of earlier writings. Later his health improved and in 1905 he was able to publish, under the title *Erkenntnis und Irrtum,* some of the lectures held at Vienna in 1895.

In 1910 he published "Die Leitgedanken meiner naturwissenschaftlichen Erkenntnislehre und ihre Aufnahme durch die Zeitgenossen," an article devoted mainly to a reply to Planck's criticism of Mach's views on atomic theory. His *Kultur und Mechanik,* mentioned earlier, was published in 1915.

Because of old age and illness, Mach's last major work, *The Principles of Physical Optics,* was only partly completed. The printing of the first part was commenced in 1916, even though he was not fully satisfied with it and wanted to experiment further to round out the work. This part was finally published in 1921 (English translation in 1926). The second part, which he was writing in collaboration with his son and colleague Ludwig, was to treat modern physical optics and relativity theory. A detailed account of Mach's views on relativity would have been most interesting, since Einstein and others regarded his work as one of the foundations of relativity theory while Mach himself discredited the theory and disclaimed to be a forerunner of it. In the preface to the first part of the projected two part study Mach wrote: "The reason why, and the extent to which, I discredit the present-day relativity theory, which I find to be growing more and more dogmatical, together with the particular reasons which have led me to such a view—the considerations based on the physiology of the senses, the theoretical ideas, and above all the conceptions resulting from my experiments—must remain to be treated in the sequel."

Unfortunately, the intended sequel was never written. Ernst Mach died on February 19, 1916, the day following his 78th birthday.

SOME LEADING THOUGHTS IN MACH'S THEORY OF KNOWLEDGE *

Mach's "positivistic" conception of science had many immediate followers, and many opponents, in the philosophy of science, and it later exerted a strong influence on the Russian "critical-empiricists," on the so-called "Vienna Circle," on the "Unity of Science" movement, and on the gradual spread of modern "logical positivism" which followed. (See Frank, 1949 and 1951, and von Mises, 1956, for historical details). Mach did not claim the title of "philosopher" and his aim was not to found a new philosophy. He sought only to adopt a view of science that he would not have to abandon each time he moved from one special area of his diverse interests to another. His search led naturally to that which the several departments of science have in common: the elements of experience on which all fundamental scientific concepts are grounded. With science reduced to these elements, the contrast between the physical and the psychical was lessened; superfluous conceptions, supported by dogma

* Mach's theory of knowledge is presented in its most mature form in his *Erkenntnis und Irrtum* (1905). For a short account see his article "Die Leitgedanken meiner naturwissenschaftlichen Erkenntnislehre und ihre Aufnahme durch die Zeitgenossen," (1910a). What follows here comes mainly from his earlier article "The Analysis of Sensations" (1890), the English translation of the fifth German edition of his book on the same subject (1914), and his *Mechanics* (1883, & 5th English edition, 1942).

and tradition rather than by experience, were called into question. Furthermore, with all the various disciplines set on a common ground the prospect of a genuine unity of science came into view.

The elements of experience According to Mach, all concepts—whether physical, physiological, or psychical—originate in and are based upon the sensations. Here he refers not only to the "sensory" sensations, but to sensations in the widest possible meaning of the term, encompassing all elements of experience. Mach preferred to use the noncommittal term "elements" because it was not his purpose to arrive at a psychological, physiological, or physical theory, but merely to proceed descriptively, as follows:

> Colors, sounds, temperatures, pressures, spaces, times, and so forth, are connected with one another in manifold ways; and with them are associated dispositions of mind, feelings, and volitions. Out of this fabric, that which is relatively more fixed and permanent stands prominently forth, engraves itself on the memory, and expresses itself in language. Relatively greater permanency is exhibited, first, by certain complexes of colors, sounds, pressures, and so forth, functionally connected in time and space, which therefore receive special names, and are called bodies. Absolutely permanent such complexes are not.
>
> My table is now brightly, now dimly lighted. Its temperature varies. It may receive an ink stain. One of its legs may be broken. It may be repaired, polished, and replaced part by part. But, for me, it remains the table at which I daily write. . . . My very manner of expressing this shows that we are concerned here with a sum-total of permanency, to which the new element is added and from which that which is lacking is subsequently taken away.
>
> Our greater intimacy with this sum-total of permanency, and the preponderance of its importance for me as contrasted with the changeable element, impel us to the partly instinctive, partly voluntary and conscious economy of mental presentation and designation, as expressed in ordinary thought and speech. That which is presented in a single image receives a single designation, a single name . . . (Mach, 1914, pp. 2-3).
>
> The useful habit of designating such relatively permanent compounds by single names, and of apprehending them by single thoughts, without going to the trouble each time of an analysis of their component parts, is apt to come into strange conflict with the tendency to isolate the component parts. The vague image which we have of a given permanent complex, being an image which does not perceptibly change when one or another of the component parts is taken away, seems to be something which exists in itself. Inasmuch as it is possible to take away singly every constituent part without

destroying the capacity of the image to stand for the totality and to be recognized again, it is imagined that it is possible to subtract *all* the parts and to have something still remaining. Thus naturally arises the philosophical notion, at first impressive, but subsequently recognized as monstrous, of a "thing-in-itself," different from its "appearance," and unknowable.

Thing, body, matter, are nothing apart from the combinations of the elements,—the colors, sounds, and so forth—nothing apart from their so-called attributes. That protean pseudo-philosophical problem of the single thing with its many attributes, arises wholly from a misinterpretation of the fact, that summary comprehension and precise analysis, although both are provisionally justifiable and for many purposes profitable, cannot be carried on simultaneously (Mach, 1914, pp. 6-7).

Not only are there more or less permanent complexes of elements to which we refer as physical bodies or substances, but there are also, according to Mach, more or less permanent complexes to which each of us refers as his own "self."

Further, that complex of memories, moods, and feelings, joined to a particular body (the human body), which is called the "I" or "Ego," manifests itself as relatively permanent. I may be engaged upon this or that subject, I may be quiet and cheerful, excited and ill-humored. Yet, pathological cases apart, enough durable features remain to identify the ego. Of course, the ego also is only of relative permanency.

The apparent permanency of the ego consists chiefly in the single fact of its continuity, in the slowness of its changes. The many thoughts and plans of yesterday that are continued today, and of which our environment in waking hours incessantly reminds us (whence in dreams the ego can be very indistinct, doubled, or entirely wanting), and the little habits that are unconsciously and involuntarily kept up for long periods of time, constitute the groundwork of the ego. There can hardly be greater differences in the egos of different people, than occur in the course of years in one person. When I recall today my early youth, I should take the boy that I then was, with the exception of a few individual features, for a different person, were it not for the existence of the chain of memories (Mach, 1914, pp. 3-4).

According to the view advanced above, the ego, our own body, external bodies, and all other things may be regarded as complexes of elements of experience:

> Let us denote the above-mentioned elements by the letters ABC . . . , KLM. . . , $\alpha\beta\gamma$. . . . Let those complexes of colors, sounds, and so forth, commonly called bodies, be denoted, for the sake of clearness, by ABC. . . ; the complex known as our own body, which is a part of the former complexes distinguished by certain peculiarities, may be called KLM. . . ; the complex composed of volitions, memory images, and the rest, we shall represent by $\alpha\beta\gamma$. . . . Usually, now, the complex $\alpha\beta\gamma$. . . KLM. . . , as making up the ego, is opposed to the complex ABC. . . , as making up the world of physical objects; sometimes also, $\alpha\beta\gamma$. . . is viewed as ego, and KLM . . . ABC as world of physical objects. Now, at first blush, ABC appears independent of the ego, and opposed to it as a separate existence. But this independence is only relative, and gives way upon closer inspection. Much, it is true, *may* change in the complex $\alpha\beta\gamma$ . . . without much perceptible change being induced in ABC. . . ; and *vice versa.* But many changes in $\alpha\beta\gamma$. . . do pass, by way of changes in KLM. . . , to ABC. . . ; and *vice versa.* (As, for example, when powerful ideas burst forth into acts, or when our environment induces noticeable changes in our body.) At the same time the group KLM. . . appears to be more intimately connected with $\alpha\beta\gamma$. . . and with ABC. . . , than the latter with one another; and their relations find their expression in common thought and speech (Mach, 1914, pp. 8-9).

Naturally, common modes of thought and speech cannot be abandoned altogether in the conduct of scientific investigations. It is necessary, however, to recognize the limitations of concepts which were developed to meet the requirements of practical life, for no matter how well suited they may be for this specific purpose it does not follow that they will be equally well suited for the more exacting requirements of science. Experience, rather than common views handed down by tradition, must be relied upon to shape and guide scientific thought.

> If, to the physicist, bodies appear the real, abiding existences, whilst the "elements" are regarded merely as their evanescent, transitory appearance, the physicist forgets, in the assumption of such a view, that all bodies are but thought symbols for complexes of elements (complexes of sensations). Here, too, the elements in question form the real, immediate, and ultimate foundation, which it is the task of physiologico-physical research to investigate. By the recognition of this fact, many points of physiology and physics assume more distinct and more economical forms, and many spurious problems are disposed of.
>
> For us, therefore, the world does not consist of mysterious entities, which by their interaction with another, equally mysterious entity,

> the ego, produce sensations, which alone are accessible. For us, colors, sounds, spaces, times, . . . are provisionally the ultimate elements, whose given connexion it is our business to investigate. It is precisely in this that the exploration of reality consists. In this investigation we must not allow ourselves to be impeded by such abridgments and delimitations as body, ego, matter, spirit, etc., which have been formed for special, practical purposes and with wholly provisional and limited ends in view. On the contrary, the fittest forms of thought must be created in and by that research itself, just as is done in every special science. In place of the traditional, instinctive ways of thought, a freer, fresher view, conforming to developed experience, and reaching out beyond the requirements of practical life, must be substituted throughout (Mach, 1914, pp. 29-31).

Idealism, realism, and solipsism The so-called "elements" of experience have been the source of much criticism of, and confusion about, Mach's theory of knowledge. Friendly supporters and bitter critics alike misinterpreted Mach's positivism as a return to the subjective idealism of Berkeley. For example, Lenin's militant polemic, *Materialism and Empirio-Criticism* (1909) was directed against the Russian followers of Mach's ideas who posed a threat to his view of the Marxist philosophy. This attack is devoted almost entirely to a "proof" that, besides being "absurd" and "confused," Mach's anti-metaphysical views were identical with, and nothing but a "sheer plagiarism" of, the views of Berkeley.

There is no question that Mach was influenced by Berkeley. (For a detailed and objective account of this influence see Popper, 1953.) Throughout his works Mach acknowledged again and again his debt to Berkeley, but at the same time he pointed out in his usual lucid way the differences between their points of view:

> I must say that anyone who, in spite of repeated protests from myself and from other quarters, identifies my view with that of Berkeley, is undoubtedly very far removed from a proper appreciation of my position.
>
> Shall I once again state the difference in a word? Berkeley regards the "elements" as conditioned by an unknown cause external to them (God); accordingly Kant, in order to appear as a sober realist, invents the "thing-in-itself"; whereas, on the view which I advocate, a dependence of the "elements" on one another is theoretically and practically all that is required.
>
> This misconception is no doubt partly due to the fact that my view was developed from an earlier idealistic phase, which has left on my language traces which are probably not even yet entirely obliterated. For, of all the approaches to my standpoint, the one by way of ideal-

ism seems to me the easiest and most natural (Mach, 1914, pp. 361-362).

Mach's statement of his position regarding realism was equally clear:

> The philosophical point of view of the average man—if that term may be applied to the naïve realism of the ordinary individual—has a claim to the highest consideration. It has arisen in the progress of immeasurable time without the purposed assistance of man. It is a product of nature, and is preserved and sustained by nature. Everything that philosophy has accomplished . . . is, compared with *it,* but an insignificant and ephemeral product of art. And in reality, we see every thinker, every philosopher, the moment he is forced away from his one-sided intellectual occupation by some practical necessity, immediately fall back on the universal point of view that all men hold in common.
>
> We seek by no means to discredit this point of view. The task that we have set for ourselves is simply to show *why* and to what *purpose* for the greatest part of our life we occupy this point of view, and *why* and for what *purpose* we are provisorily obliged to abandon it. No point of view has an absolute *permanent* validity. Each has an importance but for some one given end (Mach, 1890, p. 68).

Thus for Mach, "naïve realism" was neither to be rejected nor accepted on faith. The reasons for its acceptance or rejection were to be determined by an investigation of the foundations of knowledge. But Lenin regarded all this as "sophistry of the cheapest kind." For him, the view of the common man was to be accepted at face value and as obviously correct, and dialectical materialism deliberately and without question made the "naïve" belief of mankind the foundation of its theory of knowledge. (For English translation see Lenin, 1927.)

Many critics insisted that Mach's views would lead inevitably to solipsism, but the following quotation hardly indicates that Mach believed his own "self" to be the sole reality:

> The primary fact is not the ego, but the elements (sensations). . . . The elements constitute the I. *I* have the sensation green, signifies that the element green occurs in a given complex of other elements (sensations, memories). When *I* cease to have the sensation green, when *I* die, then the elements no longer occur in the ordinary, familiar association. That is all. Only an ideal mental-economical unity, not a real unity, has ceased to exist. The ego is not a definite, unalterable, sharply-bounded unity. None of these attributes are important; for all vary even within the sphere of individual life; in fact

> their alteration is even sought after by the individual. *Continuity* alone is important. . . . But continuity is only a means of preparing and conserving what is contained in the ego. This content, and not the ego, is the principal thing. This content, however, is not confined to the individual. With the exception of some insignificant and valueless personal memories, it remains preserved in others even after the death of the individual. The elements that make up the consciousness of a given individual are firmly connected with one another, but with those of another individual they are only feebly connected, and the connexion is only casually apparent. Contents of consciousness, however, that are of universal significance, break through these limits of the individual, and, attached of course to individuals again, can enjoy a continued existence of an impersonal, superpersonal kind, independently of the personality by means of which they were developed. To contribute to this is the greatest happiness of the artist, the scientist, the inventor, the social reformer, etc. (Mach, 1914, pp. 23-24).

In an unpublished autobiography of Mach, discovered by Herneck (1956), there is a remarkable passage in which Mach indicates that his adoption of the above view that the ego is not a sharply-bounded unalterable unity led him to an understanding of Buddhism—"A good fortune," he said, "that seldom befalls a European." Although in adopting this view he rid himself of all metaphysical ideas of personal immortality, Mach nonetheless entertained the equally metaphysical notion of an impersonal immortality, a superpersonal consciousness transcending his own experience and existing after his own death. But only the living speak of what happens after death—on this subject, as on all others, the dead are silent.

On the "subjective" and the "objective" The views of the common man on the meaning of objectivity are frequently carried over into science, but however practical these common-sense views may be, they are not necessarily appropriate in a scientific context. Mach cites the following example:

> A common and popular way of speaking and thinking is to contrast "appearance" with "reality." A pencil held in the air in front of us is seen as straight; dip it in the water, and we see it crooked. In the latter case we say that the pencil *appears* crooked, but is in *reality* straight. But what justifies us in declaring one fact rather than another to be the reality and degrading the other to the level of appearance? In both cases we have to do with facts which present us with different combinations of the elements, combinations which in the two cases are differently conditioned. Precisely because of its

> environment the pencil dipped in water is optically crooked; but it is tactually and metrically straight. An image in a concave or flat mirror is *only* visible, whereas under other and ordinary circumstances a tangible body as well corresponds to the visible image. A bright surface is brighter beside a dark surface than beside one brighter than itself. To be sure, our expectation is deceived when, not paying sufficient attention to the conditions, and substituting for one another different cases of the combination, we fall into the natural error of expecting what we are accustomed to, although the case may be an unusual one. The facts are not to blame for that. In these cases, to speak of "appearance" may have a practical meaning, but cannot have a scientific meaning (Mach, 1914, pp. 10-11).

In fact, if a pencil partly immersed in water does *not* appear crooked from some points of view, then it probably is not really straight. If two supposedly identical pieces of white paper do *not* look different when placed one on a dark background and the other on a light one, then they probably do not reflect the same amount of light. But the facts of our experience in any one case are just as real as in any other. Indeed, according to Mach, the senses neither represent things falsely nor correctly—they merely produce different sensations under different circumstances. Evidently, by "really straight" we mean something other than the mere visual appearance of straightness, and by "amount of light" we mean something other than the appearance of brightness.

In everyday life we are not too explicit about exactly what it is we do mean by "objective" or "real," but usually we mean that which is tangible:

> Colors, sounds, and the odor of bodies are evanescent. But their tangibility, as a sort of constant nucleus, not readily susceptible of annihilation, remains behind; appearing as the vehicle of the more fugitive properties attached to it. Habit, thus, keeps our thought firmly attached to this central nucleus, even when we have begun to recognize that seeing, hearing, smelling, and touching are intimately akin in character. A further consideration is, that owing to the singularly extensive development of mechanical physics a kind of higher reality is ascribed to the spatial and to the temporal than to colors, sounds, and odors; agreeably to which, the temporal and spatial links of colors, sounds, and odors appear to be more real than the colors, sounds and odors themselves (Mach, 1914, p. 8).

In science, however, we are forced to adopt a more rigorous approach than in everyday life. Again referring to Mach's classification of the elements in which ABC . . . are those complexes which we generally regard as external bodies, and KLM. . . the complex of elements making up our own body, then:

> The ascertainment of the dependence of the elements ABC on one another, KLM being disregarded, is the task of natural science, or of physics in its broadest sense. But, in reality, the ABC's are always also dependent on KLM. There are always equations of the form f(ABC. . . KLM, . . .) = 0. Now since many different observers KLM. . . , K′L′M′. . . , K″L″M″. . . are involved, we succeed in eliminating the accidental influence of the variation of KLM, etc., and we thus obtain only the element that can be stated as common property, namely the pure dependence of the ABC's on one another. In this process the KLM. . . , K′L′M′. . . , are treated like physical instruments, each with its peculiarities, its special constants, and so forth, from which the results, as finally indicated, have to be set free. But if it is a question merely of the temporal connexion of one quantitative reaction with other quantitative reactions . . .the matter is then still simpler. Everything then turns on the ascertainment of equality or identity of the ABC's under like circumstances,—that is to say, under like KLM's, which comes to saying that everything turns merely on the ascertainment of spatial identities. The kind of quality of the sensations is now indifferent; it is their equality that is alone decisive. And now a single individual suffices to fix relations of dependence which are valid for all individuals. From this point onwards we have obtained a safe basis for the whole field of scientific research,—a fact which inures to the advantage of psychophysiology as well (Mach, 1914, pp. 344-345).

We can go even farther in this direction and attempt to find "absolute" measures that are entirely independent of the observer and his senses, hoping that we will thus eliminate the "subjective" element from science altogether. But according to Mach, we fail.

> The introduction into physics of the universally comparable, or so called "absolute" measurements,—the reduction of all physical measurements to such units as the centimetre, the gramme, and the second (length, mass, and time),—has one peculiar result. There exists in any case a tendency to regard anything that can be physically grasped and measured, anything that can be stated in such a way as to become common property, as "objective" and "real," in contrast to the subjective sensations; and the absolute measures appear to give some support to this opinion, and to supplv it with a psychological, if not with a logical, motive. It looks as if what we call "sensations" in the familiar sense, were something quite superfluous in physics. Indeed, if we look closer, the system of units of measurement can be

still further simplified. For the numerical measurement of mass is given by a ratio of accelerations, and measurement of time can be reduced to measurement of angles or lengths of arcs. Consequently measurement of lengths is the foundation of all measurements. But we do not measure mere space; we require a material standard of measurement, and with this the whole system of manifold sensations is brought back again (Mach, 1914, pp. 342-343).

On absolute space, time, and motion Of all his studies on the foundations of physical science, Mach's analysis and criticism of Newtonian mechanics had the most far-reaching effect—leading ultimately to Einstein's theory of gravitation and relativity.* Concerning "absolute space" and "absolute motion," Mach wrote:

> No one is competent to predicate things about absolute space and absolute motion; they are pure things of thought, pure mental constructs, that cannot be produced in experience. All our principles of mechanics are, as we have shown in detail, experimental knowledge concerning the relative positions and motions of bodies. Even in the provinces in which they are now recognized as valid, they could not, and were not, admitted without previously being subjected to experimental tests. No one is warranted in extending these principles beyond the boundaries of experience. In fact, such an extension is meaningless, as no one possesses the requisite knowledge to make use of it (Mach, 1942, p. 280).

* Newton was not unaware of the practical problems involved in the actual measurement of absolute space and time. In the definitions prefixed to his *Principia* he wrote: "Absolute, true, and mathematical time, of itself, and from its own nature, flows equably without relation to anything external, and by another name is called duration: relative, apparent, and common time, is some sensible and external (whether accurate or unequable) measure of duration by the means of motion, which is commonly used instead of true time; such as an hour, a day, a month, a year. Absolute space, in its own nature, without relation to anything external, remains always similar and immovable. Relative space is some movable dimension or measure of the absolute spaces; which our senses determine by its position to bodies; and which is commonly taken for immovable space; such is the dimension of a subterraneous, an aerial, or celestial space, determined by its position in respect of the earth. . . . Absolute time, in astronomy, is distinguished from relative, by the equation or correction of the apparent time. For the natural days are truly unequal, though they are commonly considered as equal, and used for a measure of time; astronomers correct this inequality that they may measure the celestial motions by a more accurate time. *It may be, that there is no such thing as an equable motion, whereby time may be accurately measured. . . . It may be that there is no body really at rest, to which the places and motions of others may be referred"* (italics mine). Even so, Newton's basic view was metaphysical. He wrote: "And so instead of absolute places and motions, we use relative ones; and that without any inconvenience in common affairs; but in philosophical disquisitions, we ought to abstract from our senses, and consider things themselves, distinct from what are only sensible measures of them."

Mach expressed a similar view on "absolute time":

> As in the study of thermal phenomena we take as our measure of temperature an *arbitrarily chosen indicator of volume,* which varies in almost parallel correspondence with our sensation of heat, and which is not liable to the uncontrollable disturbances of our organs of sensation, so, for similar reasons, we select as our measure of time an *arbitrarily chosen motion,* (the angle of the earth's rotation, or path of a free body), which proceeds in almost parallel correspondence with our sensation of time. If we have once made clear to ourselves that we are concerned only with the ascertainment of the *interdependence* of phenomena, . . . all metaphysical obscurities disappear (Mach, 1942, pp. 275-276).

Einstein leaves no doubt that he was influenced by these and other views of Mach. In his eulogy of Mach he wrote:

> The significance of such minds as Mach lies by no means only in the fact that they fill certain philosophical needs of their time which a devoted specialist of science might term luxury. Concepts that have proven useful in the order of things easily gain such authority over us that we are likely to forget their worldly origin and take them for unalterable facts. They are then stamped "necessities of thinking," "given a priori," etc. The road of scientific progress is often made impassable for a long time by such errors. It is therefore by no means idle play when we are trained to analyze long-established concepts and to show the circumstances upon which their authority and usefulness depends, how they individually grew out of the results of experience. Their all-too-great authority is thereby broken; they are removed if they cannot be properly justified, corrected if their classification to the things given was too negligent, replaced by others if a new system is feasible that we for some reasons prefer.
>
> To the specialized scientist, whose mind is more directed towards the specific, such analyses appear often superfluous, pompous and, sometimes even ridiculous. The situation, however, changes when one of the customarily used concepts is to be replaced by a more precise one because the development of the science concerned demands it. Then all those who have not dealt neatly with their own concepts rise in energetic protest and complain about the revolutionary threat to the holiest goods. These cries are then joined by the voices of those philosophers who believe themselves incapable of doing without that concept because they had neatly tucked it away in their little treasure box of the "absolute," the "a priori" or, in short, in such a way that they had proclaimed its basic unalterability.
>
> The reader will already guess that I am here hinting at certain

> concepts in the teaching of space and time, as well as mechanics which, through the theory of relativity, have undergone a modification. No one can deny that students of the theory of knowledge have smoothed the path for this development; at least of myself I know that directly and indirectly I have been particularly influenced by Hume and Mach. . . .
>
> Mach clearly recognized the weak points of classical mechanics and was not very far from requiring a general theory of relativity—and all of this almost half a century ago! It is not improbable that Mach himself would have discovered the theory of relativity, if, during the time that his mind was in its prime, physicists had been concerned with the importance of the problem of the constancy of the speed of light (Einstein, 1916, pp. 102-103).

Although Einstein did much to eliminate the concept of absolute space from modern physics, his theory of gravitation still does make some use of the concept. Even in the absence of gravitating matter, that is, in empty space, the inertial coordinate systems are assumed to have meaning (see the reviews by Dicke, 1959a, b and 1962, and Dicke and Dirac, 1961). According to what is now known as *Mach's principle,* however, inertial forces are not produced by acceleration relative to empty space—the forces are due to acceleration relative to distant matter in space. As Mach points out:

> The comportment of terrestrial bodies with respect to the earth is reducible to the comportment of the earth with respect to the remote heavenly bodies. If we were to assert that we knew more of moving objects than this their last-mentioned, experimentally-given comportment with respect to the celestial bodies, we should render ourselves culpable of a falsity. When, accordingly, we say, that a body preserves unchanged its direction and velocity *in space,* our assertion is nothing more or less than an abbreviated reference to *the entire universe* (Mach, 1942, p. 286).

This principle, one gathers from Dicke's reviews, still exerts a strong guiding influence on research on the enigma of gravitation. For a detailed non-mathematical account of the significance of Mach's principle for modern cosmology, and of the case for the principle and the objections to it, see Sciama (1959).

On the atomic theory For Mach, atoms were not unchangeable "things in themselves"—they were concepts:

> The majority of natural inquirers ascribe to the intellectual implements of physics, to the concepts mass, force, atom, and so forth,

> whose sole office is to revive economically arranged experiences, a reality beyond and independent of thought. Not only so, but it has even been held that these forces and masses are the real objects of inquiry, and, if once they were fully explored, all the rest would follow from the equilibrium and motion of these masses. A person who knew the world only through the theater, if brought behind the scenes and permitted to view the mechanism of the stage's action, might possibly believe that the real world also was in need of a machine-room, and that if this were once thoroughly explored, we should know all. Similarly, we, too, should beware lest the *intellectual* machinery employed in the representation of the world on *the stage of thought,* be regarded as the basis of the real world (Mach, 1942, p. 611).

Mach's view of atomic theory was by no means well-received by some of his contemporaries. At best, it was regarded as a very weak point in his theory of knowledge; at worst, as patently incorrect. Consider Einstein's remarks in his autobiographical notes:

> In my younger years . . . Mach's epistemological position also influenced me very greatly, a position which today appears to me to be essentially untenable. For he did not place in the correct light the essentially constructive and speculative nature of thought and more especially of scientific thought; in consequence of which he condemned theory on precisely those points where its constructive-speculative character unconcealably comes to light, as for example in the kinetic atomic theory (Einstein, 1951, p. 21).

Planck (1909), one of the leading theoretical physicists of the day, was particularly outspoken in his criticism, referring to Mach as a "false prophet." Actually, however, Planck and Mach were not far apart in their views on the origin and development of physics. Both agreed that physics aims to eliminate the influence of specific observers and specific senses. Planck wrote:

> We may say briefly that the feature of the whole development of theoretical physics, up to the present, is the unification of its systems which has been obtained by a certain elimination of the anthropomorphous element, particularly the specific sense-perceptions. Seeing, however, that the sensations are acknowledged to be the starting-point of all physical research, this deliberate departure from the fundamental premises must appear astonishing, if not paradoxical. Yet there is hardly a fact in the history of physics so obvious now as this, and, in truth, there must be undoubted advantages in such

self alienations (Planck, 1960, pp. 4-5—an English translation of the original 1909 article by Planck).

The difference between the two points of view was that Planck thought that the elimination of the "anthropomorphous elements" could be complete, and that we could obtain knowledge of a fixed world picture, independent of the variation of both time and people.

> This constancy, independent of all human and intellectual individuality, is what we call reality. . . . The acknowledgment of this reality is regarded as essential to a scientist (Planck, 1960, p. 24).

Mach was not prepared to believe in the "reality" of atoms, and he was even less well-prepared to be told what he ought to believe. In his reply to Planck, written when he was 72, there was more than a trace of bitterness:

> One can see that the physicists are well on their way to becoming a church and that they are even adopting its familiar means. To this I simply reply: If the belief in the reality of atoms is so essential to you, then I will have nothing more to do with the physical way of thinking, then I do not want to be a real physicist, then I will forego any scientific esteem, in short, then, I decline with thanks any participation in the community of believers; freedom of thought is much dearer to me (Mach, 1910a, p. 233).

What could bring a world-famous physicist, writing at the beginning of the atomic age, to question the reality of atoms and similar concepts? For one thing it was the absence of the very constancy that Planck deemed so essential to reality:

> As far as the reality of atoms is concerned, I do not doubt at all that if the atomic theory is quantitatively adjusted to the sentient reality then even the deductions made therefrom will in *some* way or other be related to the *facts,* it only remains questionable in *which* way. According to Newton, the separation of glass surfaces at the first dark ring [in Newton's rings] corresponds to one-half the period of the "fits" of reflection and transmission, but according to the later Young-Fresnel theory it corresponds to one-quarter of the wavelength. In the same manner the results of the atomic theory can also still undergo multiple and *useful* new changes in interpretation, even if one does not deem them to be realities right away. Therefore, all honor to the belief of the physicists! But I cannot accept it as my own (Mach, 1910a, pp. 232-233).

For Mach, reality was to be found in the complex of sensations on which the theoretical concepts were based, not in the concepts themselves. Furthermore, he regarded the concepts as only provisional, and subject to change or even abandonment whenever the facts so warranted. Theories, he once wrote, are "like dry leaves which fall away" once they have served their function.

In any event, whatever it may be about atoms that is constant for all times, places, and persons is evidently not the atomic theory itself. It undergoes continual change. One of the most important modifications was due to Heisenberg who, in 1925, sought a firmer foundation for the mechanics of quantum theory. He noted that an essential part of previous theoretical computations involved relations between quantities that were unobservable, such as the position and period of an electron. He proposed, therefore, to build up a new quantum mechanics, "analogous to the classical mechanics, but in which only relations between observable quantities occur." In doing so, he utilized not the unobservable position of the electron, but the observable radiation emitted. Whatever one may believe about the reality of atoms, this and later modifications of the atomic theory appear to be more in accordance with the views of Mach than with those of some of his critics.* Certainly the theoretical atom of today, with its 16 (or 17?) "fundamental" particles and antiparticles differs significantly from the atom described by Planck. One or the other, therefore, must not be the real unchanging atom. Most likely, neither of the two is; Planck's concept of the atom is largely outmoded, and the current concept changes almost daily.

On physiological psychology One goal repeatedly stated by Mach was "to promote the efforts, which the positive sciences are at this moment making, toward mutual accommodation." He saw the traditional physical and psychological disciplines as too narrow, too exclusive. The investigation of the senses on which both are founded, he thought, would bring them into closer relation with benefits for both. On this subject he wrote:

> The frequent excursions which I have made into this province have all sprung from the profound conviction that the foundations

* Indeed, in an anonymous note commenting on Mach's influence on modern physics, the following statement appears: "Mach's suggestion that the physical events inside the atom should no longer be described by the motions—positions and velocities—of the subatomic particles but by the radiation that is emitted by the particles as described by *matrices,* not by coordinates . . . was the origin of the first formulation of quantum mechanics advanced by Heisenberg. . . ." (*Scientific Monthly,* 1954, *79,* 252) Unfortunately, the note gives no indication as to where, in Mach's own writings, this specific suggestion attributed to him is to be found.

of science as a whole, and of physics in particular, await their next great elucidations from the side of biology, and especially from the analysis of the sensations (Mach, 1914, pp. vii-viii).

The physicist says: I find everywhere bodies and the motions of bodies only, no sensations; sensations, therefore, must be something entirely different from the physical objects I deal with. The psychologist accepts the second portion of this declaration. For him, as is proper, sensations are the primary *data;* but to these there corresponds a mysterious physical something which, conformably with the prepossession, must be quite different from sensations. But what is it that is the really mysterious thing? Is it the Physis or the Psyche? Or is it perhaps both? It would almost appear so, as it is now the one and now the other that appears unattainable and involved in impenetrable obscurity. Or are we here being led round in a circle by some evil spirit?

I believe that the latter is the case. For me the elements . . . are immediately and indubitably given, and for me they can never afterwards be volatilized away by considerations which ultimately are always based on their existence (Mach, 1914, p. 45).

As we recognize no real gulf between the physical and the psychical, it is a matter of course that, in the study of the sense organs, general physical as well as special biological observations may be employed. Much that appears to us difficult of comprehension when we draw a parallel between a sense-organ and a physical apparatus, is rendered quite obvious in the light of the theory of evolution, simply by assuming that we are concerned with a living organism with particular memories, particular habits and manners, which owe their origin to a long and eventful race-history. The sense-organs themselves are a fragment of soul; they themselves do part of the psychical work, and hand over the completed result to consciousness (Mach, 1914, p. 71).

Every organism together with its parts is subject to the laws of physics. Hence the legitimate attempt gradually to conceive of an organism as something physical, and to establish the consideration of it in a "causal" point of view as alone valid. But whenever we try to do this we are always brought face to face with the peculiar characteristics of the organic, for which no analogy can be found in the physical phenomena of "lifeless" nature, so far as they have been investigated at present (Mach, 1914, pp. 98-99).

We do not indeed know what are the physical counterparts to memory and association. All the explanations that have been attempted are very much forced. In this respect it *seems* as if there were almost no analogy between the organic and the inorganic. It is possible, however, that in the physiology of the senses, psychological observation on the one side and physical observation on the other, may make such progress that they will ultimately come into contact,

> and that in this way new facts may be brought to light. The result of this investigation will not be a dualism but rather a science which, embracing both the organic and the inorganic, shall interpret the facts that are common to the two departments (Mach, 1914, pp. 100-101).

Investigations of the visual phenomena now known as Mach bands, which Mach discovered in 1865 while working in the field of physiological psychology, show the extent to which his expectations have been fulfilled. A later consideration will show what the special study of these and similar phenomena contributes to an understanding of the meaning of objectivity.

The brighter the light, the deeper the shadow. German proverb

CHAPTER TWO *Mach bands*

Mach's interest in the theory of knowledge occasionally caused him to turn from his study of physics to that of the senses. But early in his career he also had a practical and more compelling reason—he could not afford the expensive equipment necessary for the experiments that he wished to do in physics. As a result, much of his early work at Vienna and at Graz was devoted to the study of hearing and vision which could be carried out with relatively simple and inexpensive apparatus at that time.

Indeed, the study on vision that Mach first undertook did not require any special optical equipment at all, other than his own eyes. To determine the visual effects of combining or juxtaposing fields of various colors and intensities Mach utilized the principle of the color top, or color wheel, which had been known since ancient times. In this method colored or black and white sectors of a disc (Fig. 2.1) are visually combined by rapidly rotating the disc. At a high speed no flicker can be seen; the successive sectors appear to fuse into a single color and intensity. The greater the proportion of white to black, the brighter the rotating disc appears. Similarly, the greater the proportion of one color to another, the greater the influence of that color

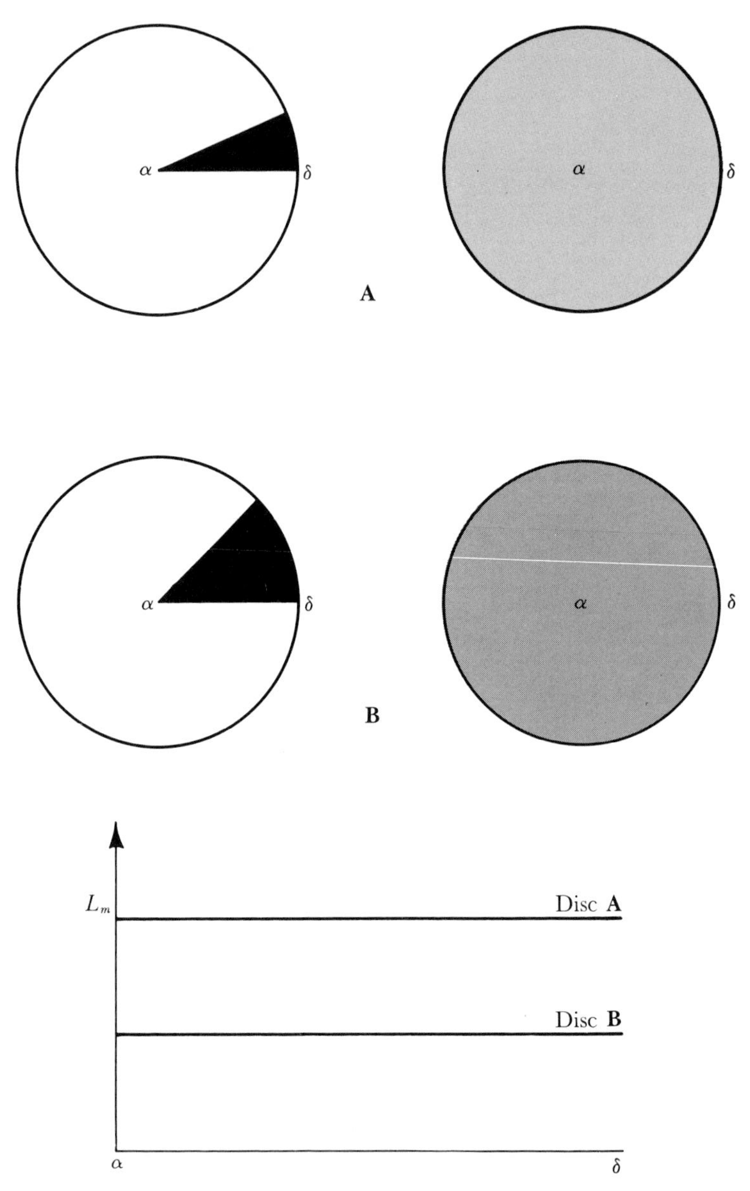

Figure 2.1. *White disc* A *with small black sector (shown on the left) appears a uniform light gray when rapidly rotated (shown on the right). White disc* B *with larger black sector (left) appears darker than disc* A *when rapidly rotated. Mean luminance of rapidly rotating discs* A *and* B *along their radii* (αδ) *shown in graph.*

on the appearance of the rotating disc.* Variations in the proportion of white to black (or of one color to another) along the radius of the disc—that is, variations in the central angles subtended by the component sectors—thus produce corresponding variations in brightness (or color) from center to circumference of the rotating disc.

The apparent brightness resulting from the visual combination of a succession of light and dark periods of illumination may be calculated by means of a simple principle that was first established by Plateau in 1829, further elucidated by Talbot in 1834, and finally formulated as a law by Plateau in 1835. In modern terms (see LeGrand, 1957), this so-called Talbot-Plateau law may be stated as follows:

> The apparent constant luminance of a succession of uniform flashes of brief duration with a frequency above the critical fusion frequency is the mean value L_m of the real varying luminance L taken over any one period or over any time t comprising an integral number of periods:

$$L_m = \frac{1}{t} \int_0^t L \, dt.$$

Empirical tests of the law show it to be exact, or at least to hold within a fraction of one percent, as long as the fusion frequency is exceeded.

According to the Talbot-Plateau law, the discs shown in Figure 2.1 should—and do—appear uniformly bright from the center (α) to the circumference (δ) when rapidly rotated. During rotation the proportion of black to white at every point along any radius is the same because the angular dimensions of the sectors are the same from center to circumference. With a small black sector (disc *A*) the proportion of black to white is correspondingly small and the disc appears a uniform bright gray. With a large black sector (disc *B*) the proportion of black to white is large, and the rotating disc appears a uniform dark gray.

While experimenting with similar but slightly more complex rotating discs, such as the one illustrated in Figure 2.2, Mach noticed a curious phenomenon. The black sector in this disc is merely a combination of the two sectors shown in Figure 2.1; the inner zone of the sector in disc *A* and the outer zone of the sector in disc *B* are linked to one another with a uniformly graded intermediate zone in which the central angle subtended by the sector varies linearly with the radius. Assuming that the Talbot-Plateau law is general, the mean luminance of this disc should

* A color wheel devised later by Maxwell utilized interlocked discs cut along one radius, thus enabling the size of the sectors to be varied as desired. These "Maxwell discs" are still commonly used to demonstrate the basic laws of color mixture.

be given, as shown in Figure 2.2, simply by connecting with a straight line the luminance curves for disc *A* and disc *B* that correspond to the inner and outer zones respectively. Accordingly, the disc shown should

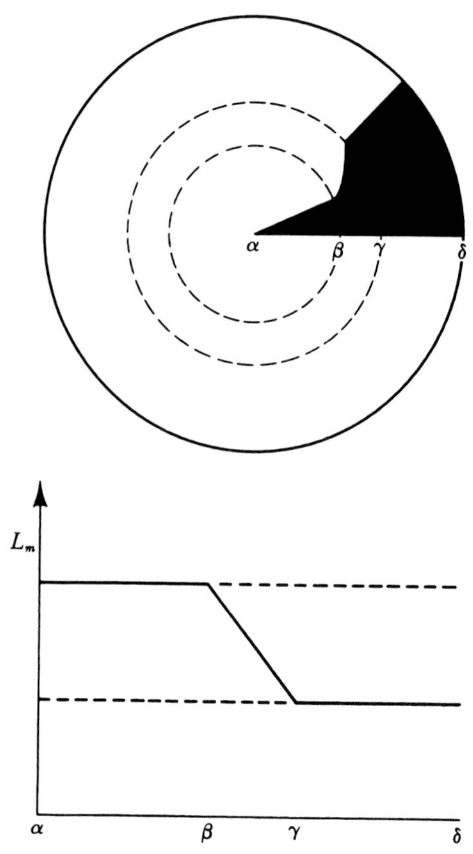

Figure 2.2. *Stationary white disc with black sector combining the inner zone (αβ) of the disc* A, *the outer zone (γδ) of the disc* B *(both shown in Fig. 2.1), and a graded intermediate zone (βγ). Graph shows the calculated mean luminance of the three zones along the radius αδ when the disc is rapidly rotated.*

The intermediate zone of the black sector is bounded below by a radius of the disc and above by a portion of an Archimedes spiral with the equation $\theta = kr$, where θ is the central angle, r the radius, and k a constant which is the slope of the gradient of the desired light curve. The origin of the spiral (θ = zero) is chosen so that the spiral from β to γ forms the upper boundary of the dark sector. The disc shown here is slightly simpler than the one actually used by Mach in his first experiment (see Part Two). The multiple black sectors in Mach's disc are represented in this figure by a single sector. Furthermore, this sector is constructed so as to yield a simple rectilinear light curve.

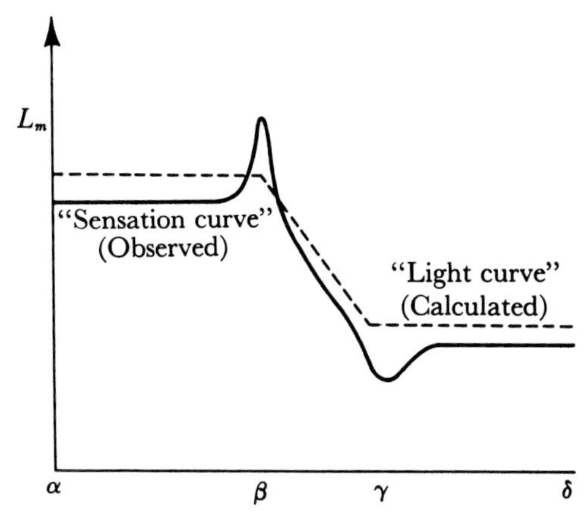

Figure 2.3. Calculated mean luminance or "light curve" (dashed line) and apparent luminance or "sensation curve" (solid line) of the disc shown in Figure 2.2 when set in rapid rotation.

appear a uniform and fairly bright gray from α to β when set in rapid rotation. The proportion of black to white is small but constant throughout that zone. From β to γ, the zone where the proportion of black to white gradually increases, the disc should become increasingly darker. From γ on to the edge of the disc δ, the zone where the proportion of black to white is greatest but again remains constant, the disc should appear darkest, and uniform.

The rotating disc does appear gray, and—in general—the three zones appear as expected (Fig. 2.3). The transition from each zone to the next is interrupted, however, by a distinct narrow ring—a bright ring at point β and a dark ring at point γ. On the basis of the Talbot-Plateau law one would predict that the brightness of the rings at β and γ would lie between that of the next outer and inner rings. At no point is the proportion of black to white less than at any point in zone $\alpha\beta$, or greater than at any point in zone $\gamma\delta$. Yet the narrow ring at β is the brightest place on the disc; the narrow ring at γ, the darkest. These striking and completely unexpected bright and dark rings are now known as Mach's rings or, more generally, *Mach bands.*

The principal visual features of Mach bands and the stimulus conditions which determine them were elucidated in Mach's original investigations. These are only summarized below because translations of the original papers are presented in full in Part Two. The numerous psychophysical investigations that later grew out of Machs' work, however, are surveyed in some detail.

A SUMMARY OF MACH'S OBSERVATIONS

Mach first demonstrated the generality of the visual phenomena that bear his name by constructing a wide variety of forms of light and dark sectors on rotatable discs and cylinders. For example, he constructed a disc which, when rapidly rotated, gave a negative image of one such as that shown in Figure 2.2. This negative disc showed dark rings where the positive one appeared bright, and bright rings where the positive one appeared dark. In both cases, everywhere that the curve representing the light distribution had a significant flection, the corresponding point on the disc was brighter or darker than its surroundings. The point was brighter where the flection was concave with respect to the abscissa, darker where the flection was convex.

These phenomena are not peculiar to rotating discs, nor are they dependent upon fusion of intermittent light. Mach demonstrated these facts by photographing the rotating discs and then observing the still pictures. Positive photographs of the rotating discs appeared almost exactly like the rotating discs themselves.

The fact that the Mach bands can be photographed seems to indicate that they must be physical, rather than physiological or psychological phenomena. Indeed, the first question that most persons ask when they see the bands for the first time is, "Can they be photographed?" The natural assumption is, of course, that if a physical instrument such as the camera can "see" the bands, then they must be a purely physical effect. This reasoning is faulty, as Mach showed in the following way.

First, Mach carefully determined that the photographic effect resulting from equal light intensities depended only upon the exposure time, irrespective of whatever interruptions of the light may occur. In short, he found that something like the Talbot-Plateau law for vision also holds for the photographic process. In addition, he demonstrated that time and intensity of exposure to light could be interchanged to produce a constant photographic effect.* Consequently, the photographs present essentially the same distribution of light to the eye as do the rotating discs. Therefore, as Mach pointed out in his first paper (see Part Two):

> It must not be concluded that the bright and dark rings are objective phenomena because they appear in the photograph. On the contrary, I have shown that objective photography follows the Talbot-Plateau law and since the rings are not explainable in terms of this law, their subjective nature is demonstrated. Only when the

* These latter observations by Mach were probably an independent discovery of the Bunsen-Roscoe law of photochemical equivalence.

> objective photograph gives the same brightness relations as the rotating disc must they appear subjectively equal. Both must, of course, be viewed by eye. I would not emphasize this fact if I had not often heard this objection.

This is a most important point in making the proper distinction between so-called "objective" and "subjective" phenomena. This problem will be discussed in more detail in Chapter 5.

The fact that the bands appeared in still photographs showed that neither intermittent light nor movement of the illuminated surface was necessary for the phenomena. The controlling factor in these experiments was the spatial distribution of the illumination, rather than the particular method of obtaining that distribution. Mach found that the following simple principle of spatial distribution was common to all of the diverse conditions under which the phenomena were seen:

> Wherever the light intensity curve of an illuminated surface (whose light intensity varies in only one direction) has a concave or a convex flection with respect to the abscissa, that place appears brighter or darker, respectively, than its surroundings.

In other words, the location and magnitude of the bright and dark bands are given approximately by the location and magnitude of the maxima and minima in a curve representing the *negative* of the second derivative of the light intensity curve.

Mach bands are noticed under a number of common conditions, once the underlying principle of their dependence upon a particular kind of spatial distribution of illumination is known. One can observe them at the edges of almost any shadow cast on a fairly uniform surface by an object in the sunlight. The transition from the full shadow to the graded half-shadow provides the convex flection; the transition from the half-shadow to the fully illuminated space provides the concave flection. At these points dark and light bands, respectively, are seen.

The simple principles underlying the production of such patterns by means of shadows cast in sunlight, or in the light of any extended source, are illustrated in Figure 2.4. The Mach bands appear at once in the shadow cast on a piece of white paper by the edge of a card held under a fluorescent desk lamp, which provides an extended source of light. Covering the ends of the lamp, which usually are not uniformly bright, somewhat enhances the effect. From α to β the paper is illuminated by light from the full length of the exposed part of the lamp. In the half-shadow, however, the illumination becomes progressively dimmer from β to γ because more and more of the source is occluded by the card.

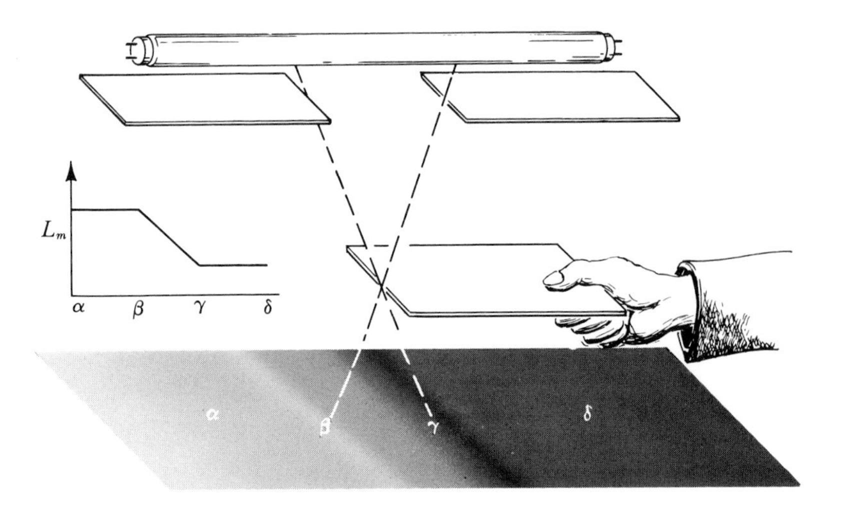

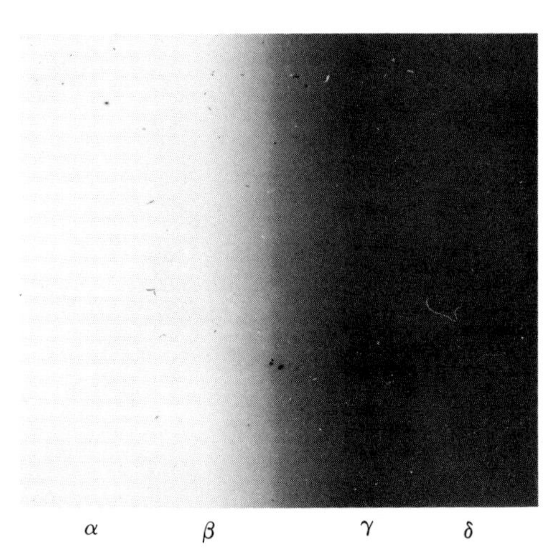

Figure 2.4. *Simple method for producing Mach bands. If the lamp is about one foot above the white paper, the height of the card should be about one or two inches. Slight lateral movements of the card will enhance the visibility of the bands.*

The Mach bands in the diagram (above) were painted with an air brush and were exaggerated somewhat for illustrative purposes. The photograph (below) was obtained by casting a half-shadow directly on a photographic plate and the bands in it are more realistic. The photographic process and other steps involved in the reproduction of a figure in continuous tone, however, can produce spurious bands and "edge" effects (see Chapter 5). Therefore the light curve of the reproduction shown here may not correspond exactly to the original photograph or to the ideal curve described in the text and shown in the sketch. This caution applies to all similar photographs reproduced in this book.

Finally, from γ to δ the direct light from the source is completely occluded; only scattered light and light from other sources reaches this region. Ideally, the curve representing this pattern of illumination is uniformly high from α to β, uniformly low from γ to δ, and uniformly graded from β to γ with sharp flections at these latter two points.

Mach found, however, that the flections need not be sharp. The phenomena also result from slight degrees of curvature, but then the bright and dark lines are somewhat weaker and less distinct. Furthermore, the pattern of illumination need not be essentially one-dimensional as those described above. Patterns of illumination that vary nonuniformly and in many directions show similar phenomena.

Such a complex pattern of illumination and the corresponding pattern of apparent brightness may be visualized in the following way. Let the distribution of light on the retina resulting from the pattern be represented by a continuous surface. Elevations of this surface correspond to regions of increased intensity; depressions correspond to regions of diminished intensity. Similarly, let the sensation of brightness also be represented by a continuous surface. Elevations of this surface correspond to regions of increased brightness; depressions correspond to regions of diminished brightness. According to Mach, the following general principle expresses the relation between the "light surface" and the corresponding "sensation surface" in any complex pattern of illumination:

> Where the light surface, on the average, is concave with respect to the retina there appears an increase in brightness; the opposite where it is convex, on the average. In its gross features, the sensation surface follows the light surface. However, to the concave curvature of the light surface with respect to the plane of the retina there corresponds a greater elevation of the sensation surface; to the convexities, on the other hand, a greater depression of the sensation surface.*

In both the simple and complex patterns Mach noticed that, in addition to enhanced sensations of brightness and darkness, many of the graded distributions of illumination gave remarkable impressions of depth. For example, the graded distribution of illumination on the plane surface of a rotating disc may be the same as that reflected from some curved surface illuminated from a particular direction. From this graded distribution of illumination on the plane surface the eye (or rather, the whole visual system) reconstructs the equivalent, and perhaps more fa-

* For convenience, curves and surfaces representing light distribution may be referred to hereafter as "light curves" and "light surfaces." Similarly, the corresponding curves and surfaces representing the apparent brightness are called "sensation curves" and "sensation surfaces." Spatial distributions of illumination in which the Mach bands are seen are called "Mach patterns."

miliar, three-dimensional surface. The information available to the eye is ambiguous, however; a particular three-dimensional surface is not uniquely indicated by a particular distribution of light. One and the same distribution of illumination on a plane surface can, for example, yield equally well the appearance of a depression lighted from the left or an elevation lighted from the right. These phenomena are described in detail by Mach in his original papers (see Part Two) and need not be considered further here. It is worth noting, however, that Mach's systematic and rigorous treatment of this subject presaged a number of present-day studies on the influence of gradients on visual perception.

The marked dependence of the light and dark bands on the spatial distribution of illumination led Mach to conclude that both phenomena must originate in a functional interdependence of neighboring elements of the retina. He believed that this interdependence was a reciprocal inhibitory influence and that it was mediated, with gradually diminishing effect, over the lateral network of neural interconnections in the retina. The "purpose" of the inhibitory influence, Mach believed, was to enhance the appearance of contours and borders in the spatial distribution of illumination.

Mach's early insight into this problem was quite remarkable, as is shown by a comparison of his views with the modern quantitative formulations of neural mechanisms in the retina that have been proposed to explain Mach bands. But this comparison must be deferred until the next chapter. To understand fully the merits and shortcomings of these several formulations it is first necessary to understand the phenomena to be explained and the manner in which a number of significant variables influence them.

METHODS FOR THE PRODUCTION OF MACH BANDS

The appearance of Mach bands depends upon particular spatial distributions of illumination, rather than upon the particular methods used to obtain these distributions. Since any one distribution may be produced in countless ways—some complex and devious, others simple and direct—the choice of a method is usually based on practical considerations alone. A few simple and practical methods are illustrated below, but they by no means exhaust the possibilities.

Fusion of moving patterns Because of its simplicity, the rotating disc, or one of its many variants, is frequently used to produce the desired distribution of illumination. As indicated above, these methods depend upon fusion; the eye itself integrates and finds the approximate mean of fluctuations in luminance produced at any point by a rapidly moving or flickering pattern. The mean luminance at any point along the radius of a rotating disc with black and white sectors thus depends upon the proportion of black to white along the circumference of the circle that would be inscribed by that point. That is, the radial angle subtended by a sector at any point, rather than absolute size of the arc subtended, is a direct measure of the contribution of that sector to the luminance of that particular point on the rotating disc (Fig. 2.1). Then it is a simple matter to calculate the spatial distribution of luminance that sectors of various shapes yield when the discs are rotated.

The slight inconvenience of laying out and painting sectors on polar coordinates and making calculations of luminance in terms of angular measurements may be avoided by using rotating cylinders or belts (Fig. 2.5). If the belt shown in the figure is viewed from above and through the aperture indicated by the dashed lines, the critical motion is along a straight line in the plane perpendicular to the line of sight. Thus the painted white sectors on the surface may have essentially the same form as the desired intensity distribution. That is, if we call the direction of motion *Z*, the plane of motion *XZ*, and the mean luminance at any point on this plane *Y*, then any *Y* is simply proportional to the corresponding *Z* dimension of the white sector of the stationary pattern. The light surface is thus given by erecting such an ordinate *Y* at every point on the plane *XZ* and interconnecting all the end points. Note that this method has the advantage of producing a rectilinear pattern in both the *X* and *Z* dimensions. With the rotating discs, of course, the pattern is curved in the *Z* dimension.

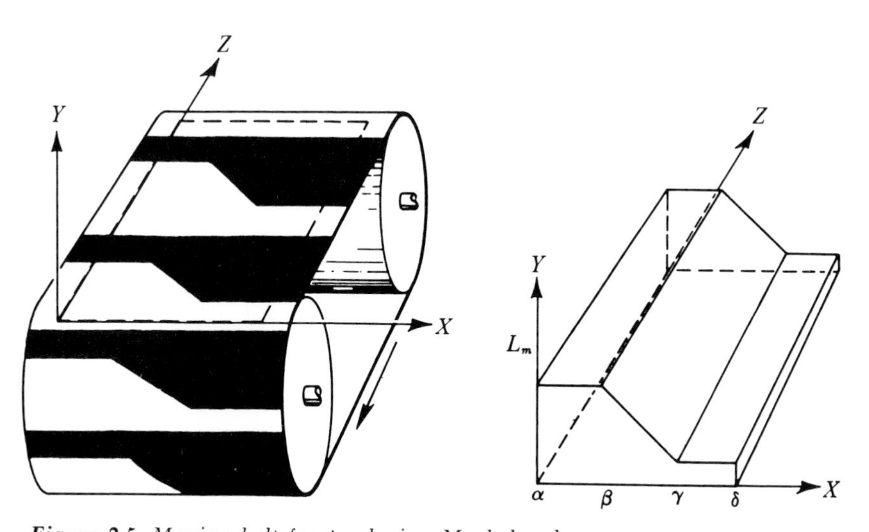

Figure 2.5. Moving belt for producing Mach bands.

In an interesting application of the Fourier series, Mach synthesized various complex spatial patterns by integrating—that is, visually fusing on a moving belt—their sinusoidal components. (See his third paper in Part Two.) The method was perfectly analogous to the more familiar synthesis of a complex periodic sound wave by superposition of the appropriate sine waves. This was probably the first application of Fourier methods to the analysis and synthesis of optical images. Mach was ahead of his times; it was not until the mid twentieth century that these methods were widely applied to the study of optical systems (cf. Duffieux, 1946). Only very recently have the Fourier methods been applied to the study of the optical and physiological properties of the visual system (see Chapter 4).

A variant of the fusion method in which the illuminated pattern itself is held stationary was devised by Békésy (1960b). The image of the stationary pattern is swept repetitively across the retina by a rapidly rotating cube prism placed between the observer's eye and the stationary pattern (Fig. 2.6). The result is essentially the same as that obtained with a rotating disc or a cylinder. The intensity of any point of the fused pattern seen by the observer is determined by the mean intensity on the stationary pattern along the line which passes through that point perpendicular to the axis of rotation of the prism. The advantage of this method is that the pattern may be changed easily, even during observation, simply by changing the shape of the opening of the stop. Furthermore, it is easier to obtain wide ranges of intensities and high contrasts between light and dark areas with this method than with light reflected from the surfaces of discs or cylinders.

Shadow patterns One of the simplest and most useful methods is based on the common natural cause of Mach bands mentioned above: the

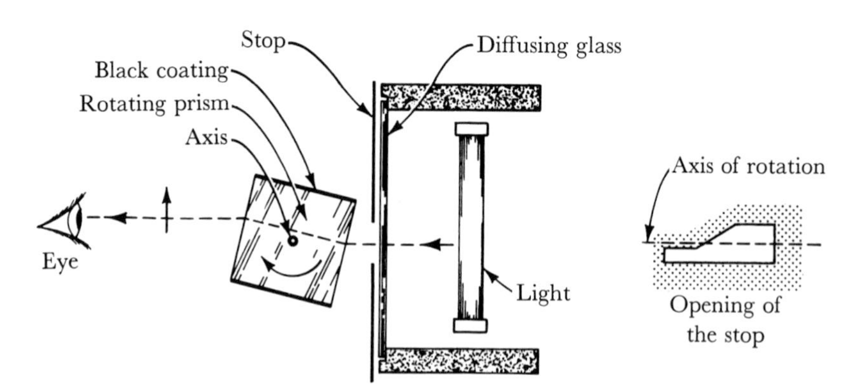

Figure 2.6. *Békésy's rotating prism method for producing Mach bands. From Békésy (1960b).*

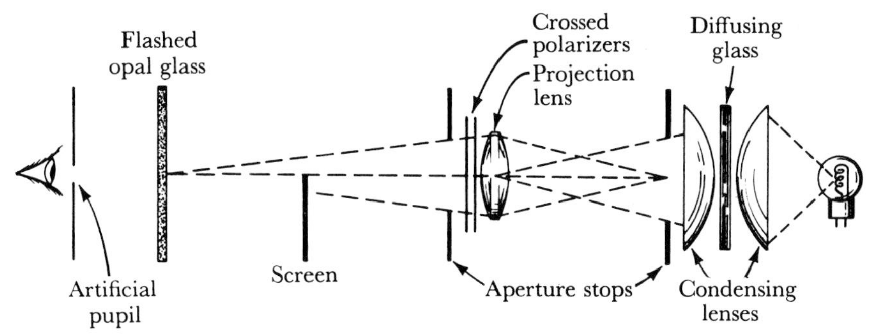

Figure 2.7. *Fry's projection method for producing Mach bands. Redrawn after Fry (1948).*

gradient of illumination at the edge of a shadow cast in the light of an extended source such as the sun. For example, the projection apparatus used by Fry (1948) is essentially a shadow-casting device (Fig. 2.7). A diffusing glass is placed between the condensing lenses of an ordinary lantern slide projector and a circular aperture stop is placed in the slide holder. Intensity is controlled by crossed polarizers in front of the projection lens. A screen placed in the projected beam of light casts a shadow onto a sheet of flashed opal glass viewed from the rear by the observer. The shape of the illumination gradient in the half-shadow is determined by the shape of the effective source, which in turn is controlled by a simple aperture stop in front of the projection lens. The pattern may be modified during observation by using an adjustable aperture.

Moving the screen which casts the shadow produces motion of the half-shadow in the pattern. Fiorentini and Ercoles (1957) obtained oscillating Mach patterns in this way in an apparatus similar to Fry's; the fixed screen was simply replaced by a rotatable eccentric disc. (If the radius of the disc is fairly large the slight arc in the pattern may be neglected.) Frequency of motion was controlled by the frequency of rotation of the disc, and amplitude was controlled by the eccentricity of the axis of rotation. A similar controlled movement of a Mach pattern may be obtained by viewing a fixed pattern in a moving mirror (Bittini, Ercoles, Fiorentini, Ronchi, and Toraldo di Francia, 1960).

The shadow-casting method also lends itself to the study of color effects. Colored gradients of illumination are obtained by inserting colored filters at some point between the source and the screen. Fairly narrow bands of wavelengths may be obtained by this method. In this respect it is superior to using rotating discs and cylinders made with painted sectors or colored papers because they generally reflect very broad bands of wavelengths. Hence, the spectral composition of such colors is impure and difficult to determine exactly.

Complex patterns Superposition of two simple one-dimensional patterns ordinarily produced by rotating discs or cylinders yields complex patterns of illumination that vary in two dimensions. For example, one pattern may be viewed directly through a piece of unsilvered plane glass. Then by tilting the glass to the proper angle, the reflected image of a second pattern may be caused to appear superimposed upon the first. Simple patterns produced by the shadow-casting methods may also be combined into more complex patterns by merely superimposing the separate images formed on the screen by different projectors.

In a similar manner, separate still photographs taken on translucent glass plates may be combined to yield more complex patterns by placing the plates together and viewing them against a uniform field of illumination.* Also schlieren photographs, X-ray photographs, and photographs of diffraction patterns, all yield complex distributions of illumination. There is no scarcity of Mach patterns; the problem is how to measure rather than how to produce them.

Photometric measures of the Mach pattern The distribution of illumination, or light curve, can be determined by conventional methods —some direct, others indirect. For example, a photometer with a very small aperture yields a more or less direct measure of every point on the light curve when scanned across the image plane of a projected pattern of illumination. More often, however, the light curve is determined indirectly. The size and arrangement of critical components of the apparatus—such as the light and dark sectors of rotating discs, or the source, aperture, and shadow-casting screen in a projection apparatus—provide a sufficient basis for calculating the shape of the light curve. Physical or visual photometric measurements at one or two points in the extended light and dark areas of the pattern combined with the above calculations are sufficient to determine the absolute values of every point on the light curve.

Conventional methods of visual photometry cannot ordinarily be used directly to measure the small critical regions of the light curve where sharp bends occur. The aperture of the usual instrument is so large that a sizeable portion of the nonuniform Mach pattern would appear in it. Not only would it be difficult to adjust the uniform comparison field in

* In photographing Mach patterns the development process itself may produce spurious "contrast" effects. The cause of these effects—the so-called "Mackie lines"—is photochemical, not physiological. Great care must be taken to avoid confounding the photographic Mackie lines with the physiological Mach bands. This problem is considered in detail in Chapter 5.

the instrument to match the nonuniform pattern, but it is also possible that with a considerable portion of the pattern exposed the Mach phenomenon itself might significantly influence the appearance of that part of the pattern being measured. Thus, the usual methods of visual photometry are suitable only to measure the extended and more or less evenly illuminated areas of the Mach pattern.

Although there are pitfalls for the unwary in any of the conventional photometric measurements described, the methods are relatively straightforward and simple, at least in principle. Unfortunately, the next problem, that of the proper quantitative measurement of the distribution of the apparent brightness and color of the Mach bands, or the sensation curve, is not so straightforward and simple. Indeed, as late as 1906, Mach remarked that no proper measurement of the sensation curve could be made.

PSYCHOPHYSICAL MEASURES OF THE APPEARANCE OF MACH BANDS

It is easy to see that certain general regions of the Mach pattern appear brighter or dimmer than others, but to determine exactly where the pattern is brighter or dimmer and by exactly how much it varies requires more than unaided observation. To obtain quantitative data, precise psychophysical measurements are required. Contrary to Mach's opinion, such measurements can be made.

Brightness of the Mach bands Estimates of the relative magnitudes of the Mach bands seen under various conditions may be made either by a comparison of the different appearances of the bands in a particular pattern as it is changed, or by a comparison of the bands in two different patterns presented simultaneously. By these methods one can determine quantitatively what changes in a particular pattern lead to an increase or decrease in the brightness of the bands, or how much two patterns must differ to produce dissimilar bands. Such observations, however, do not indicate exactly how the brightness is distributed in a particular pattern or how much the brightness distributions in two patterns will differ. Precise quantitative measures of the distribution of the apparent brightness in the Mach pattern require a further refinement of these simple comparisons.

This refinement consists of determining independently by visual photometry the luminance of some uniform extended field at several levels of intensity. These several calibrated stimuli may then be used as a quantitative scale with which to compare the unknown brightness of the Mach bands. But now the experimenter faces a dilemma. Placing the comparison stimulus close enough to the Mach pattern to permit an accurate comparison may cause either the brightness of the comparison stimulus to be modified by the pattern or the Mach bands themselves to be distorted by the stimulus. If the comparison stimulus is placed far enough from the pattern to avoid these difficulties, however, then it becomes very difficult to make an accurate comparison of the two. The only solution to this predicament is a compromise somewhere between the two extremes. For example, the comparison stimulus can be kept fairly small and located at some distance from the Mach pattern, but still be large enough and close enough to permit a reasonably accurate comparison of the two. Perhaps a better solution is to view the pattern with one eye and the comparison stimulus with the other. This reduces the interaction between the comparison stimulus and the Mach pattern still further because binocular interactions are generally somewhat weaker than monocular interactions and effects of light scatter from one stimulus area to the other are eliminated. Therefore the two stimuli can be closely juxtaposed without deleterious effects by binocular fusion of the two fields as in a stereoscope (Fig. 2.8a).

Another problem still remains, due to the peculiar nature of the dark bands. When they are very dark, these bands cannot be matched by a simple comparison stimulus of any intensity because they are darker than the darkness produced by total absence of light in the comparison field. To extend the range of the comparison stimulus downward to match this unusual darkness, it is necessary to subject the comparison stimulus itself to contrast influences by surrounding it with an illuminated field, as in Figure 2.8b. (See Heinemann, 1955; and Fiorentini and Radici, 1957.) Now these contrast influences must also be measured in order to provide quantitative units for the extended scale. Thus the quantitative psychophysical measurements of the darkest Mach bands are necessarily indirect, and, unfortunately, the more indirect a method of measurement is, the more questionable is its validity. At present, however, we have no choice in the matter; there are no alternative methods for this particular kind of measurement.

The thresholds at which the Mach bands appear can be determined without reference to special comparison stimuli. To do this, some significant part of the Mach pattern, such as the gradient of the half-shadow, is gradually altered until a point is reached at which either the bright or the dark band makes its first appearance; if the band is already visible the pattern is altered in the opposite way until a point is reached at which the band begins to disappear. The observer has only to compare the brightness of the band with the immediately adjacent uniform field. Thus the Mach pattern itself provides the necessary comparison stimulus.

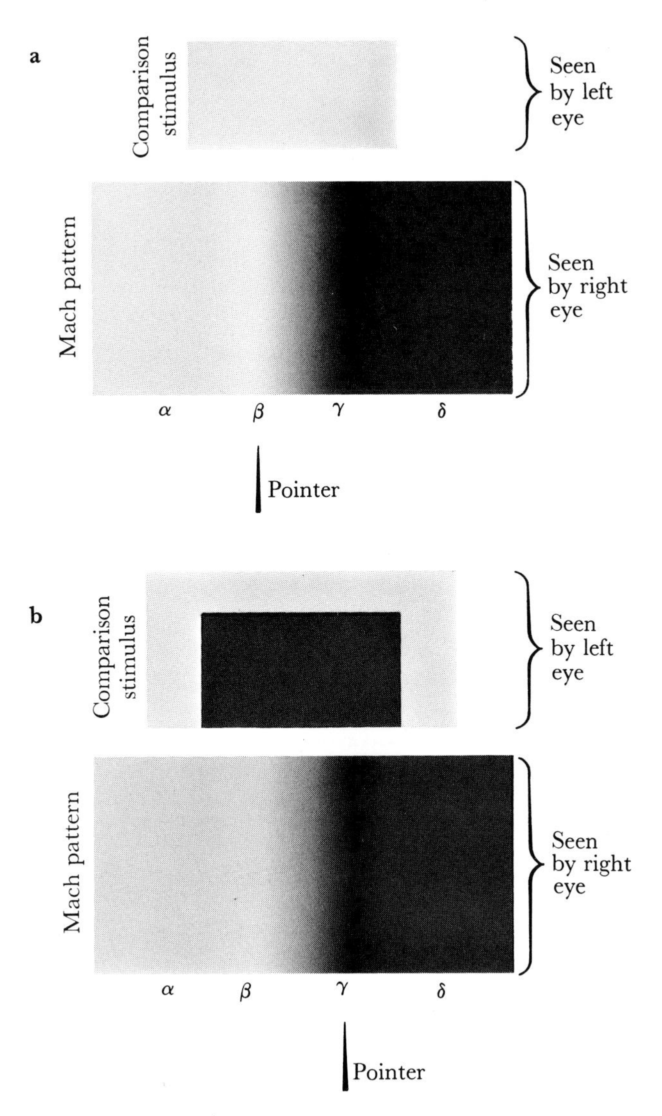

Figure 2.8. *Schema of patterns of illumination for binocular comparison method of measuring* (a) *the brightness and location of the light band, and* (b) *the brightness and location of the dark band. Redrawn after Fiorentini and Radici (1957). The Mach patterns in this figure were painted with an air brush. The light and dark bands are exaggerated for illustrative purposes.*

These threshold measures are analogous to psychophysical measures of minimum conditions on which the Weber-Fechner law was originally based—such as a just detectable real increment in the intensity of an already illuminated field, or in the weight of an object lifted by the observer. The slight difference between the threshold measurements on the Mach pattern and the conventional increment thresholds is that the increment producing the detectable change in the brightness of the bands need not be placed in the same region where the bands are seen. The real illumination intensity at the critical point where the brightness appears to change may even remain constant; the actual change in brightness may be produced, for example, by a change in the gradient of the neighboring half-shadow.

Of course visibility of real increments of illumination at various locations on the Mach pattern may be measured in the usual manner. This is done by momentarily superimposing a small spot of light of low intensity on the region of the pattern under investigation and having the observer report whether or not he detects this small change. As a result of repeated observations with the spot at different levels of intensity, the increment that produces a just noticeable difference at any particular point in the pattern may be determined.

The location of the Mach bands The alignment of two objects is a common instrumental adjustment and observation that can be made easily and accurately. Many investigators have determined the location of the Mach bands in this way. A slender sharp pointer (as in Fig. 2.8) is placed in front of the pattern and adjusted laterally until it is aligned with one edge of a bright or dark band, or with the center of the region of maximum brightness or darkness. Superimposing the pointer directly on the pattern, of course, would change the pattern of illumination reaching the observer's eye, and this change might be sufficient to alter the appearance of the bands. Fortunately, parallel straight line segments of some length may be accurately aligned even when there is a considerable gap between their ends. Thus if the pointer is parallel with the Mach bands, the end of the pointer may be placed some distance from the critical region of the pattern where it presumably has little or no effect.

Another method of locating the bands is to project a very small spot of light on the surface of the rotating disc or other Mach pattern. The observer then adjusts the spot to indicate the location of the maxima, minima, or edges in the pattern of brightness. If the spot is small and rather dim, its effects on the Mach bands are probably correspondingly localized and weak. The spot may be turned off from time to time to permit the observer to reassess his judgment of the location of the feature in question. A small dark fleck on a sheet of glass through which the pattern is observed may be similarly aligned with critical features of the pattern.

AN ANALYSIS OF THE INFLUENCE OF SEVERAL VARIABLES ON THE APPEARANCE OF MACH BANDS

A typical rectilinear Mach pattern, Figure 2.9, in which one edge of a uniform bright field shades gradually into a uniform dark field is essentially one-dimensional and may be represented adequately by the single light curve shown by the heavy line.

Two values of x and two values of y determine the figure of this curve: y_1, the luminance of the dimly illuminated field; y_2, the luminance of the brightly illuminated field; and x_1 and x_2, the locations of the two flections of the curve. (Assume that the pattern extends for a considerable distance along both the x dimension and the z dimension so that "edge-effects" need not be considered here.) Over large ranges of luminances y_1 and y_2, and slopes of the curve from x_1 to x_2, all observers see in this pattern a bright band at x_1 and a dark band at x_2. Usually, the bright band is seen as slightly narrower, more prominent, and more nearly centered on its corresponding flection in the light curve than is the dark band. The exact appearance of the bands in any case is strongly dependent upon the values of the four variables x_1, x_2, y_1, and y_2—that is, upon the slopes and field luminances in the pattern of illumination.

The influence of the slope of the gradient between the uniform fields The main features of a series of observations by Fiorentini and Radici (1958) are summarized in Figure 2.10. As a result of increasing the slope between x_1 and x_2 and keeping y_1 and y_2 constant, the bright band generally becomes slightly narrower and more distinct, but it disappears altogether when the slope becomes an abrupt step. A series of abrupt

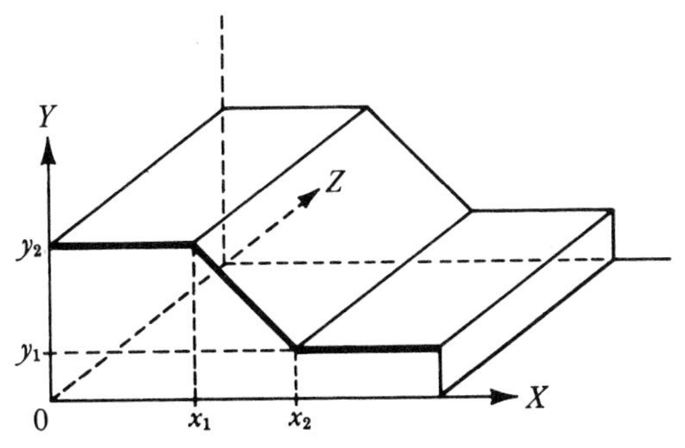

Figure 2.9. *Luminance of typical rectilinear Mach pattern.*

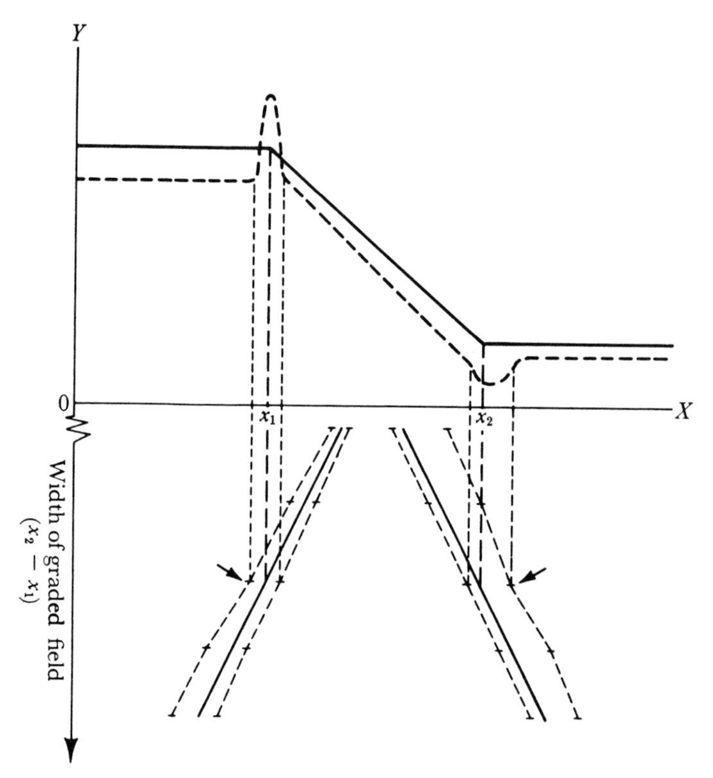

Figure 2.10. *The influence of the slope of the gradient between the uniform fields in a Mach pattern on the widths of the Mach bands. The schema of the Mach bands and the graph of the intensity distribution (above) refer to the set of data points (below) indicated by the arrows. Graph of data redrawn after Fiorentini and Radici (1958). See also Fiorentini (1956) and Ercoles (1957).*

steps, however, does show a curious fluted or scalloped appearance. As the slope is decreased, the bright band becomes wider and less distinct until finally, with very gradual slopes, it disappears altogether. Similarly, the dark band becomes darker and more distinct with increasing slope from x_1 to x_2, but it is not apparent when the slope is an abrupt step. Compared with the behavior of the bright band, the dark band also becomes indistinct when the slope is made very gradual but, in contrast, its width appears to remain constant over a considerable range of change in slope. The bright band generally appears narrower than the dark band in the same pattern and is nearly centered on the flection at x_1 in these rectilinear patterns. For some observers it shifts slightly off center into the uniform bright field when the slope is decreased. The greater part of the dark band, however, always appears in the uniform dark field. The results obtained from different observers commonly reveal consistent individual differences.

McCollough (1955) observed earlier that the width of the bright band decreases markedly as the slope of a concave gradient increases, while the field luminance remains constant. As in the work described above, some observers reported that as the slope decreased the position of the bright band shifted slightly in the direction of the bright field and did not appear to be symmetrically positioned around the flection in the curve. This change in position varied greatly with the individual observer. (No observations were made on similar properties of the dark band because the pattern used in these experiments consisted of the uniform bright field and the adjacent graded field only.)

Using the method of binocular comparison previously described, Fiorentini and Radici (1957, 1958) measured the apparent brightness of the Mach bands. Boundaries of the bands were not determined exactly.

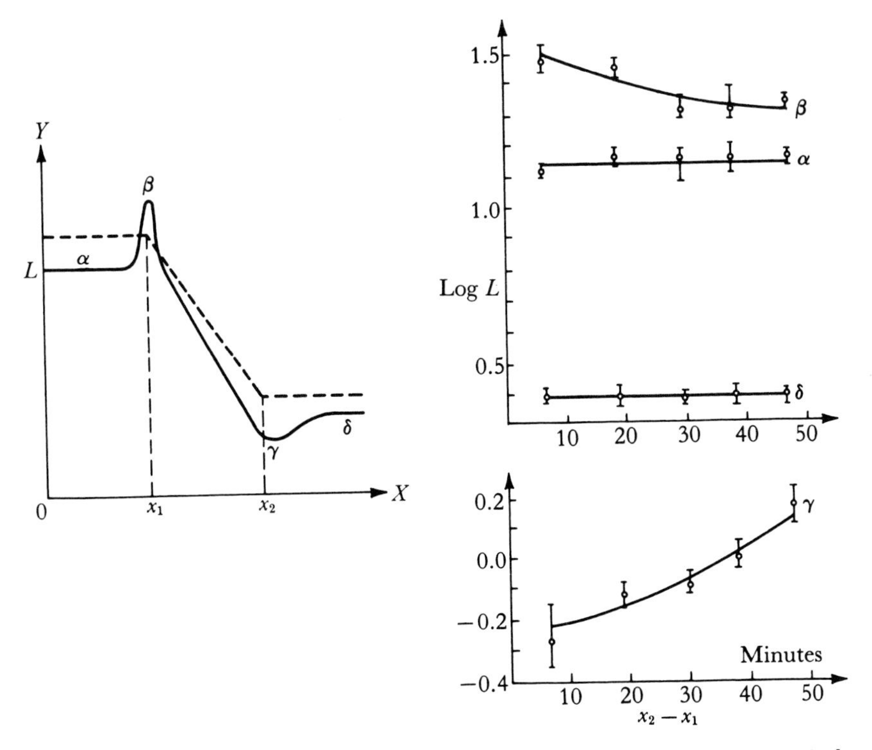

Figure 2.11. Graph on the right shows measurements by one observer of the brightness of a Mach pattern at the four points α, β, γ, and δ (indicated in the graph on the left) with various slopes of the gradient of the zone x_1, x_2. Graph of data from Fiorentini and Radici (1958).

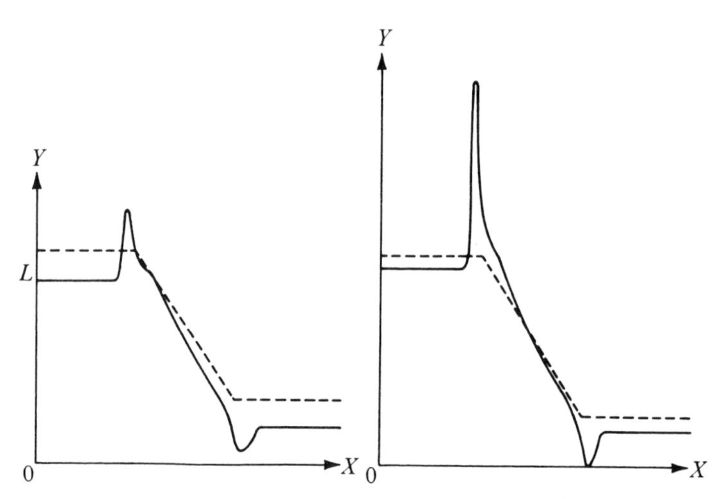

Figure 2.12. *Measurements of the brightness of the same Mach pattern made by two skilled observers. From Fiorentini and Radici (1957).*

Measurements were made only at single points in the uniform bright field (α), at the maximum of the bright band (β), the minimum of the dark band (γ), and in the uniform dark field (δ). The luminances of the bright and dark fields were held constant and the effects of changing the slope of the gradient between them were determined. Brightness measurements made by one observer are shown in Figure 2.11. In general, the brightnesses of the uniform fields at some distance from the intervening gradient remain constant for all slopes. The amplitude of the bright band increases slightly with the increasing slope of the gradient, although some observers report no change, and the brightness of the dark band decreases significantly. Individual differences are great; absolute magnitudes of measurements by different observers under comparable conditions may vary by factors of as much as 3 to 1 (Fig. 2.12).

It is not surprising, therefore, to find that measurements made by other experimenters using quite different methods do not agree exactly with those illustrated above. For example, some measurements by Lowry and DePalma (1961) showed little change in the amplitudes of the bright and dark bands with variations in the slope of the gradient over an intermediate range. As in the above experiments, they did find that the bright band was more pronounced than the dark band and that it became significantly narrower with increasing slopes.

To make these measurements, a narrow slit of light was placed next to the Mach pattern and both were viewed with the same eye while the brightness of the slit was adjusted to match the adjacent zone of the pattern. By moving the slit along the pattern, several points on the sensation curve were determined. The advantage of this method is that the locations of the points measured can be determined precisely. But as far as the brightness measurements themselves are concerned, the method seems questionable because the apparent brightness of the comparison slit itself may be affected by the distribution of light in the Mach pattern. In addition, measures of the brightness of the dark band are restricted to the narrow range from zero to the low luminance of the uniform dark field. If the band should appear darker than the darkness produced by the absence of light, as is often the case, the luminance of the comparison slit cannot be set below zero to match it. Although the exact coincidence of the light and sensation curves in the uniform fields that was reported by Lowry and DePalma should not be expected, according to most of the current theories, the results in general agree qualitatively with those obtained by others.

Hartwig (1958) measured the magnitude of the bright band by introducing an adjustable step increment in the bright field and matching it with the maximum of the bright band. According to Hartwig, it is possible to superimpose the step upon the band itself without altering the brightness of the band. But this method, which actually consists of changing the luminance of the entire bright field and adding an abrupt step to the gradient, seems questionable since both the gradient and field luminance are known to affect the appearance of the bands. Nevertheless, Hartwig's findings are in general agreement with those obtained by other methods.

Although there are differences in detail among the results obtained by different observers and by the use of different methods, there is satisfactory agreement on the basic character of the phenomena. As illustrated schematically in Figure 2.13, the effects usually become more

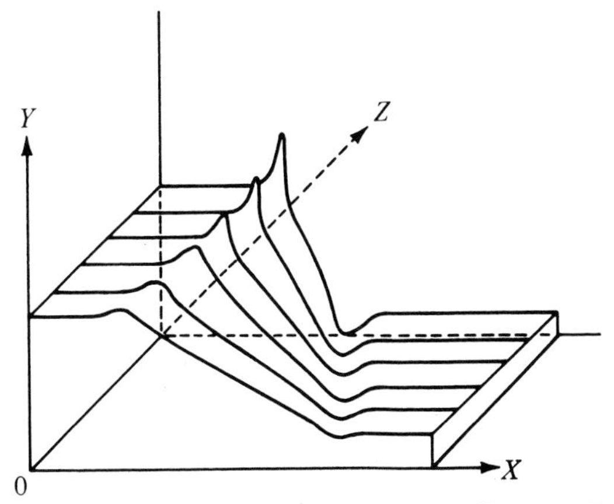

Figure 2.13. *Schema showing influence of slope of gradient on the appearance of Mach bands. Compare with actual data in Figures 2.10-2.12.*

pronounced as the slope of the gradient is increased between bright and dark fields of constant luminance. The amplitude of the bright band becomes much greater and its width narrower. The amplitude of the dark band becomes somewhat greater, but its width remains about the same. The bands are not seen at all when the slope is very small or very large. In the latter case, however, less sharply localized "border contrast" effects may be seen.

It is important to note that in patterns with constant field luminances the width of the graded zone and the slope of the gradient are not independent variables. On the basis of these experiments, therefore, one cannot say whether the effects observed depend upon width, or slope, or both.

It is evident that the bright and dark bands are not symmetrical. This asymmetry also appears in measurements of the increment threshold, that is, the visibility of small spots of light added to the Mach pattern (Fiorentini, Jeanne, and Toraldo di Francia, 1955). The threshold luminance ΔL follows neither the objective luminance curve nor the apparent brightness changes throughout the pattern. The elevation of the threshold corresponds fairly well to the increase in brightness, but there is no minimum in the threshold corresponding to the minimum in the brightness of the dark band. As the slope of the gradient is decreased with the luminance of the bright and dark fields held constant, the maximum value of the increment required to reach threshold decreases (Fig. 2.14). Changes in this peak value correspond roughly to changes in the brightness of the Mach band. Of course there is no reason, a priori, to expect to find any particular relation between the increment threshold and the appearance of the Mach bands, but it is rather surprising to find that the threshold is markedly affected by the bright band and is not at all affected by the dark band.

The observations above were made using central (foveal) vision. Viewed at an angle some degrees from the fovea, the typical Mach pattern does not give rise to Mach bands. Instead the whole gradient appears as a more or less uniformly bright stripe between the two uniform fields, and is the brightest region in the pattern. Correspondingly, the increment threshold is generally higher across the entire gradient than when the pattern is viewed foveally (Fiorentini, 1957).

Luminance of the uniform fields In his original investigations, Mach concluded that the appearance of the bands is unaltered if the illumination at every point on the pattern is multiplied by some constant factor, but the bands tend to vanish if a large uniform increment is added to the entire pattern. These observations were only qualitative, however; and with the methods of illumination then available the changes were

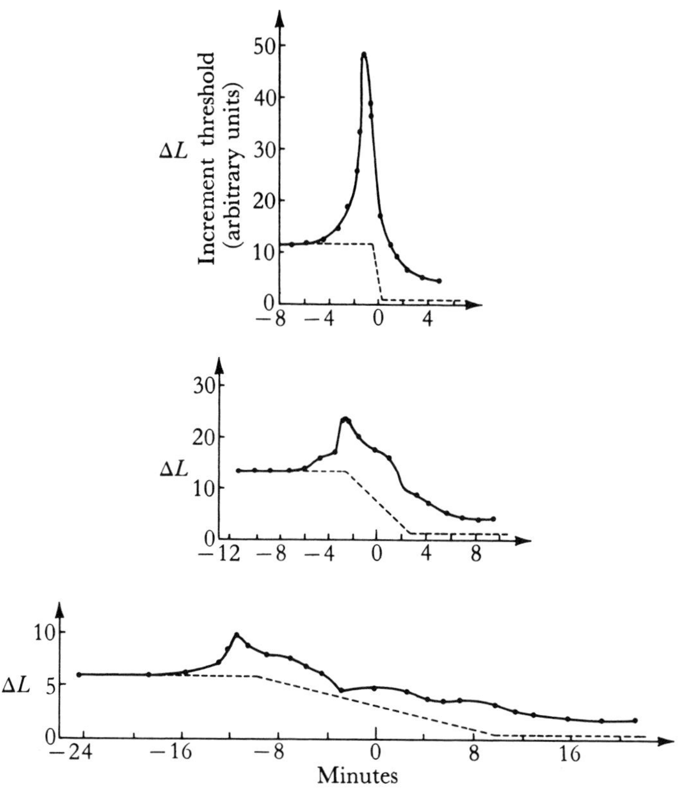

Figure 2.14. *Increment threshold in arbitrary units (points and solid lines) plotted against distance (minutes of visual angle) from center of Mach pattern. Location of pattern and slope of gradient indicated by dashed line. From Fiorentini, Jeanne, and Toraldo di Francia (1955).*

probably limited to small ranges. Unfortunately, this general problem has not yet been studied in detail. There have been only a very few quantitative studies on the effects of the levels of field luminances (y_1 and y_2 in Fig. 2.9) on the appearance of the Mach bands.

Observing a pattern with a uniform bright field and a graded darker adjacent field (which produces the bright band only) McCollough (1955) found that the width of the band decreased with an increasing luminance of the bright field when the slope of the gradient remained constant. Hartwig (1958) found that with a constant width of the half-shadow and an increasing bright field luminance, which also increased the slope of the gradient, the amplitude of the bright band increased. Corresponding measurements on the dark bands have not yet been made.

The visibility threshold of the bright and dark bands as a function of the luminance of the neighboring bright and dark fields respectively was

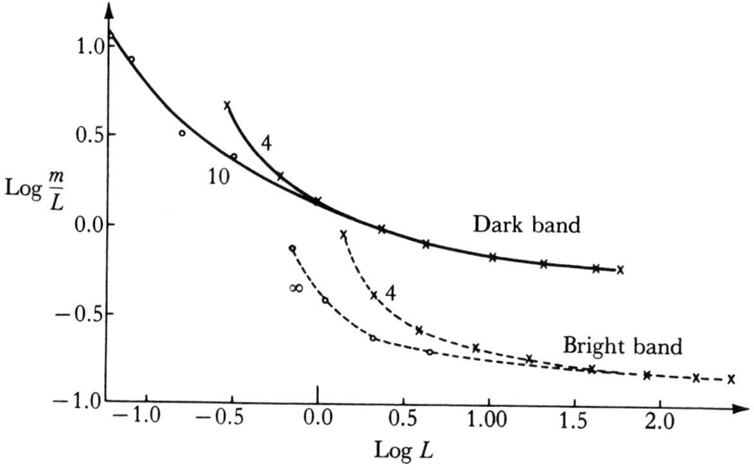

Figure 2.15. Log m/L plotted against L for the dark band (solid lines) and for the bright band (dashed lines). From Ercoles and Fiorentini (1959).

investigated by Ercoles and Fiorentini (1959). The measure of the threshold was the minimum slope m of the gradient between the bright and dark fields (with field luminances held constant) that was just sufficient to produce visible bands. Figure 2.15 shows results for several luminance levels of the fields with constant ratios of bright field luminance to dark field luminance. For the infinite ratio, the dark field was totally dark. All values of L used to plot the curve for the bright band refer to the bright field luminance; for the dark band, the dark field luminance. The number near each curve is the ratio of the bright field luminance to the dark field luminance for that particular curve.

At very low values of L, the bands are not visible at all. As L is increased, the bands become visible and the ratio m/L required for visibility decreases rapidly; that is, as the field luminance increases the necessary slope decreases. At low intermediate levels of luminance, m/L decreases almost directly with increasing luminance; in other words, over a short range of low intermediate luminances approximately the same slope is required to produce bands that are just visible. At still higher luminances the ratio m/L decreases very slowly with increasing L, which means that the slope necessary for the bands to be just visible increases.

The influence of color on the Mach bands Since no color phenomena are seen when the bands are produced with white light, Mach concluded that all of the component colors in this light must be strengthened or weakened to the same degree. This conclusion is supported by the fact that when a disc with black and white sectors is illuminated with monochromatic light of any color, it shows the brighter and darker rings in much the same way as when it is illuminated with white light.

Mach did observe that if the white sectors of his discs were replaced by one color, and the dark sectors by a second color, then in place of the bright line there was a prominence of the first color and in place of the dark line a prominence of the second color. But these effects are not very pronounced. If instead of using two colors, for example if one sector of the disc is colored red and the other is gray, then at the flection in the predominantly red zone of the disc a reddish band is seen, at the flection in the predominantly gray zone a complementary greenish band. This latter result is analogous to "induced" colors in shadows.

Observations made since by Thouless (1922-23), Koffka and Harrower (1931), Fry (1948), and Ercoles-Guzzoni and Fiorentini (1958) show that the color effects observed in Mach patterns depend mainly upon luminance differences, rather than color differences. If fields of illumination

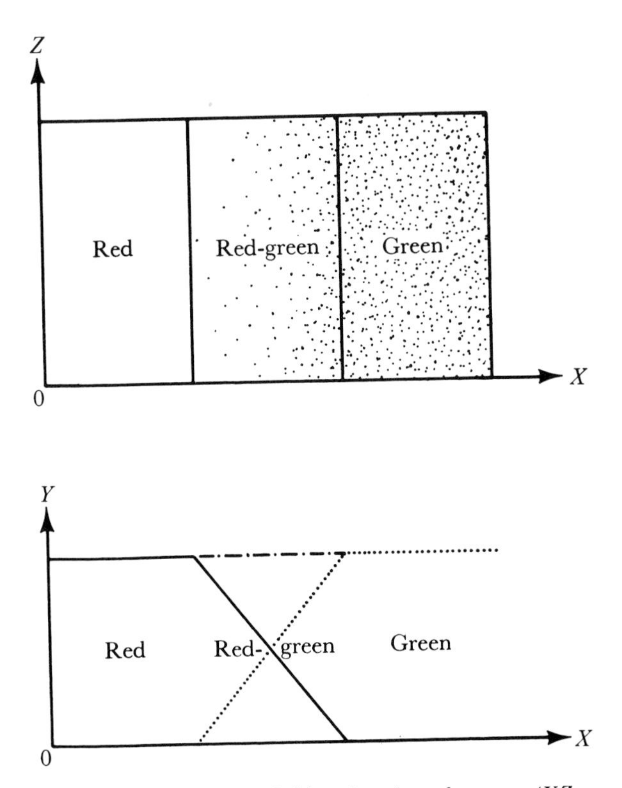

Figure 2.16. *Partially overlapping fields of red and green (XZ coordinates) which are graded and superimposed so as to yield a field of constant luminance (XY coordinates).*

are produced that have color gradients but no luminance gradients (Fig. 2.16), then no visual effects comparable to the Mach bands are seen. How these findings are to be reconciled with the known facts of color contrast is a problem requiring further study.

Mach bands in microscopic images The bands seen in microscopic images (Watrasiewicz, 1963; Charman and Watrasiewicz, 1964) differ markedly from those seen in the macroscopic distributions of illumination described above. The basic difference is a multiple band structure as shown in Figure 2.17. At least one bright band and two dark bands were always observed on the low intensity side of the field and one bright band on the high intensity side. Occasionally a narrow dark band was also seen in the high intensity field, adjacent to the bright band. The bright and dark bands are more pronounced if the cone of illumination is narrow (small condenser lens aperture).

In these experiments the amplitudes of the Mach bands were measured

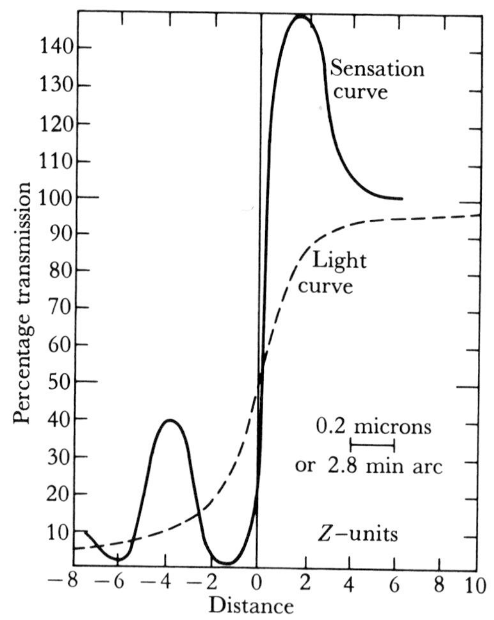

Figure 2.17. *Objective distribution of illumination (dashed line) and corresponding subjective distribution (solid line) in a microscopic image. Distances perpendicular to the edge are indicated in terms of three different but equivalent units. These are: linear units (microns) in the object space; angular subtense (minutes) in the image space of the microscope; and dimensionless diffraction units (Z-units). The diffraction units are defined by the relation $Z = 2\pi/\lambda\,(NA)\eta$ where η is the linear measure in the object space, NA is the numerical aperture of the microscope objective, and λ the wavelength of the light. From Watrasiewicz (1963).*

by a monocular photometric matching technique similar to the one described earlier in this chapter. The comparison slit, of which the luminance could be varied, was projected into the focal plane of the eye piece of the microscope. It was parallel to and below the edge which produced the Mach bands. Measurements of the position of the bands were carried out with a fine pointer made of wire 1μ in diameter, placed in the focal plane of the eye piece, perpendicular to the bands. The pointer could be adjusted laterally by means of a micrometer. The physical distribution of light was determined by photoelectric scanning of the image through the same microscope used for the visual observations. All measurements were made using green light of wavelength 530 ± 50 mμ.

The bands have been seen before by microscopists, but they have assumed them to be diffraction bands resulting from the coherent illumination of the object in the image plane. According to Watrasiewicz (1963), the relative positions of the bands with different cones of illumination and the physical measurements of the distribution of illumination both rule out the possibility that the bands are diffraction effects.

Charman and Watrasiewicz (1964) note that from the point of view of the microscopist such a subjective enhancement of the sharpness of an edge may be beneficial; it may aid in the detection and recognition of detail in the image. Also, it will improve the precision, though not the accuracy, of measurements of object size. There is the disadvantage, however, that the subjective fringes may be mistaken for real detail in the object, such as a surrounding membrane, and considerable care is therefore necessary in interpreting the image. These problems are considered in more detail in Chapters 4 and 5. See also Kühl (1928 and 1951).

EYE MOVEMENTS AND THEIR INFLUENCE ON THE MACH BANDS

Our eyes are continually in motion, even when we attempt to fixate steadily on an object. To demonstrate these small involuntary eye movements, observe the position of a small afterimage relative to some reference mark on an object that is viewed normally. The afterimage and the mark cannot be kept in perfect register; therefore, fixation on the mark is not steady. This procedure was the method used by Dodge (1907) to make quantitative measurements of this so-called physiological nystagmus.

The physiological nystagmus is even more apparent if the afterimage of a grid rather than a point is used (Verheijen, 1961, 1963). Fixate steadily on the black dot at the center of the grid in Figure 2.18 for 30 seconds or more, and then fixate on the white dot in the center of the

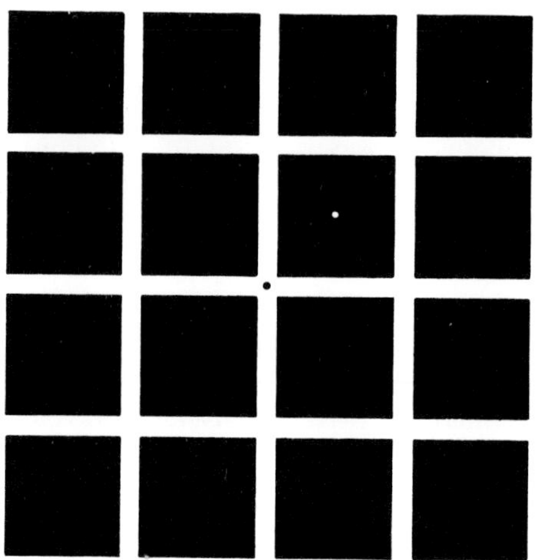

Figure 2.18. *Grid for subjective demonstration of eye movements by means of after images. From Verheijen (1961).*

black square to the right and above the black dot. The negative after-image of the entire figure can soon be seen distinctly. It is somewhat blurred, of course, because your eyes were actually moving while you attempted to fixate on the black dot. For the same reason, no matter how carefully one attempts to control fixation on the white dot, the negative afterimage of the grid will seem to move considerably with respect to the real grid. This figure also shows an interesting contrast phenomenon: shadowy dark patches appear at the intersections of the white bars. They are not seen at the intersection which is directly fixated, however, but are quite distinct at all the others.

Records of the frequency and amplitude of minute eye motions have been obtained by means of an optical lever (Fig. 2.19) provided by light reflected from a mirror on a contact lens tightly fitted to the eye (Ratliff and Riggs, 1950). Analysis of the records show four main components of the eye movements: (1) small rapid motions with a median extent (peak to trough) of about 20 seconds angle of rotation, and frequencies ranging from 30 to 70 or more cycles per second; (2) larger and slower oscillatory motions of very irregular frequency and extent; (3) slow drifts of a few minutes of arc in one direction or another; and (4) rapid jerks with an average extent of about 5 minutes of arc occurring at irregular intervals, sometimes apparently compensating for the drifts. The total movement due to the combined effects of these motions over a period of three or four seconds is usually less than ten minutes of arc during the steadiest fixations.

On the basis of these results, the following conclusions may be drawn regarding the motions of the retinal image of the object being fixated. (1) During a fixation period of three or four seconds the image of the object being fixated may move across a total of 25 to 50 receptors. (2) The slower motions, drifts, and jerks may carry the retinal image across approximately a dozen receptors. (3) The small rapid motions move the retinal image across two or three receptors at most. The amplitudes of these rapid motions are so small, however, that under optimal conditions of fixation the retinal image of an object exposed for a hundredth of a second or so is virtually stationary. (See Riggs, Armington, and Ratliff, 1954.)

Spark illumination of the Mach pattern Although they had not been measured precisely, these involuntary eye movements were known to exist at the time of Mach's original investigations. Therefore he considered the possibility that the bright and dark bands might be a special

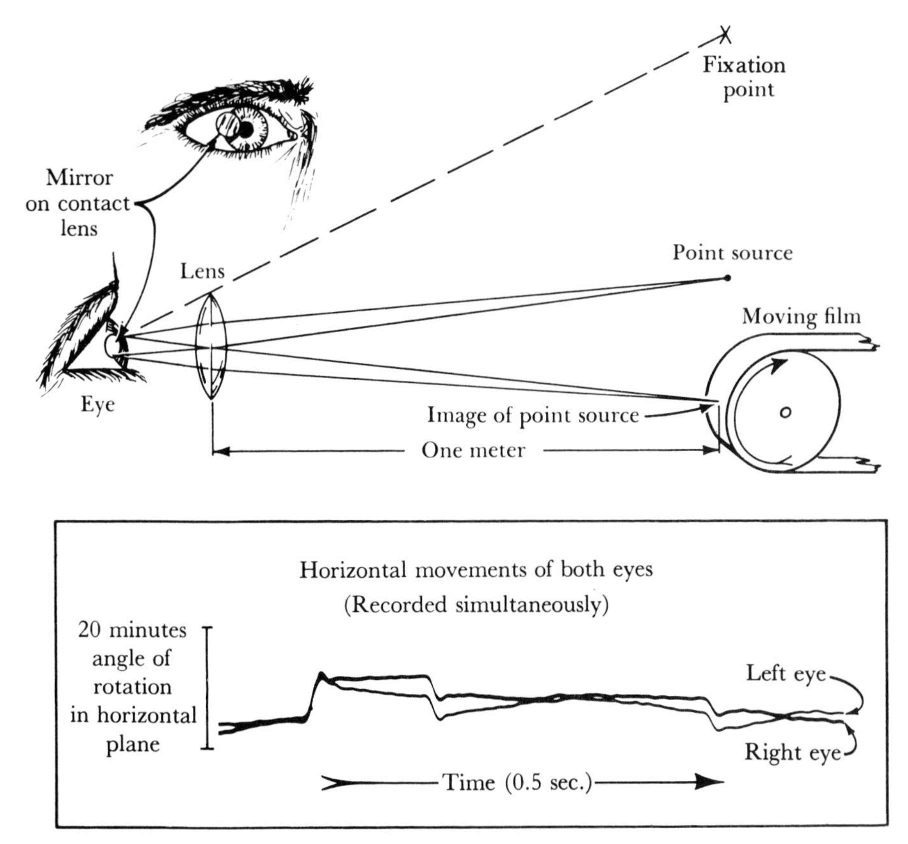

Figure 2.19. *Contact lens and mirror technique for objective recording of eye movements. Schematic redrawn after Ratliff and Riggs (1950).*

case of "successive contrast"—that is, an enhancement or diminution of the apparent brightness as a particular receptor moved successively from the bright field to the dark field and back again. In order to test this possibility, Mach observed stationary patterns illuminated by an electric spark from a Leyden jar. On photographs of the usual rotating discs, the bands were either very weak and indistinct or not seen at all. They could be seen fairly distinctly, however, on the striped patterns Mach used (see Plate III in Mach's first paper in Part Two), although they were broader and less distinct than when viewed under steady illumination.

The fact that the bands can be seen under these conditions, even though indistinctly, indicates that eye movements are not their sole cause. But it is uncertain from this experiment whether the indistinctness results from the extremely short duration of the illumination or from the effective elimination of motion. Some answers have been provided by two other methods of study: controlled movement of the Mach pattern, and optical compensation of eye movements to produce a motionless image on the retina. The latter method, unlike Mach's momentary electric spark, permits prolonged viewing of the stationary pattern on the retina.

Controlled movement of the Mach pattern Bittini, Ercoles, Fiorentini, Ronchi, and Toraldo di Francia (1960) investigated the visibility of moving Mach bands by oscillating a typical Mach pattern perpendicularly to the line of sight. The results of several experiments are shown in Figure 2.20. Visibility of the bands was measured in terms of the greatest visual angle (α) subtended by the gradient at which the bands could just be seen. Field luminances were held constant. For a given angular amplitude of motion (ϑ), visibility at first increases with increasing frequency of motion, passes through a maximum at a frequency in the neighborhood of two to four cycles per second, and then decreases with higher frequencies of motion. For the several amplitudes investigated, the larger the amplitude of motion, the larger the maximum width of the gradient that produced just visible bands, and the smaller the frequency of motion corresponding to this maximum. The results for the bright band and the dark band are similar, but not identical.

These results were also analyzed in terms of the time gradient of illumination. If the oscillation has the amplitude ϑ, the luminance at a fixed point in a gradient of angular width α varies by the amount $L_1 - L_2 = (L_a - L_c)\ \vartheta/\alpha$. If t is the half period of the oscillation, then the ratio $(L_1 - L_2)/t$ is the mean variation of the luminance per second at any point remaining within the gradient. Results plotted in these terms are shown in Figure 2.21.

As the time gradient $(L_1 - L_2)/t$ increases from zero, the spatial gradi-

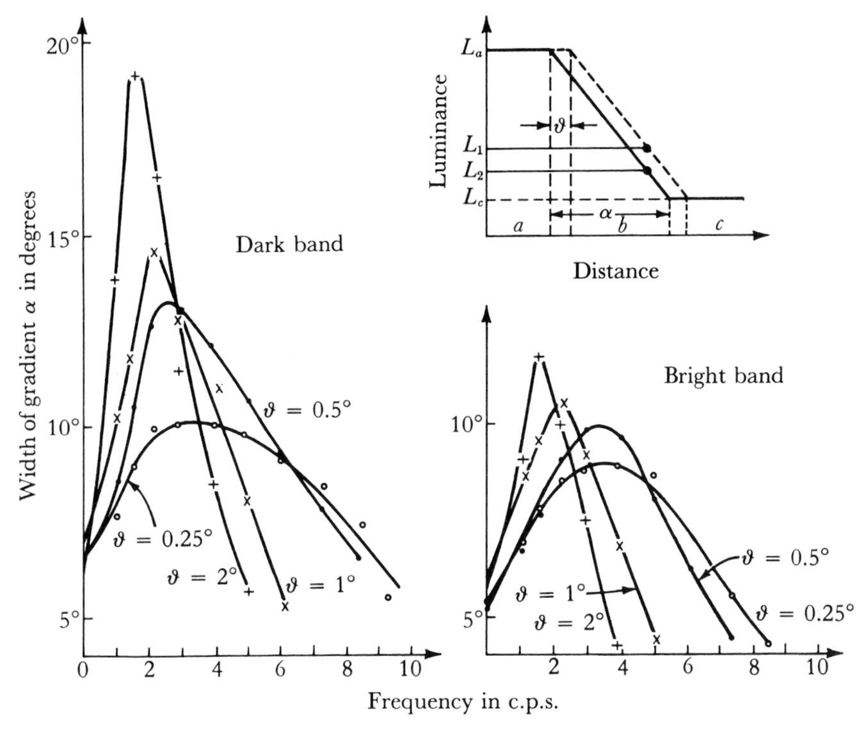

Figure 2.20. *Width of gradient (α) required for bands to be visible in Mach pattern oscillated at various frequencies (c.p.s.) for four amplitudes of motion (ϑ). From Bittini, Ercoles, Fiorentini, Ronchi, and Toraldo di Francia (1960).*

ent $(L_a - L_c)/\alpha$ required for the bands to be just visible decreases at first. As the time gradient increases further, the spatial gradient necessary for visibility of the bands passes through a minimum and then begins to increase. The greater the angular amplitude of the motion, the lower the minimum spatial gradient, the higher the time gradient required to reach the minimum, and the smaller the slope of the subsequent increase.

Thus if the image of the Mach pattern is oscillated on the retina, a smaller luminance gradient is required at the lower temporal gradients for the bands to be just visible. Small temporal gradients enhance the visibility of the bands by approximately the same amount no matter what the frequency and amplitude of the movement. At low frequencies, however, there is less real difference in the motion of the image on the retina with different amplitudes and frequencies than one might expect. The explanation is simple. Using the contact lens and mirror technique described above, Fiorentini and Ercoles (1957) found that the eye tended to follow the oscillation of the pattern when the frequency of movement

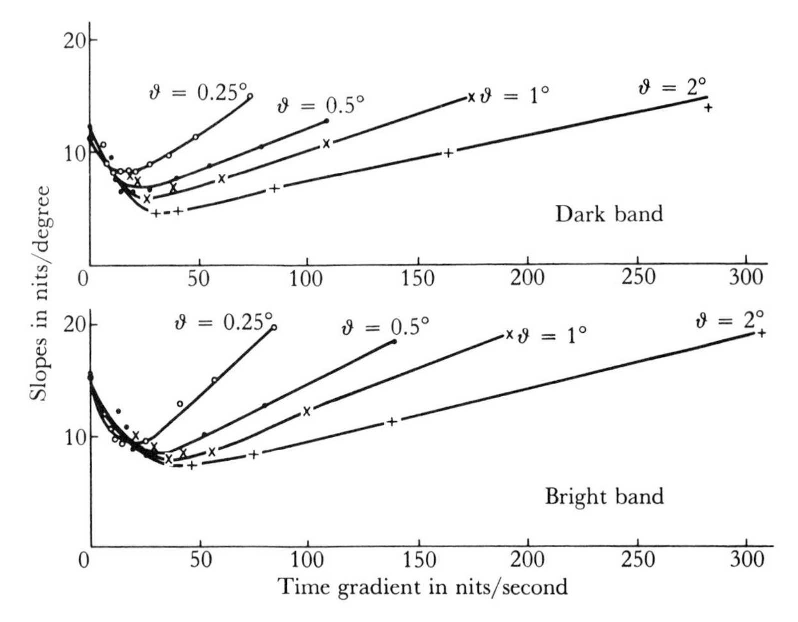

Figure 2.21. *Slope of luminance gradient (nits/degree) required for bands in oscillating Mach pattern to be visible plotted as a function of the temporal gradient of the luminance (nits/sec). (The nit is a unit of luminance equal to 1 candela per square meter). From Bittini, Ercoles, Fiorentini, Ronchi, and Toraldo di Francia (1960). (See also Ronchi and Toraldo di Francia, 1957.)*

was slow. (See also Fender and Nye, 1961; and Dallos and Jones, 1963.) If these movements are considered and proper corrections are made in the calculations of the temporal gradients, then the descending branches of the curves in Figure 2.21 coincide and all reach approximately the same minimum value. At higher frequencies the eye cannot follow the moving pattern with any precision and the effects of different amplitudes and frequencies of motion become evident.

These experiments show that the visibility of the Mach bands is improved significantly by slow oscillatory movements of the observed pattern. Thus if the temporal gradients are not too steep, they, as well as spatial gradients, contribute to the appearance of the Mach bands. The possible physiological bases of these phenomena are considered in Chapter 4. (See also Fiorentini, 1958 and 1961.)

Appearance of Mach bands with a motionless retinal image When Mach observed the Mach bands by illuminating the field with a spark from a Leyden jar, the illumination was so brief that significant eye movements were unlikely to occur. Naturally the short duration of the illumination alone would be expected to have a deleterious effect on the visibility of the bands. The method used by Riggs, Ratliff, and Keesey (1961) has the advantage of providing a stationary image on the retina which can be observed for long periods of time. Furthermore, the stationary image can be compared directly with an identical image moving normally on the retina. (The stationary image is obtained by projecting the pattern on the viewing screen by way of a mirror mounted on a contact lens fitted to the observer's eye so that the pattern moves as the eye moves. This method is described in detail in Chapter 4.)

Earlier experiments (Ditchburn and Ginsborg, 1952; Riggs, Ratliff, Cornsweet, and Cornsweet, 1953) had shown that contours and discontinuities in stabilized retinal images gradually fade from view, and the visual field where the image had appeared takes on a uniform appearance even though the image is physically unchanged on the retina. Stabilization of the retinal image also has this effect on the appearance of the Mach bands.

In these experiments a split field of the Mach pattern was shown to the subject; the half just above the fixation point was viewed normally, and the lower half was motionless on the retina. The subject reported whether the fields appeared to be the same or different. During a one-second exposure, observers report that the two images appear the same. With longer exposure intervals, however, the stationary image fades significantly; and sooner or later, depending upon the slope of the gradient in patterns with fixed field luminances, the stationary image always appears dimmer than the normal moving image. The bands and eventually the entire pattern, fade out and disappear altogether; the more vivid the bands are, the longer is the time required for them to disappear. Of course, if one stares fixedly at any object the retinal image is stabilized to some extent and the contours fade out. Therefore the normally viewed bands may tend to disappear also, but their disappearance times are generally much longer than those for the properly stabilized images.*

The stabilized image technique offers an improved method for the study of the effects of controlled motion. The Mach patterns can first be immobilized on the retina and then moved with any desired frequency and amplitude of motion by deviating the projection path in the stabilization system. This eliminates altogether the effect of uncontrolled eye movements; the controlled motion introduced into the system is the only effective motion. A preliminary investigation found that relatively large slow movements (1 minute of arc, 3 cycles per second) lengthen the time

* A curious effect is seen if, after the Mach patterns viewed under the motionless condition have disappeared completely, a uniform field is substituted for the field containing the pattern. A distinct negative afterimage of the previously invisible pattern then appears.

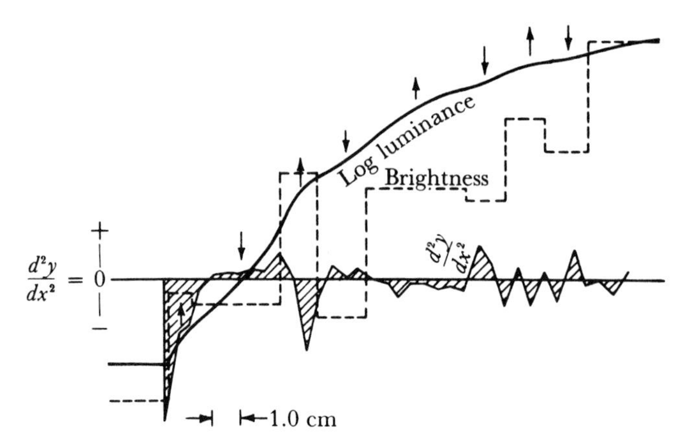

Figure 2.22. *Log luminance curve of radial cross section of electron diffraction pattern, brightness curve through same cross section showing relative brightness of Mach rings, and second derivative function of log luminance curve derived by numerical differentiation. From Burnham and Jackson (1955).*

during which the images remain visible. Smaller and faster movements do not seem to help maintain the visibility of the bands. These results are in general agreement with those reported by Bittini et al., (1960) but the problem has not yet been investigated in detail.

As Mach concluded, the typical appearance of Mach bands is not directly dependent on eye movements. For the bands to be visible, however, may require transient effects produced either by the onset and cessation of illumination under the stationary retinal image conditions, or by motion of the image on the retina, but motion *per se* is not required. (The effects of eliminating both spatial and temporal transients could be investigated by means of a gradual temporal onset and termination of the illumination of a spatially stabilized retinal image of a Mach pattern, but the appearance of the pattern in such an arrangement has not yet been studied.)

MACH BANDS AND SIMILAR PHENOMENA IN COMPLEX PATTERNS

Mach noted in his first investigations that sharp flections in the light curve are not necessary for the production of the bands. Although light distributions which have rounded curves do also show the bands, they are less pronounced than in the patterns with sharper curvatures.

It is probable that the Mach bands or analogous phenomena occur in all patterns of illumination. They are more noticeable in the simple rectilinear patterns described above not only because they are more pronounced but also because the actual rectilinear physical distribution of light in these simple, essentially one-dimensional patterns is easy to visualize and remember. In short, deviations from the expected brightness are noticed only when the physical pattern is extremely simple or when there is some reason to measure a complex pattern exactly.

An example of the latter situation, in which microdensitometric traces were made of the electron diffraction patterns of certain gas molecules, was described by Burnham and Jackson (1955). In this method films are exposed to the diffraction pattern, developed, and then diffusely illuminated from behind. A characteristic series of concentric rings of various widths and brightnesses, which may be used to identify the gas molecules, is seen. For more exact measurements, a microdensitometer is used to measure the varying density of the film along a radius of the circular pattern. The light and dark rings seen on the transilluminated film do not conform closely to the densitometer tracing (Fig. 2.22). In general, however, the light and dark bands correspond to and are approximately centered on upward and downward undulations, respectively, in the log luminance curve of the diffraction pattern, that is, on minimum and maximum values of d^2y/dx^2.

Such complex curvilinear patterns are, of course, much more typical than the simple rectilinear patterns. As Mach pointed out, because of the dioptric imperfections of the eye the retinal image, even that of a simple rectilinear pattern with sharp flections, will always be blurred. The sharp flections in the external physical stimulus will actually be mere curves in the image on the receptor mosaic. Thus, if we think of the proximal (or retinal) stimulus rather than the distal (or external) stimulus, we are nearly always dealing with a more complex curvilinear pattern (cf. Ludvigh, 1953a and 1953b). We will return to this problem in Chapter 4.

The influence of an "edge" on remote parts of a visual pattern All of the above investigations suggest that a particular part of a visual pat-

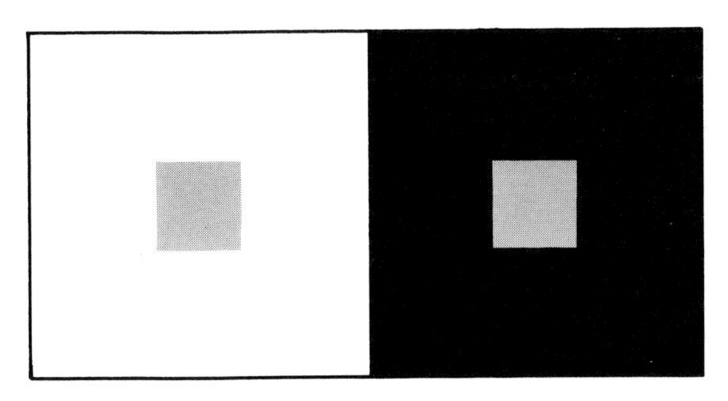

Figure 2.23. *Simultaneous brightness contrast. The two gray squares in the figure are physically identical, i.e., printed by the same process, but the one surrounded by black appears much brighter than the one surrounded by white.*

tern has an influence mainly on the appearance of nearby parts and that this influence diminishes rapidly with distance. But some contrast phenomena are not consistent with this view. Many familiar brightness contrast and color contrast effects appear surprisingly uniform over extended areas where, assuming some graded influence in the visual system, graded changes in brightness or color would be expected (see Fig. 2.23).

O'Brien (1958) has reported some remarkable effects in which the brightness over the entire surfaces of two adjacent areas appears to depend strongly upon the nature of the transition from one area to the other, that is, upon the nature of the "edge" common to the two areas. Some examples using rotating discs are shown in Figure 2.24. The familiar border contrast is observed by means of a simple step. With a very gradual S-shaped transition, no edge is apparent and the disc appears uniform from the center to the circumference. Finally, with a sharp edge next to the black sector and a gradual slope away from it, the inner portion of the disc appears as bright or brighter than the outer portion. The apparent brightness relations are the reverse of the actual physical intensity relations. (See also MacLeod, 1947, and Hake and Auerback, 1956.)

A similar phenomenon (Fig. 2.25) has been described by Cornsweet

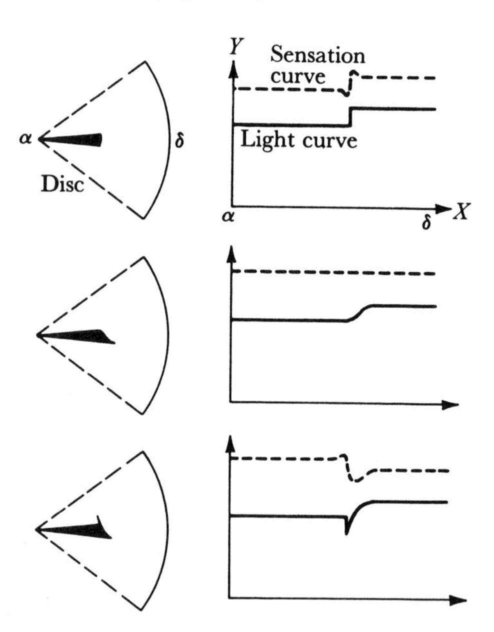

Figure 2.24. Light curve (solid line) and sensation curve (broken line) measured from center (α) to circumference (δ) of three white discs with black sectors when in rapid rotation. One quadrant of each disc is shown at the left of the corresponding graph. Redrawn after O'Brien (1958).

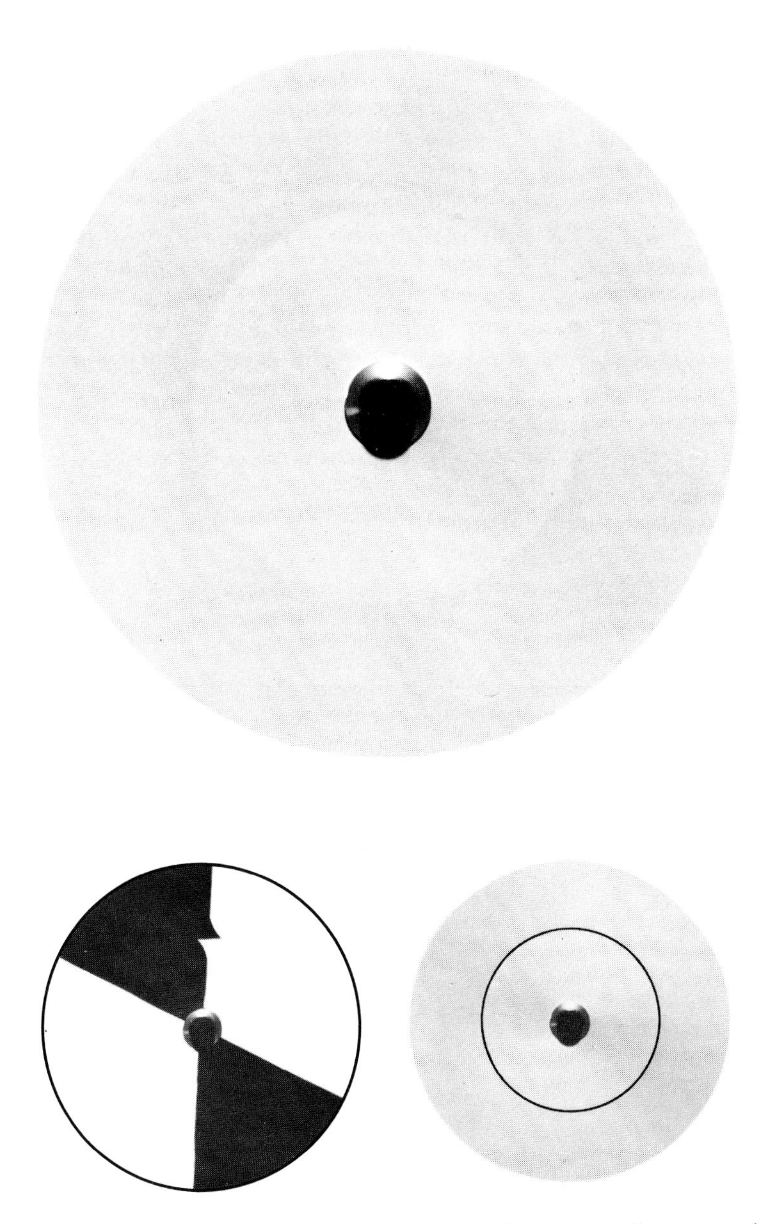

Figure 2.25. *Difference in brightness of two adjacent annular zones of equal luminance caused by the nature of the transition from one zone to the other. Photograph courtesy of T. N. Cornsweet.*

(personal communication). The inner and outer zones of the disc shown in the left inset appear quite different when the disc is rotated, but if there were no discontinuity in the sector the disc would appear uniformly bright from center to circumference (as in Fig. 2.1). When the transition is masked with a heavy line as in the right inset, making it a simple step down and up in intensity, then the inner and outer zones of the same disc appear equally bright. This apparent difference in brightness takes some time to develop. The reader can easily demonstrate this for himself by cutting a ring out of black paper and observing the disc while alternately covering and uncovering the transition from the inner to the outer zone.

These "edge" effects, the Mach bands, and other contrast phenomena in vision no doubt must be intimately related. All are strongly dependent upon the spatial distribution of illumination and all must share some underlying physiological mechanisms in common. What these mechanisms may be is a most important problem in visual physiology.

Who hath measured the waters in the hollow of his hand, and meted out heaven with the span, and comprehended the dust of the earth in a measure, and weighed the mountains in scales, and the hills in a balance? Isaiah 40:12

CHAPTER THREE *Mathematical models of neural networks*

In the one hundred years since the discovery of Mach bands a number of explanations have been proposed for them. Generally, the explanations have been expressed in the form of mathematical models of neural networks in which opposing excitatory and inhibitory influences are integrated to yield patterns of neural responses that could account for the phenomenon. The earliest models of the neural processes were necessarily based on indirect evidence from psychophysical experiments, but the later models draw on the direct electrophysiological evidence that has more recently become available. On the basis of this direct evidence the unit of neural activity can now be identified as the nerve impulse, and the problem facing the model builder is how to represent an extremely complex visual phenomenon in terms of the spatial and temporal pattern of a large number of these essentially identical units of activity.

From a physiological point of view the various models to be discussed have much in common because the fundamental integrative process governing the pattern of response in each and every one is a reciprocal inhibition among neighboring elements in the retinal network. The particular form of the inhibition, however, is not the same for all models. In some, the inhibition is assumed to be primarily stimulus dependent; in others, response dependent. The mathematical descriptions, too, are all basically similar but not identical, expressed variously in terms of linear equations, of nonlinear equations, and simultaneous linear equations.

The six models to be considered fall into these several categories as follows:

Stimulus dependent:
  (linear equations)
    1. Huggins and Licklider (1951)
    2. Békésy (1960)
  (nonlinear equations)
    3. Mach (1865)
    4. Fry (1948)
Response dependent:
  (simultaneous linear equations)
    5. Hartline and Ratliff (1954)
    6. Taylor (1956)

In the present survey the models are first described in the order listed above and in essentially the same forms as the originals. For clarity, however, a few minor modifications have been made in the models, always following the apparent original intent of the author. Another change, the adoption of a common notation for all wherever possible, has been made to facilitate comparison. Following the examination of the mathematical formulations, we consider in detail certain of their principal features—some that are common to all the models and some that are unique in particular ones. This later section aims to search out fundamental principles of neural interaction that may be of some significance not only in explaining the Mach bands themselves, but also in reaching a fuller understanding of the neural mechanisms underlying all visual perception.

HUGGINS AND LICKLIDER (1951)—DOUBLE-DIFFERENTIATION AND WEIGHTING FUNCTION MODEL

The model developed by Huggins and Licklider grew out of Békésy's suggestion (1928) that some process such as that underlying the Mach bands was necessary to supplement the physical mechanisms of frequency analysis in the cochlea. By direct observation of the vibration of the cochlear partition, Békésy had found that it appeared to be too broadly tuned to account fully for our perception of pitch. (See Békésy, 1960a, for a survey of his work including translations of early papers.) The apparent importance of the negative second derivative in the Mach bands (see Mach's original papers in Part Two) led Huggins and Licklider to consider how the nervous system might compute derivatives.*

The authors suggest that the nervous system makes this computation by the approximate method of differentiating based on finite differences. Before considering the details of their model and the others which follow, however, it will be worthwhile to examine two basic "principles" that Huggins and Licklider set forth for the guidance of those who make models of the nervous system. The first they call "the principle of sloppy workmanship"; the second "the principle of diversity."

> The principle of sloppy workmanship states that it is dangerous to postulate a neural structure that is precisely arranged in detail. The nervous system is the product of a superb architect and a sloppy workman, and in his plans the architect took into account the fact that the workman would not get all the terminal boutons where they belonged. One of the basic facts of neurophysiology is that the nervous system works despite a considerable amount of misarrangement of detail. That fact should be taken into account in constructing theory. Taking it into account is often incompatible with simplicity of representation. One neuron in the diagram must represent a thousand in the nervous system. Nevertheless, it is important to keep in mind that a statistical interpretation of details is required. Thus, in our opinion, the hypothesis that the nervous system computes an exact derivative, as by a digital process, is hardly to be taken seriously. But, for example, the hypothesis that the nervous system performs, in its statistical and analogical way, an operation that may be roughly described as differentiation, and one that we may represent by differentiation in a mathematical model, seems to account economically for a considerable range of facts.
>
> The principle of diversity states that the nervous system often hedges. Instead of presenting a single transform of the peripheral stimulation to the higher centers, the . . . [afferent] tract may present a number of transforms. Given a number of views of the stimulus, the cortex may look them over and take the most useful one. Or it may accept them all and operate upon them all, trying to piece together a consistent picture of the outside world. As a rough analogy, one can improve upon the transmission of a message in noise by using a number of channels, one for the message itself, one

* Although this particular model is concerned specifically with a central problem of the theory of hearing, that is, how to reconcile the acute perception of pitch with the broad tuning of the cochlear analyzing mechanism, the problem it treats was derived from and is so closely related to the problem of Mach bands in vision that it is appropriate to consider the model here.

for its time derivative, another for its second time derivative, perhaps another for its time integral. These several transforms of the message protect different aspects of the message from the effects of the noise. The receiver, trying to reconstruct the original message, can come much closer by operating upon the set of transforms (though they are all contaminated) than it can with only the noisy message itself to work on. The principle of diversity is in a sense opposed to the principle of parsimony. It suggests that we look not for the simplest explanation consistent with the data at hand but for an explanation consistent both with the data and with the demands of efficiency in the processing of information. The principle of diversity suggests that a simple description of the. . .process may not be possible because the process may not be simple. Theories that appear at first thought to be alternative may in fact supplement one another (Huggins and Licklider, 1951, p. 299).

The double-differentiation hypothesis Figure 3.1 shows an excitatory function, $I(x)$, which represents the stimulus distribution on the receptor mosaic. This function I is sampled by the receptors at closely and equally spaced values of x. The first-order elements, which amplify the samples, end on second-order elements where the neural response R is to be measured. The "gain" of the amplifiers may be either positive or negative.

Assume that the first-order elements have a gain of $+1$ and that they make one-to-one connections with the second-order elements, but are not

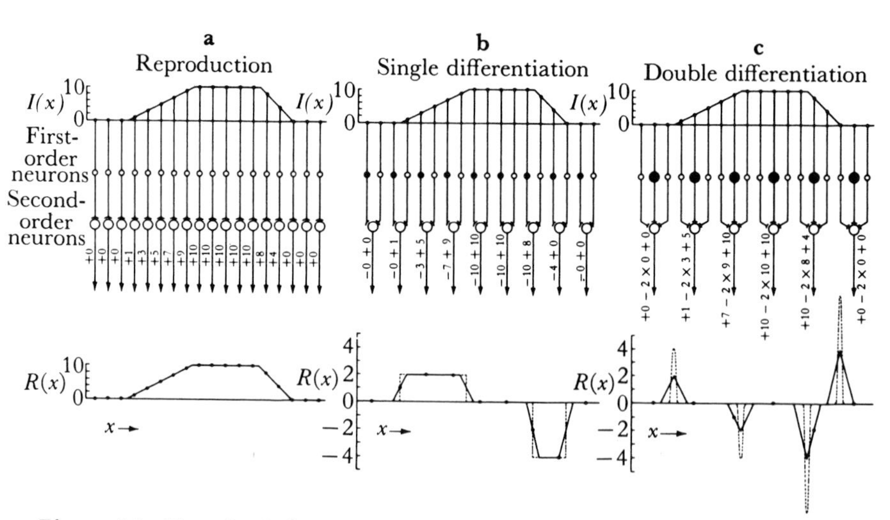

Figure 3.1. *Hypothetical neural mechanisms for* (a) *reproduction,* (b) *single differentiation, and* (c) *double differentiation of a stimulus distribution. Redrawn after Huggins and Licklider (1951).*

interconnected with one another. The response of a particular second-order element, then, is simply the gain of +1 multiplied by the value of I at the point sampled. In other words, the response $R(x)$ of the whole system is simply a reproduction of the excitatory function $I(x)$. It would be slightly blurred, however, because of the finite dimensions of the sampling receptors and their interspaces.

In the single differentiation system the first-order elements act in pairs. The right-hand member (unfilled circle) has a gain of +1; the left-hand member (filled circle) has a gain of −1; the second-order element, on which they converge, adds the two signals. The net effect depends upon the difference $\Delta I = I_2 - I_1$; that is, the difference between the values of I at the two points sampled. The difference, ΔI, is proportional to $\Delta I/\Delta x$; therefore, the response R is an approximation of the first derivative $I' = dI/dx$.

The mechanism for double differentiation is similar. In it the first-order elements act in trios. The lateral members (unfilled circles) have gains of +1, the central member (filled circle) has a gain of −2. The second-order element on which the trio of first-order elements converges adds the three signals. The net effect depends on the second difference $\Delta^2 I = (I_3 - I_2) - (I_2 - I_1) = I_3 - 2I_2 + I_1$. This second difference $\Delta^2 I$ yields a response R that is an approximation of the second derivative $I'' = d^2I/dx^2$. (See also Bracewell, 1955.)

In the figure fair approximations to the actual values of the first and second derivatives, I' and I'', are shown (broken lines) along with the rough approximations to them that the networks produce in the neural response R (solid lines). Values of the approximations that result from the particular samples operated on by the reproducing and differencing mechanisms are indicated by the points on the curves directly below the second-order adding elements.

In the Mach bands the modification of the response appears to be related to the negative of the second derivative. Changing the signs of the gains for the first-order elements achieves this in the present model of the network for double differentiation. That is, positive gains would be associated with the elements represented by filled circles; negative gains with the unfilled circles. In physiological terms, the positive gains would be identified with excitation, the negative gains with inhibition.

The model becomes more realistic if each element in Figure 3.1 is thought of as representing many neurons. Thus the trio of first-order elements, for example, may be regarded as a relatively large number of central excitatory neurons flanked by inhibitory neurons. The outer terminations of the excitatory neurons would be confined to a restricted region of the receptor mosaic; the outer terminations of the inhibitory

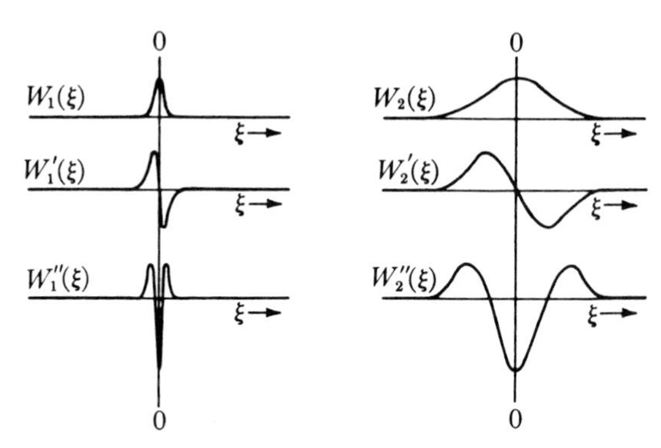

Figure 3.2. *Weighting functions which yield approximate reproduction, differentiation, and double differentiation of the curves to which they are applied. From Huggins and Licklider (1951).*

neurons would reach a larger surrounding region of the receptor mosaic. Overlap of diffuse and somewhat random branchings would be expected and the whole schema would thus take on a statistical interpretation. For this reason, a continuous weighting function, based on differentiation by finite differences, provides a more realistic analog of the neural process than do the simple units, pairs, or trios of neural elements.

Weighting-function hypothesis Figure 3.2 shows weighting functions which provide approximate reproduction, differentiation, and double differentiation of the curve to which they are applied. Weighting functions providing fairly close approximations are shown at the left; functions providing rough approximations at the right. The two functions $W_1(\xi)$ and $W_2(\xi)$ are smoothing functions; that is, they yield approximate reproductions of the original curves with some smoothing of irregularities, depending on the width and shape of the functions. Differentiation of these functions yields W'_1 and W'_2; double differentiation yields W''_1 and W''_2.

These latter weighting functions are analogs, in continuous x, of the discrete weights used in various methods of numerical differentiation based on finite differences. For example, Burnham and Jackson (1955) in their study of the location of Mach bands in electron diffraction patterns (Fig. 2.22 above) used weights based on the second derivative of Stirling's interpolation formula. With certain simplifications, and using terms only through and including the sixth difference, the second derivative at the point x_0 becomes

$$\frac{d^2y}{dx^2} = 0.011y_{-3} - 0.150y_{-2} + 1.501y_{-1} - 2.724y_0 + 1.501y_1 - 1.50y_2 + 0.011y_3.$$

The weighting function for the second derivative used by Huggins and Licklider is analogous to the central negative weight and the two immediately adjacent positive weights in this formula. Note also that the amplitudes of the weighting functions W, W', and W'' in Figure 3.2 are analogous to the gains of the units, pairs, and trios of neural elements in Figure 3.1.

The discussion of this and other models will be primarily concerned with symmetrical weighting functions such as W and W'' which give approximate reproduction and double differentiation of curves to which they are applied. (The asymmetrical function may be of significance in directionally sensitive networks to be considered later, however, and should be kept in mind.) As indicated above, the brightness and magnitude of the Mach bands appear to be related to the *negative* of the second derivative. Therefore, in the present application we shall *invert* the weighting function W''. The graphical interpretation of the use of these weighting functions is illustrated in Figure 3.3.

In Figure 3.3a the excitatory function $I(x)$ is operated on by the

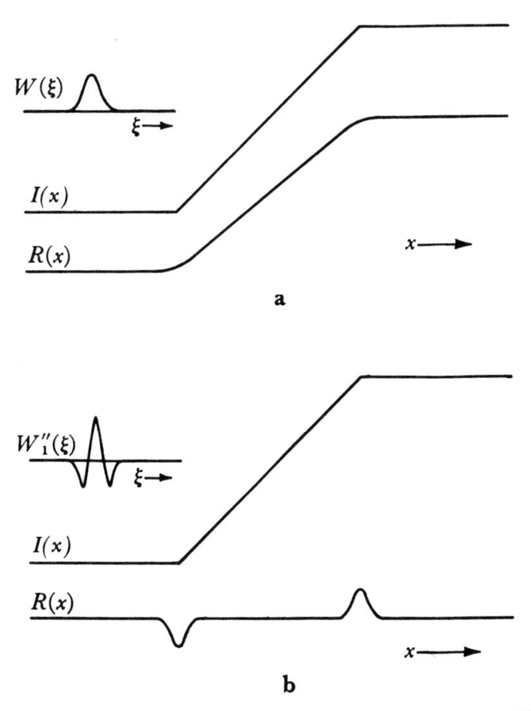

Figure 3.3. *The use of weighting functions to obtain curves which are an approximate reproduction* (a) *and the negative of the approximate second derivative* (b) *of the original function.*

weighting function $W(\xi)$ to obtain a neural response curve $R(x)$ which is a close replica of $I(x)$. The operation may be expressed in mathematical terms as

$$R(x) = K \int_{-\infty}^{+\infty} I(x - \xi) W(\xi)\, d\xi,$$

where K is a normalizing constant.

Graphically, the operation is performed as follows. Take I as a function of $x_p - \xi$, instead of x. Center the weighting function $W(\xi)$ at x_p with ξ increasing to the left. Multiply the ordinates of the excitatory function by the ordinates of the weighting function and integrate the product over ξ. Plot the integral above x_p. Repeat the process for all (or representative) values of x. The points thus determined and plotted generate $R(x)$ as a function of x. (The direction of ξ is of no significance except when the weighting function is asymmetrical.)

A response curve which is the negative of the approximate second derivative is obtained similarly (Fig. 3.3b) by simply inverting the weighting function $W''(\xi)$ for approximate double differentiation illustrated in Figure 3.2 and applying it to the excitatory function as described above. Note the maxima and minima in the response curve that correspond to the flections in the light curve.

If the weighting function and the above operations are considered in neural terms, the subscript p identifies a particular cell body in the neural network. A considerable number of first-order neurons, some excitatory and some inhibitory, converge on this cell. The receiving terminals of these neurons are distributed along the receptor mosaic about some central point (x_p). The relative numbers of inhibitory and excitatory terminals at various distances along the receptor mosaic from x_p determine the weighting function $W''(\xi)$. Thus the excitatory function $I(x)$ on the receptor mosaic influences the activity of the second-order neuron p by an intervening operation in which the values of $I(x_p - \xi)$ are, in effect, multiplied by $W''(\xi)$. Now the weighting function may be thought of as representing a small elemental network in the larger network formed by the entire retina. In one of these elemental networks converging on the neuron p the central influences are excitatory and the peripheral influences are inhibitory (the negative of the trio of elements for double differentiation illustrated in Fig. 3.1). The response of the neuron p depends upon the difference between the sum of the excitatory influences and the sum of the inhibitory influences. Since this difference is the integral $R(x)$ in the equation above, the response of p is some function of the negative of an approximate second derivative $I''(x)$ of the excitatory function $I(x)$ at the point x_p.

If, as in the graphical procedure illustrated above, the operation is repeated by a large number of similar networks, each of which partially overlaps its immediate neighbors, then the responses of all the second-order neurons acting together will yield a spatial pattern of neural activity that is approximately the negative second derivative of the entire pattern of excitation on the receptor mosaic. As the slope of the gradient in the excitatory function $I(x)$ is increased (Fig. 3.4), the maxima and minima in the pattern of neural activity $R(x)$ become more pronounced. In this respect they resemble the bright and dark Mach bands that are seen in comparable distributions of illumination (compare with Fig. 2.13 above).

One major feature of the visual appearance of a Mach pattern is missing in these responses—the general shape of the excitatory function $I(x)$. The uniform bright field, the uniform dark field, and the gradient between them all yield the same response. The only deviations from this uniform response are at or near the points in the response curve that

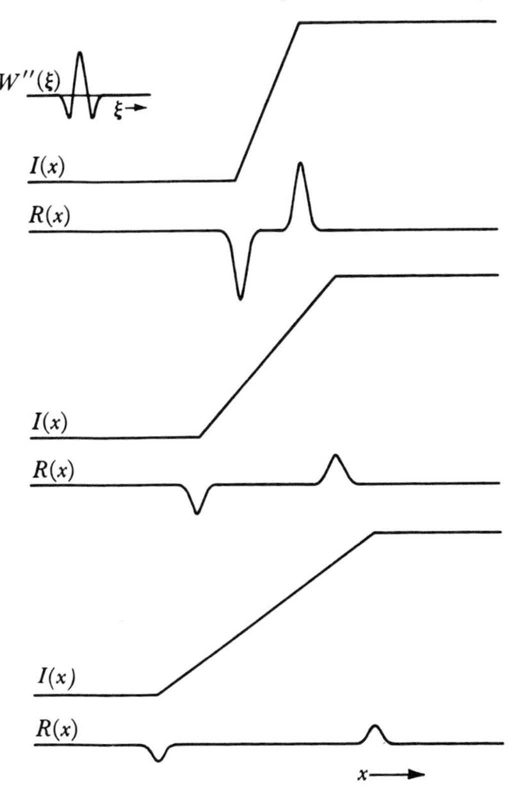

Figure 3.4. *Influence of slope of gradient in the excitatory function on the amplitude of the maxima and minima in the response curve obtained by application of a weighting function representing an inhibitory neural network.*

correspond to the flections in the excitatory function. As Huggins and Licklider suggest, however, information about the amplitude of the curve could be carried in a different channel which utilizes another transform, such as the weighting function for approximate reproduction of the curve (illustrated in Fig. 3.3a). Or, more economically, as in the other models to be described later, the information about both the amplitude and the changes of slope of the light curve might be carried in the same channel.

BÉKÉSY (1960)—"NEURAL UNIT" AND SUPERPOSITION INTEGRAL

As was mentioned above, in 1928 Békésy suggested that contrast effects similar to the Mach bands probably were not limited to the visual system. Considering the nature of the neural network in the ear and auditory areas of the brain, he reasoned that fibers in this network might interact with one another as they do in the retina, so that the operation of a stimulus at a particular point on the basilar membrane could be affected by stimuli on neighboring points. (This hypothesis has since been borne out; there is now abundant neurophysiological evidence that such inhibitory interaction does take place in the auditory system. See, for example, Galambos and Davis, 1944, and Katsuki, Watanabe, and Suga, 1959.) Furthermore, Békésy hypothesized and succeeded in demonstrating by psychophysical methods that an analogous phenomenon occurs in the tactual sensitivity of the surface of the skin. Since then, the neural mechanisms of afferent inhibition in the cutaneous system have been observed directly. (See, for example, Mountcastle and Powell, 1959.)

Békésy's model of inhibitory interaction to be described here grew out of his early work, but it is based mainly on some of his later experiments on the perception threshold of two points on the surface of the skin. In these experiments two von Frey test hairs with small balls on their ends were pressed against the skin as shown in Figure 3.5. (The

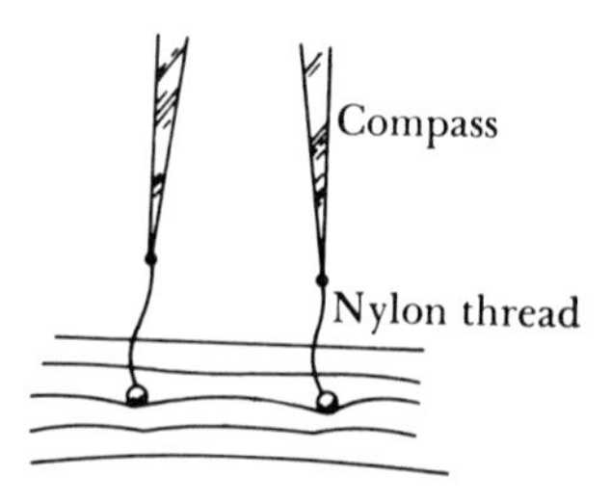

Figure 3.5. *Von Frey test hairs for study of two-point discrimination. From Békésy (1960b).*

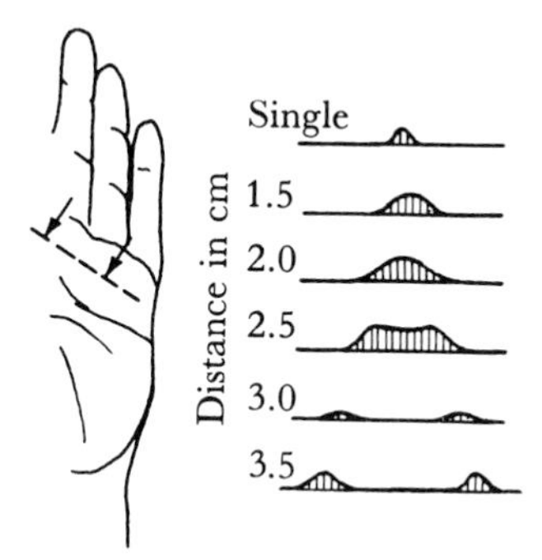

Figure 3.6. *Changes in distribution and amplitude of sensation on palm of hand with increasing separation of the two points pressed against the skin. From Békésy (1960b).*

flexible threads assured a uniform maximum pressure for every measurement.) The observer then made a sketch of the spatial distribution of the sensation magnitude for different distances between the test hairs. The results for one observer are shown in Figure 3.6. As the distance between the two stimuli was first increased the sensation magnitude also increased, but with a greater separation it became smaller for each of the two points of stimulation than for a single stimulus. With still greater separations, the sensation magnitudes for the two points increased until finally each equaled that for a single stimulus. This experiment seemed to indicate that when the two stimuli are near one another their excitatory influences summate; at a certain greater distance from one another, each partially inhibits the sensation produced by the other; and at a still greater distance there is no interaction at all. On the basis of these results Békésy concluded that every stimulus on the receptor mosaic produces a local field of *sensation* (or excitation) surrounded by a more extended *refractory* (or inhibitory) field (Fig. 3.7a). Békésy called the combination of these opposed influences acting as a whole a "neural unit." Because similar interactions occur in the afferent neural networks of the eye, ear, and skin, with suitable modifications the concept of the neural unit applies to all three. (See Békésy, 1958, 1959a, and 1959 b.)

Inhibition generally decreases with increasing distance from the point of stimulation. But, as Békésy points out, a graded diminution of the inhibition with distance is not absolutely essential for the production of Mach bands. A network in which the inhibition spreads out to a certain point with the same effectiveness, but with no effect beyond that point, will also yield the bright and dark bands. Therefore, for purposes of calculation he made use of the simplified, and essentially equivalent, rectangular neural unit shown in Figure 3.7b.

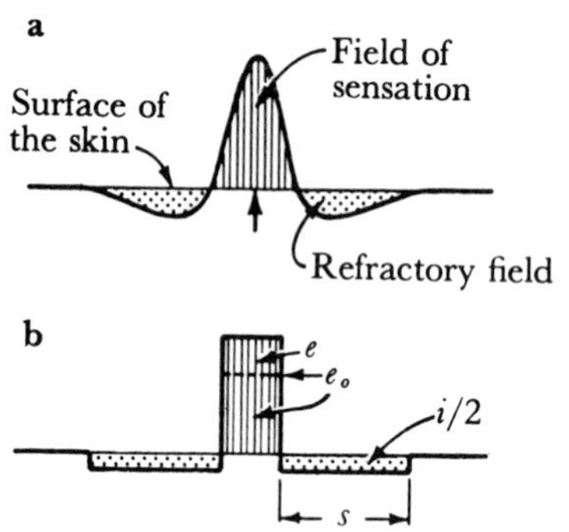

Figure 3.7. (a) *Graphical representation of a neural unit. The field of sensation and the surrounding refractory field is produced by the pressure of a stimulus at the point on the surface of the skin indicated by the arrow.* (b) *Simplified rectangular neural unit for purposes of calculation. The excitatory area under the curve is labeled e and the inhibitory area on one side is labeled i/2. The excitatory area limited by the broken line e_0 is equal to the total inhibitory area i. The width of one half of the inhibitory field is labeled s. From Békésy (1960b).*

Thus far, only the effects of local or point stimulation on the receptor mosaic have been considered. Next an examination should be made of a stimulus that consists of a continuous and extended distribution. Since the receptors are discrete elements, this continuous stimulus may be cut into thin vertical sections, each of which is assumed to act independently as a local point of stimulation on the corresponding receptor. Now, assume that: (1) every vertical section produces an excitatory field and an inhibitory field in accordance with the shape of the neural unit (the amplitudes of the excitatory and inhibitory fields are adjusted to the amplitude of the stimulus distribution at the center of the neural unit); and (2) overlapping excitatory fields (positive) and inhibitory fields (negative) combine to give the magnitude of the sensation at a given point.

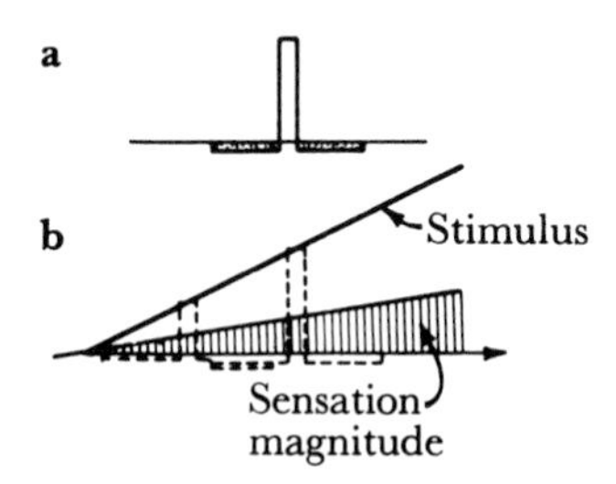

Figure 3.8. *The sensation magnitude is proportional to the stimulus magnitude where there are no changes of slope in the stimulus distribution. The neural unit* (a) *was used to construct the sensation magnitude* (b). *From Békésy (1960b).*

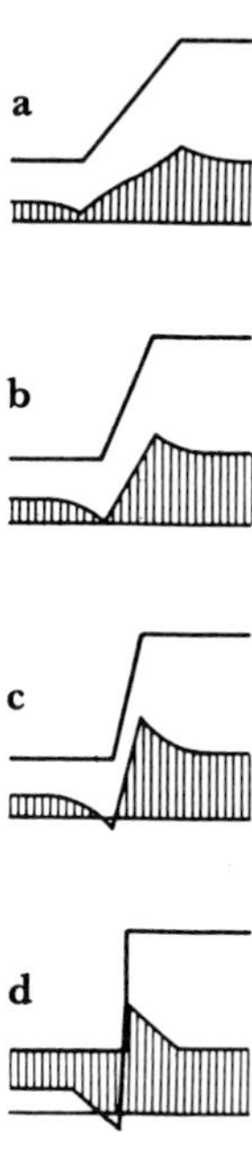

Figure 3.9. *Dependence of the magnitude of Mach bands on the slope of the gradient in the stimulus distribution. Bands were calculated using the rectangular neural unit for the eye shown in Figure 3.11. From Békésy (1960b).*

Where the entire stimulus distribution has no changes of slope, as in Figure 3.8, the sensation magnitude given by this summation of opposed excitatory and inhibitory influences is simply proportional to the amplitude of the stimulus distribution. Indeed, with the proper ratio of excitatory to inhibitory influences in the neural unit (that is, a ratio of 2:1 of the positive and negative areas under the curve representing the unit) a uniform stimulus will be reproduced exactly. The transformation from stimulus to sensation by the neural unit significantly affects only those places with a *change* in the stimulus distribution. The more pronounced the change, the more pronounced are the effects produced in the sensation distribution. For example, as the slope of the gradient in a Mach pattern is increased the magnitudes of the corresponding Mach bands increase (Fig. 3.9). Similarly, the sharper the curvature where the gradient turns over into the uniform field, the greater is the effect (Fig. 3.10).

The dimensions of the simplified rectangular forms of the hypothetical neural units can be estimated from the dimensions of bands in the observed sensation curves. The width (s) of each half of the refractory (inhibitory) field (i) is simply one-half the width of the Mach band that the neural unit produces—assuming the width of the excitatory field to

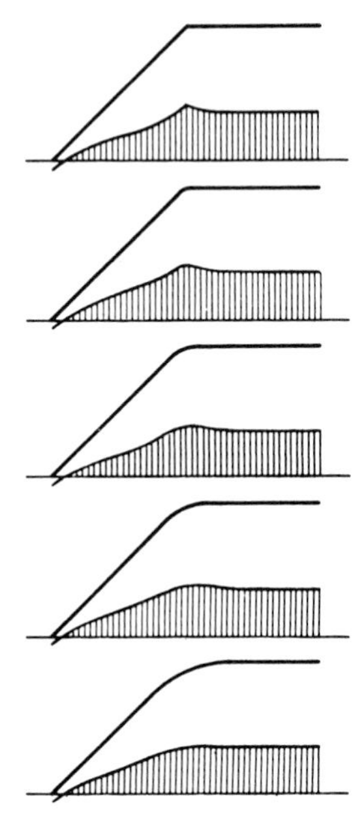

Figure 3.10. *When the slope of the stimulus distribution is constant but the radius of the curvature is increased so that the curve becomes less sharp, the magnitude of the Mach band decreases. From Békésy (1960b).*

be negligible. The dimensions of the units for the eye and the skin, calculated the same way, are shown in Figure 3.11. Sensation curves computed using these hypothetical neural units are shown in Figure 3.12.

Although the width of the inhibitory field can be estimated from the width of the observed Mach bands, the width of the central excitatory field (e) is more difficult to determine. Those excitatory fields illustrated in Figures 3.11 and 3.12 are merely rough estimates. Fortunately, the

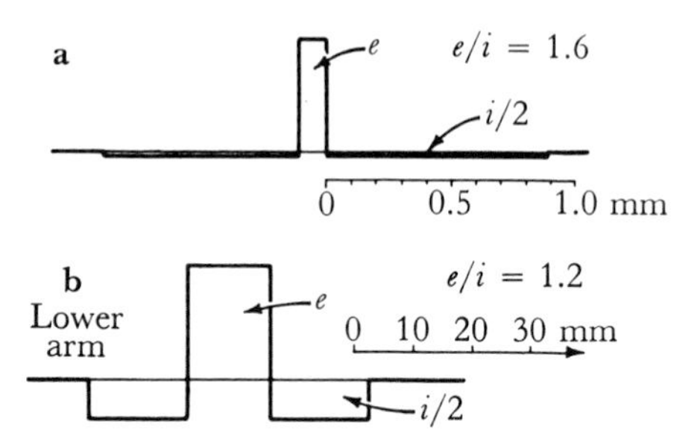

Figure 3.11. *Neural units for the eye* (a) *and for the skin of the lower arm* (b). *Dimensions of units calculated from observed sensation curves. From Békésy (1960b).*

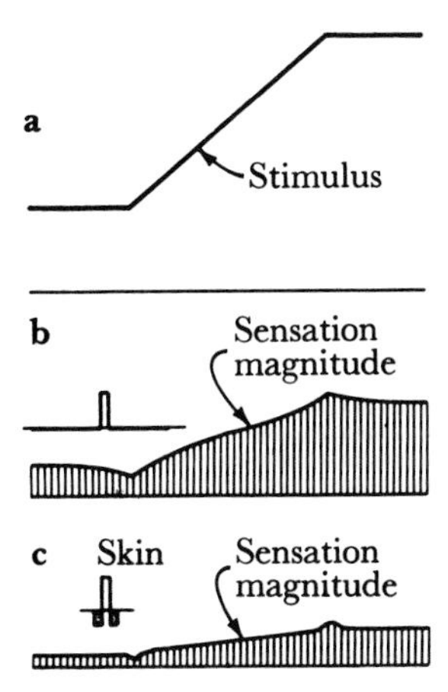

Figure 3.12. (a) *Stimulus distribution;* (b) *corresponding sensation magnitude for the eye, and* (c) *for the skin, computed using the neural units inset in the figure. From Békésy (1960b).*

exact dimensions of the excitatory field are not too critical in the formation of Mach bands as long as the extent of e is much less than the extent of i. In fact, the width of the excitatory field may be changed considerably and still not produce a significant effect on the sensation curve provided that the ratio of the excitatory to inhibitory influences remains constant. That is, if the area under the excitatory component of the curve remains the same, changing the width will have little effect (Fig. 3.13).

Mathematical expressions for the neural unit As Figure 3.8 showed, the sensation curve can be obtained geometrically by drawing overlapping neural units with amplitudes corresponding to the amplitudes of small vertical sections of the stimulus distribution, and then subtracting

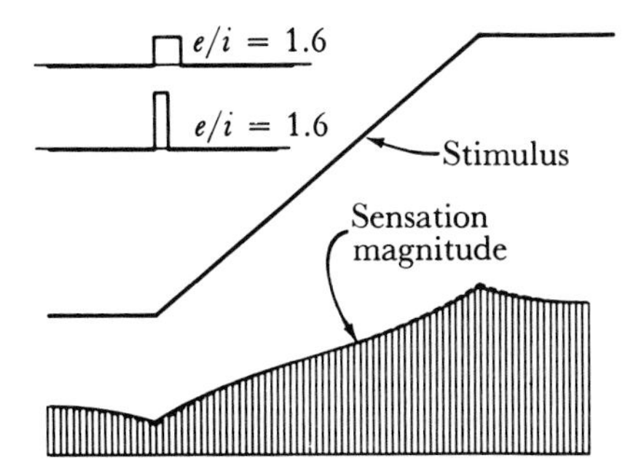

Figure 3.13. *Sensation magnitudes calculated using a neural unit with a broad excitatory field (solid line) and with a narrow excitatory field (broken line). From Békésy (1960b).*

the sum of the inhibition at every point or at representative points from the sum of the excitation. An equivalent continuous mathematical equation for the sensation magnitude produced by a given stimulus distribution may be deduced, however, by applying the superposition theorem.

Figure 3.14 illustrates that any stimulus distribution $I(x)$ can be approximated by a series of equal steps. The equivalent sensation magnitude for each step may be drawn from the neural unit. For a simple unit in which the two opposed influences e and i are equal, the sensation distribution produced by each equal step is the same and is independent of the magnitude of the stimulus. For the unit shown (with $e = i$) and the stimulus step below, the sensation distribution with the magnitude $A_s(x)$ results. (It is similar to the distribution resulting from the large abrupt step shown in Figure 3.9, except that, because $e = i$, the uniform areas some distance from the step produce no effects and, except in the vicinity of the step, the magnitude of $A_s(x)$ is zero.)

The sum of all these distributions along the x axis gives the sensation magnitude corresponding to the stimulus distribution $I(x)$. As the steps get smaller and smaller, an integral is approached. The excitatory and inhibitory influences (the shaded areas above and below the zero line) are equal in the local sensation distribution $A_s(x)$ produced by each step. Therefore, for any stimulus distribution represented by a straight line, $\Sigma A_s(x) = 0$. Thus only a curvature of the stimulus function $I(x)$ can produce a sensation magnitude; it will be negative for a stimulus distribution convex with respect to the axis of abscissae and positive for a

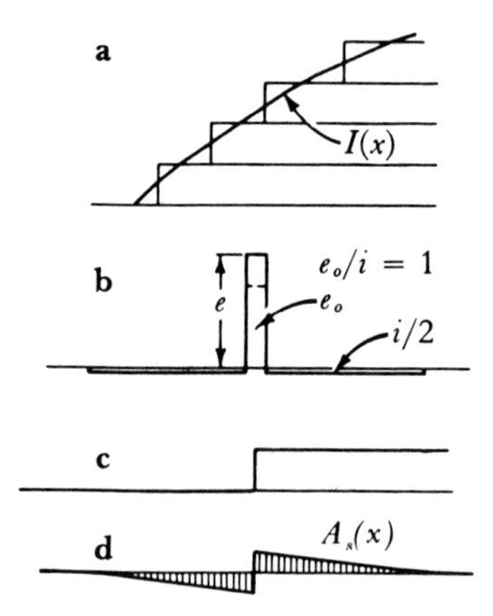

Figure 3.14. *The stimulus distribution may be regarded as consisting of a number of discrete steps* (a). *Applying the neural unit* (b) *to each such step* (c), *the corresponding sensation distribution* (d) *can be computed. When added together these individual sensation distributions yield an approximation to the complete continuous stimulus distribution. From Békésy (1960b).*

concave stimulus distribution. This method is analogous to the rough approximation to the negative of the second derivative obtained using the weighting function proposed by Huggins and Licklider.

As the steps become infinitesimal the superposition theorem may be used and the sensation magnitude R_0 for the special case of a neural unit in which $e_0 = i$ is thus:

$$R_0 = \int_{-\infty}^{+\infty} A_s(x - \xi) \cdot I'(\xi)\, d\xi$$

where $I'(\xi)$ is the derivative of $I(\xi)$.

Considered in terms of the component neural network that it might represent, the graphical analog of this superposition integral describes the influences that arise at a particular point on the receptor mosaic and diverge from it to several second-order neurons. Conversely, the similar (but not identical) graphical analog of the integral equation used by Huggins and Licklider to represent their weighting function describes the influences that arise from several points on the receptor mosaic and converge on a particular second-order neuron. Both methods give the same results, of course, when the influences are finally integrated. (The mathematical relation between the two methods is discussed in a later section of this chapter.)

For the general case, one in which the ratio e/i may not be equal to 1 in the neural unit, the sensation magnitude may be determined first by finding the magnitude with a unit in which $e = i$ and then adding to it at every point a sensation magnitude corresponding to the excess $e - e_0$ according to the formula

$$R = (e - e_0)I(x) + R_0.$$

This method is roughly equivalent to applying a weighting function for approximate reproduction of a curve and adding to this the approximate second derivative of the curve. Thus, the neural unit proposed by Békésy yields in the neural response *both* an approximate reproduction of the stimulus distribution $I(x)$ and the overshoots and undershoots corresponding to the bright and dark bands.*

Békésy proposed a second mathematical equation for calculation of the sensation magnitude using an angular measure of the change in slope,

* An analysis of the Mach bands by O'Brien (1958) is similar in many respects to this one. The stimulus distribution on the retina is an approximate, but somewhat blurred, reproduction of the external stimulus. The addition of a second-difference correction to this blurred reproduction rectifies the blur somewhat, but the rectification is imperfect, and maxima and minima are produced which correspond to the bright and dark bands. O'Brien obtains the second difference in essentially the same way as in the neural net proposed by Huggins and Licklider (Fig. 3.1 above). A similar mechanism was also postulated in a study of the Mach bands by Greene (1957).

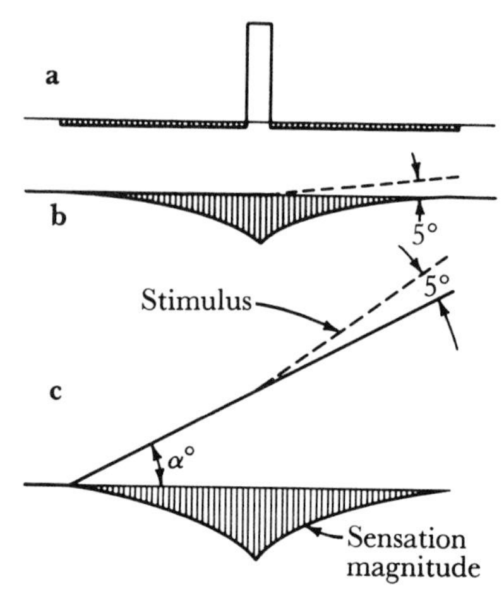

Figure 3.15. *The angular increment method for obtaining a formula for the Mach bands. From Békésy (1960b).*

that is, a unit angle of change instead of a unit step, as the basis for the calculation (Fig. 3.15). The first step in this method is to compute the response to a unit angular change in a stimulus distribution with a slope of zero. This is done, for example, by applying the neural unit (a) to a 5 degree angular increment (b), using either the graphical method or the superposition integral described above. This procedure yields a unit response—the shaded area shown in (b)—with the magnitude $A_a(x)$. All responses to successive 5 degree increments in the curvature of the stimu-

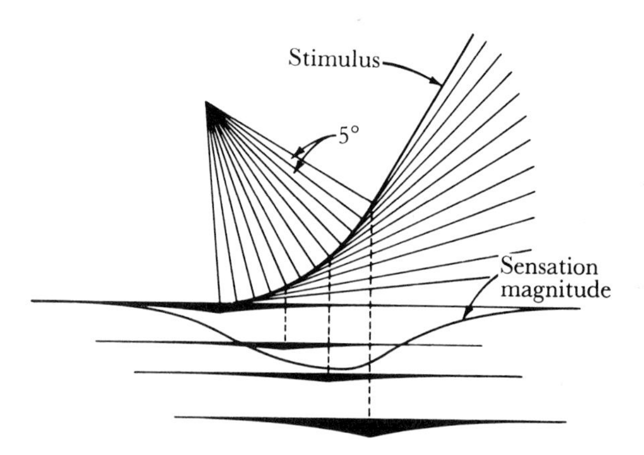

Figure 3.16. *The construction of the composite sensation magnitude curve by summation of the unit responses (shaded areas) to angular increments in the stimulus distribution. (Only four representative unit responses are shown.) From Békésy (1960b).*

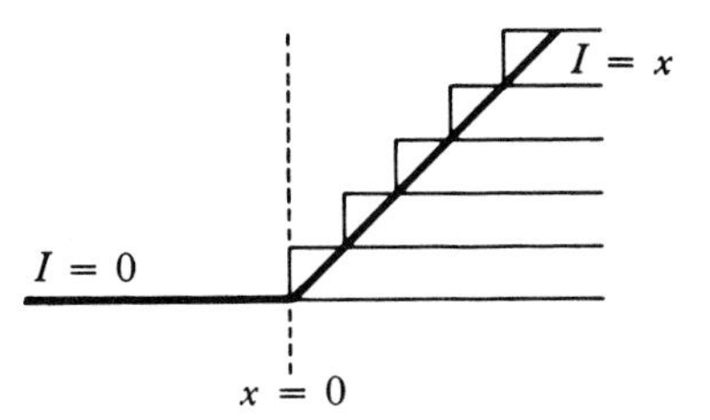

Figure 3.17. The approximation of a stimulus distribution by a series of equal steps.

lus distribution have the same form as this response to the initial increment. The magnitude of the response, however, depends upon the magnitude of the angle α to which the unit increment is added, as is illustrated in (c). Let $A_a{}^\alpha(x)$ represent the amplitude of the response to the unit increment on the angle α, as is given by the equation

$$A_a{}^\alpha(x) = A_a(x)(1 + \tan^2 \alpha).$$

Thus, in place of the step in stimulus magnitude that is the basis for calculations using the superposition integral, use a unit of angular change in the slope of the stimulus distribution to calculate the response. For each given unit change in slope, say 5 degrees, draw the corresponding sensation magnitude according to the formula given above, as is illustrated in Figure 3.16. The unit responses to each of the several successive 5 degree steps then are summed to yield the composite response $R_0(x)$ for the whole stimulus distribution. With a curvature convex to the axis of abscissae as illustrated, a depression in the sensation curve analogous to a dark Mach band results. A curvature in the opposite direction would yield an elevation in the sensation curve analogous to a bright Mach band.

Sensation curves obtained by this angular increment method are identical in the small angle limit to those obtained using the magnitude step method and the superposition integral. The proof follows.* Consider a stimulus distribution I of the form shown in Figure 3.17. This distribution may be approximated by a series of equal steps as the same figure indicates. That is,

$$I(x) \cong \sum_n s(x - x_n)\,\Delta x_n$$

where

$$s(x) = \begin{cases} x & x > 0 \\ 0 & x < 0 \end{cases}$$

* Proof of this identity was omitted in Békésy's original account. The author is indebted to Bruce Knight for derivation of the proof presented here.

or

$$I(x) = \int_0^x s(x - \xi)\, d\xi.$$

The amplitude of the response to this distribution is

$$A_c(x) \cong \sum_n A_s(x - x_n)\, \Delta x_n$$

or

$$A_c(x) = \int_0^x A_s(x - \xi)\, d\xi = +\int_0^x A_s(y)\, dy$$

where A_s is the response to each step as was illustrated in Figure 3.14, and $A_c(x)$ is the response to the entire angular distribution and is analogous to the unit response to a small angle shown in Figure 3.15b. The above gives:

$$\frac{dA_c(x)}{dx} = +A_s(x).$$

Now, using the superposition theorem as before:

$$R_0(x) = \int_{-\infty}^{+\infty} A_s(x - \xi) I'(\xi)\, d\xi$$

$$= -\int_{-\infty}^{+\infty} \frac{dA_c(x - \xi)}{d\xi} I'(\xi)\, d\xi$$

and integrating by parts gives

$$R_0(x) = -\int_{-\infty}^{+\infty} \left\{ \frac{d}{d\xi} (A_c(x - \xi) I'(\xi)) - A_c(x - \xi) \frac{d}{d\xi} I'(\xi) \right\} d\xi$$

$$= -\left\{ A_c(x - \xi) I'(\xi) \Big|_{-\infty}^{+\infty} - \int_{-\infty}^{+\infty} A_c(x - \xi) I''(\xi)\, d\xi \right\}$$

so

$$R_0(x) = \int_{-\infty}^{+\infty} A_c(x - \xi) I''(\xi)\, d\xi$$

which will be used presently.

Now

$$I'(x) = \tan \alpha$$

thus

$$\alpha = \arctan I'(x)$$

$$\frac{d\alpha}{dx} = \frac{1}{1 + \{I'(x)\}^2} I''(x) = \frac{1}{1 + \tan^2 \alpha} I''(x)$$

giving

$$I''(x)\,dx = (1 + \tan^2 \alpha)\,d\alpha$$

and the equation for $R_0(x)$ above becomes

$$R_0(x) = \int_{\text{range of }\alpha} A_c(x - x_\alpha)(1 + \tan^2 \alpha)\,d\alpha.$$

This equation may be approximated by

$$R_0(x) = \sum_n A_c(x - x_{\alpha_n})\,\Delta\alpha_n(1 + \tan^2 \alpha_n).$$

If $\Delta\alpha_n$ is set equal to 5 degrees, then it is evident that $A_c(x - x_{\alpha_n})$ is identical to the unit response $A_n(x)$ in Békésy's equation. (Note that all of the proof above uses a neural unit in which the excitatory component e is equal to the inhibitory component i. If $e > i$, then the excess $e - e_0$ must be determined separately and added to the response as was done with the superposition integral.)

In summary, Békésy's neural unit model consists of a weighting function with a central excitatory component flanked by inhibitory components. In this respect the model is similar to the Huggins-Licklider model described above. It has the added feature, however, of reproducing the general form of the stimulus distribution, which is essential in a model of the Mach bands. The model accomplishes this in a very economical way, simply by making the ratio of the excitatory component to the inhibitory component in the weighting function greater than one.

MACH (1865 AND LATER)—RECIPROCAL INHIBITION

Wherever there is a significant flection in the curve representing the light intensity of an illuminated surface, that region generally appears brighter (or darker) than its surroundings. This fact at once led Mach to consider whether the relation between the apparent brightness and light intensity might be expressed in terms of the second derivative of the light curve, as follows.

Let I be the intensity of illumination. On a plane surface $I = f(x,y)$, and the corresponding sensation of brightness (or the underlying neural response) R is given approximately by

$$R = I - m\left(\frac{d^2I}{dx^2} + \frac{d^2I}{dy^2}\right)$$

where m is a constant. Where the expression in parentheses is positive the sensation of brightness is reduced; where it is negative it is increased. Thus R is determined by the intensity I, and by the *negative* of its second derivatives.

It is to be understood, of course, that this is not a standard formula. The perceived brightness increases and decreases with the value of R but does not follow it exactly. For example, infinite values of $(d^2I/dx^2 + d^2I/dy^2)$ do not result in the appearance of infinitely bright (or infinitely dark) and infinitely narrow lines. Obviously, the equation cannot be taken at face value. The retina is not a continuum but a mosaic of discrete elements of finite extent, and one can properly speak only of Δx, Δy (and not dx, dy) when referring to the illumination on it.

Mach recognized these and other shortcomings of this first approximate version of his model. The *exact* dependence of apparent brightness on the distribution of illumination in the stimulus he later attempted to formulate in terms of the physiological events in the retina that are elicited by the stimulus, rather than in terms of the stimulus distribution itself. He dismissed as meaningless all of the then current explanations such as "It results from an unconscious inference," or "It must be only an illusion." Such statements, he said, are not explanations, they are merely another way of expressing the unexplained facts. Mach sought his explanation in the function of the neural network that was known to exist in the retina.

At that time, it was not possible to study directly the neural events in the retina. But the indirect evidence Mach obtained from his psychophysical experiments enabled him to conclude that "the phenomena discussed can only be explained on the basis of a reciprocal action (*Wechselwirkung*) of neighboring areas of the retina." Mach expressed this reciprocal action in a variety of ways, as shown by his original papers in Part Two. Only a brief account of the discrete form of one version which seems most in keeping with the modern electrophysiological evidence is presented here.

Assume that any two retinal points j,p or, properly, receptors with surface area Δa, stand in a reciprocal relation which is determined by a function ϕ of the distance x_{jp} between them. From the phenomena, it seemed evident that points nearest to one another predominantly exert the greatest influence upon one another. Mach assumed, therefore, that the magnitude of the reciprocal influences expressed by ϕ must diminish with distance, somewhat as shown in Figure 3.18. The neural activity, r_p, discharged from a particular point p illuminated with the intensity I_p is

$$r_p = I_p \cdot \frac{I_p \sum_j \phi(x_{jp})\,\Delta a_j}{\sum_j I_j \phi(x_{jp})\,\Delta a_j}.$$

In the denominator, I_j refers to the intensity on each of the several separate neighboring points j or, rather, small areas Δa_j.

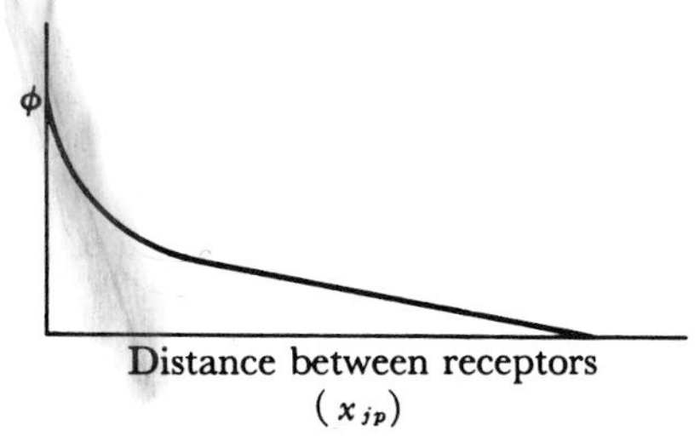

Figure 3.18. The diminution of inhibition with distance in Mach's model. Redrawn after Mach (1868).

The effects of various simple distributions of illumination on the response r are immediately evident from the form of the equation. If the intensity of illumination across the retina is uniform, then the intensity of illumination I_p on a particular receptor is equal to the illumination I_j on neighboring receptors. In this event, $I_p \Sigma_j \phi(x_{jp}) \Delta a_j$ is equal to $\Sigma_j I_j\phi(x_{jp}) \Delta a_j$, and the fraction they form is equal to one. The response r_p is thus determined solely by I_p and is the same for every element. If, however, the intensity of illumination I_p is greater than the intensity I_j on neighboring elements, the value of the fraction is greater than one, and r_p will be correspondingly greater. If the intensity of illumination I_j on neighboring elements is greater than I_p, then the value of the fraction is less than one and r_p will be less than if the illumination were uniform. If there is illumination only on element p, then the denominator approaches zero, the value of the fraction approaches infinity, and the response becomes infinitely large. This embarrassment to the physiological reality of the model may be avoided, however, by assuming that the group of elements j includes the element p. (Mach was not explicit on this point.) Then there is an upper limit to the value of the fraction since I_p will always appear in both the denominator and the numerator.

Thus the response of any particular element is determined by the product of the intensity of the stimulus to it and a fraction representing two reciprocal influences. One of these influences, the numerator of the fraction in Mach's equation, is excitatory. This excitatory influence is itself a product of two factors, I_p and $\Sigma_j \phi(x_{jp}) \Delta a_j$. Assuming ϕ to be the same function everywhere in the network and Δa to be the same for all of the elements in the network, the second term may be expressed as a single number. Since the response r increases with the value of this term, it can be called an excitatory coefficient K. The whole numerator may thus be expressed as the product I_pK. The other influence, the denominator in Mach's equation, is inhibitory. The component of influence exerted by any one element j similarly may be expressed as I_j multiplied by an inhibitory coefficient. The intensity I_j may be different on each element in the network, however, and the value of the inhibitory coefficient is a function ϕ of the distance between the elements p and j. For this reason, there must be a separate coefficient, called $k_{p,j}$, to represent the inhibitory action of each element j on p. Each I_j and the corresponding $k_{p,j}$ must thus be expressed as a separate product $I_j k_{p,j}$. The total inhibitory influence is represented by the sum of these separate influences, $\Sigma_j I_j k_{p,j}$. Stated in these simpler terms, Mach's equation becomes

$$r_p = I_p \cdot \frac{I_p K}{\sum_j I_j k_{p,j}}$$

where p represents the particular element in question and j represents each of the other elements. Note that the single excitatory coefficient K is equal to the sum of the separate inhibitory coefficients $\Sigma_j k_{p,j}$.

With coefficients based on the distance function illustrated in Figure 3.18 above, this equation was used to calculate the responses to the patterns of illumination shown in Figure 3.19. In each case, the general form of the distribution of intensity is reproduced, with maxima and minima appearing where the intensity curve is concave and convex, respectively, toward the axis of abscissae. Note, however, that the re-

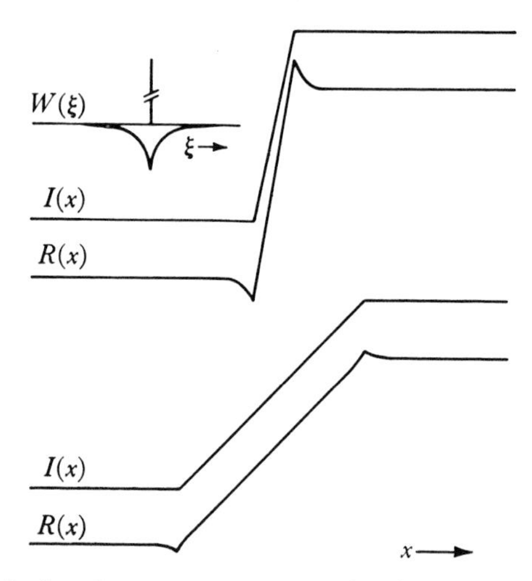

Figure 3.19. Calculated responses to two stimulus distributions using Mach's equation. The equation may be represented graphically by the weighting function shown in the inset. (The narrow excitatory component is not drawn full-scale.) Note that in this case there are actually two separate weighting functions, the excitatory component and the inhibitory component, each of which must be applied to the stimulus distribution separately, just as the values of the numerator and the denominator in Mach's equation must be determined separately.

sponse is not symmetrical. The maxima are more pronounced than the minima, as they are in the observed Mach bands (see Fig. 2.12).

In summary, the neural network in the retina as Mach described it may be regarded as composed of elemental networks in each of which there is a central excitatory component surrounded by an inhibitory component that diminishes with distance. The magnitude of the influence at the excitatory center and in the inhibitory surroundings is proportional to the intensity on the central element. The individual inhibitory influences exerted on any particular element are additive. The discharge of impulses into the central nervous system from any element, however, is the product of the intensity on that element and the ratio of the excitatory influence to the total of the inhibitory influences acting on it. Therefore, unlike the two models described above, this system is nonlinear.

FRY (1948)—ELECTRICAL INHIBITORY FIELDS

Fry's model assumed that stimulation of any given point of the receptor mosaic sets up a graded electrical field in which there is a potential difference between the front and the back of the retina. The potential difference is greatest at the point of stimulation and gradually diminishes with increasing distance from it. The extent of the field is fixed, but the magnitude of the potential difference at each and every point in the field is proportional to the magnitude of the stimulus generating it. A strong stimulus sets up a larger potential difference than a weak stimulus.

A potential difference at any particular point in the field is assumed to reduce the frequency of nerve impulses transmitted by the bipolar or second-order neurons of the retina at that point. Because the inhibition is greatest where the potential difference is greatest, the inhibition is maximal at the point of stimulation itself and gradually diminishes with increasing distance from that point.

The inhibitory fields produced by stimulation of closely neighboring points may overlap. Where they do, the potentials at any point common to two or more fields are assumed to be additive. Thus the amount of inhibition produced at such a point is determined by the sum of all the inhibitory potentials acting there. It is also assumed that the inhibitory influences are generated at some point in the retinal pathway closer to the receptors than the point at which the influences subsequently act. Consequently, the generation of inhibitory potentials in one pathway is unaffected by inhibitory potentials generated in adjacent pathways, as in the previous models. Only the transmission of nerve impulses is affected by the inhibitory influences.

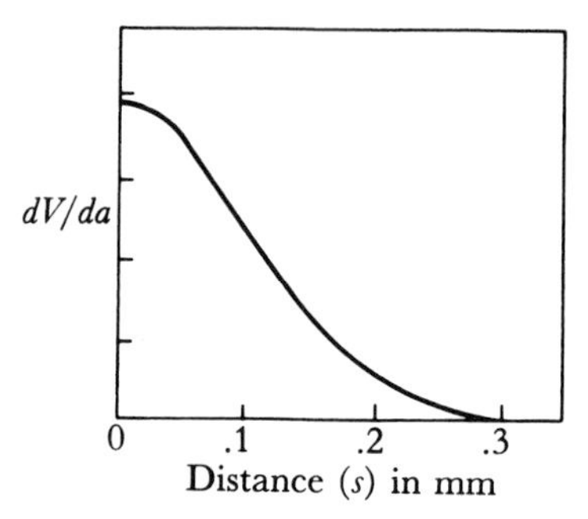

Figure 3.20. *Diminution of the inhibitory potential with distance in Fry's model. Redrawn after Fry (1948).*

The electrical mechanism postulated for this model is based primarily upon two electrophysiological studies by Granit (1933, 1946). In the first study, Granit discovered an inhibitory component in the so-called retinal action potential—that is, the potential difference between the front and the back of the retina that is generated in response to illumination. In the second study he demonstrated that passing a current through the retina from an external source either enhanced or inhibited the responses of retinal ganglion cells, depending upon the direction of current flow. (See also Granit and Therman, 1935.) Thus Fry's model was the first to be based on direct electrophysiological observations.

Mathematical formulation of the model An element of area da at a point on the retina is stimulated with an intensity of retinal illuminance I. This stimulation supposedly sets up an electrical field in which the potential difference dV at any point in the field is some function of the distance s separating that point and the point of stimulation. The exact function is not known. Assume that

$$dV/da \propto I \exp(-s^2/\sigma^2).$$

The constant σ expresses the extent of the inhibitory field around the point of stimulation. The value assumed for σ (0.1 mm. on the retina) was based on psychophysical measurements of certain contrast phenomena in human vision. Using this assumption the radius of the effective field (Fig. 3.20) is about 0.3 mm., which corresponds to a visual angle of approximately one degree.

Since the inhibitory potentials produced by overlapping fields at any particular point are assumed to be additive, the total potential difference V produced at any point p may be obtained by integration. Let p be the center of a coordinate system x,y, and let j be any point with the coordinates x,y. Thus, at any point j the area da equals $dy\ dx$, and s^2 equals $x^2 + y^2$. Therefore

$$V_p \propto \int_{-\infty}^{+\infty} \int_{-\infty}^{+\infty} I(x, y) \exp(-x^2/\sigma^2) \exp(-y^2/\sigma^2)\, dy\, dx.$$

The frequency r_p of the impulses discharged in the bipolar neurons underlying a particular point on the receptor mosaic is assumed to be proportional to the logarithm of the excitatory influence which is directly related to the intensity I_p at that point and inversely related to the total inhibitory potential V_p. Fry expresses these relations in the following general equation:

$$r_p \propto \log \frac{I_p}{1 + V_p}.$$

(For simplicity, a constant of proportionality and a normalizing constant which appeared in Fry's original equations have been omitted.)

In the above equations all values of I, and therefore all values of V also, are assumed to be positive. Note that the value of the inhibitory term $1/(1 + V)$ cannot be less than 1. That is, if there were no inhibition at all ($V = 0$), then r would be determined solely by the intensity of I.

Fry compared the visual appearance of several patterns of illumination with the neural responses predicted by his model when applied to the same distribution. A pattern with significant flections in it shows the expected bright and dark bands and, corresponding to them, maxima and minima in the calculated neural response (Fig. 3.21). A blurred stimulus

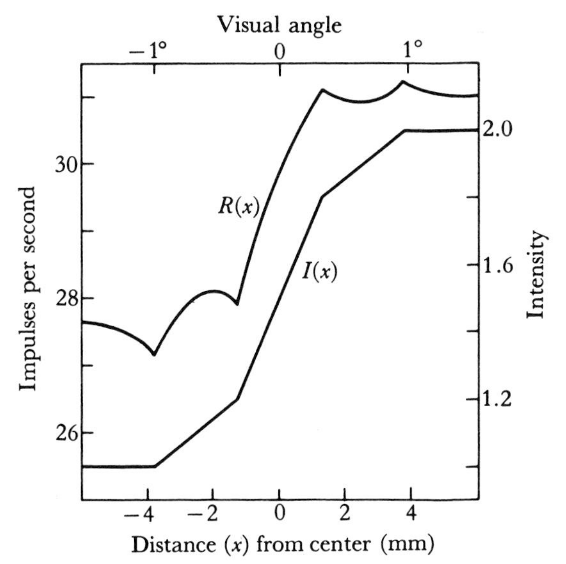

Figure 3.21. *The response to a stimulus distribution consisting of linear segments calculated with Fry's equation. From Fry (1948).*

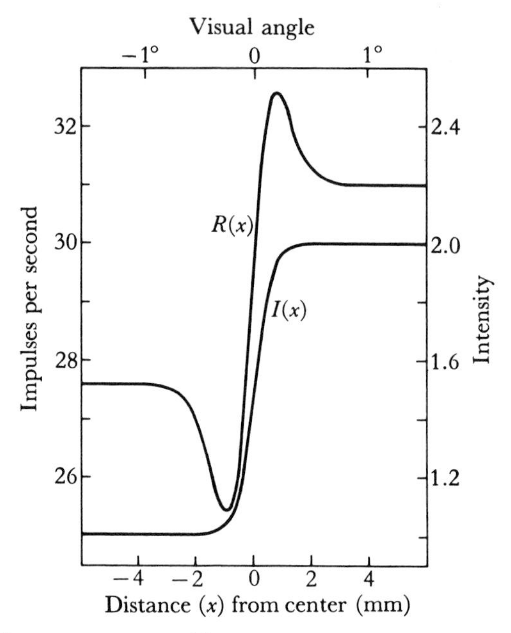

Figure 3.22. *The response to a blurred stimulus distribution calculated with Fry's equation. From Fry (1948).*

distribution having a steeper gradient, however, showed more pronounced and rounded maxima and minima (Fig. 3.22).

Although gray patches on brighter and darker backgrounds (Fig. 3.23) also yield pronounced maxima and minima in the response $R(x)$ calculated along the line drawn across the pattern, the comparable effects seen by the observer are slight. A striking difference is actually seen in the brightnesses of the two identical patches, however, as is predicted

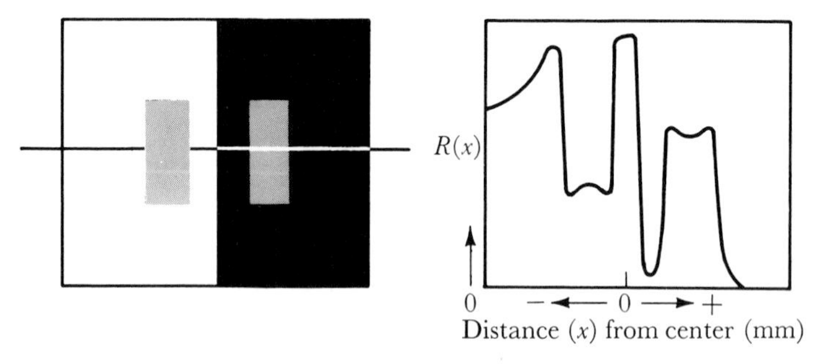

Figure 3.23. *The response to gray patches on bright and dark backgrounds calculated along one dimension across the center of the stimulus pattern (as indicated by the horizontal line) using Fry's equation. From Fry (1948).*

from the model, but the brightness of each patch is nearly uniform across its entire extent (see Fig. 2.23). As was mentioned in the discussion of "edge effects" above, many color contrast and brightness contrast effects are surprisingly uniform over areas of great extent. None of the neural models discussed here accounts fully for these phenomena. Fry suggests, however, that there may be some "frequency equalizing" mechanism elsewhere in the visual system that, to a certain extent, smooths out the frequency differences in the responses of elements within uniform fields, and yet maintains the over-all contrast between differently illuminated fields themselves.

In summary, this model is similar to the ones already described and to those to be described later in that it consists of a narrow excitatory component surrounded by an extended inhibitory component that diminishes with distance. But, like Mach's model, it differs from the Huggins-Licklider and Békésy models in one important respect—it is nonlinear. The inhibitory influences add arithmetically, but their ultimate effects depend upon the *ratio* of excitatory to inhibitory influences.

HARTLINE AND RATLIFF (1954 AND LATER)—RECURRENT INHIBITION WITH THRESHOLDS AND DELAYS

The next model to be considered is a description of the general properties of a neural network in the lateral eye of the horseshoe crab *Limulus*. Unlike the other models it is empirical rather than inferential; all terms in the quantitative expressions refer to directly observable electrophysiological phenomena in an actual retina—none of the functions are hypothetical and none of the constants are arbitrary.

The eye of *Limulus* provides an especially favorable preparation for the quantitative analysis of the functional properties of a neural network that arise from inhibitory interaction. This eye has a relatively small population of interacting elements; it contains a three-dimensional network, or plexus, of neural interconnections which form a true retina; the interaction mediated by this plexus is purely inhibitory; and both the excitatory and the inhibitory influences in the retina may be observed directly.

The lateral eye of *Limulus* (Fig. 3.24a) is a compound eye containing approximately 1,000 ommatidia (literally "little eyes"), each of which appears to function as a "receptor unit." Nerve fibers arise from these ommatidia in small bundles (Fig. 3.24b) and come together to form a larger bundle—the optic nerve—which then proceeds to the optic lobe of the brain. A plexus of nerve fibers interconnects the small bundles immediately behind the photoreceptor layer. By recording the electrical

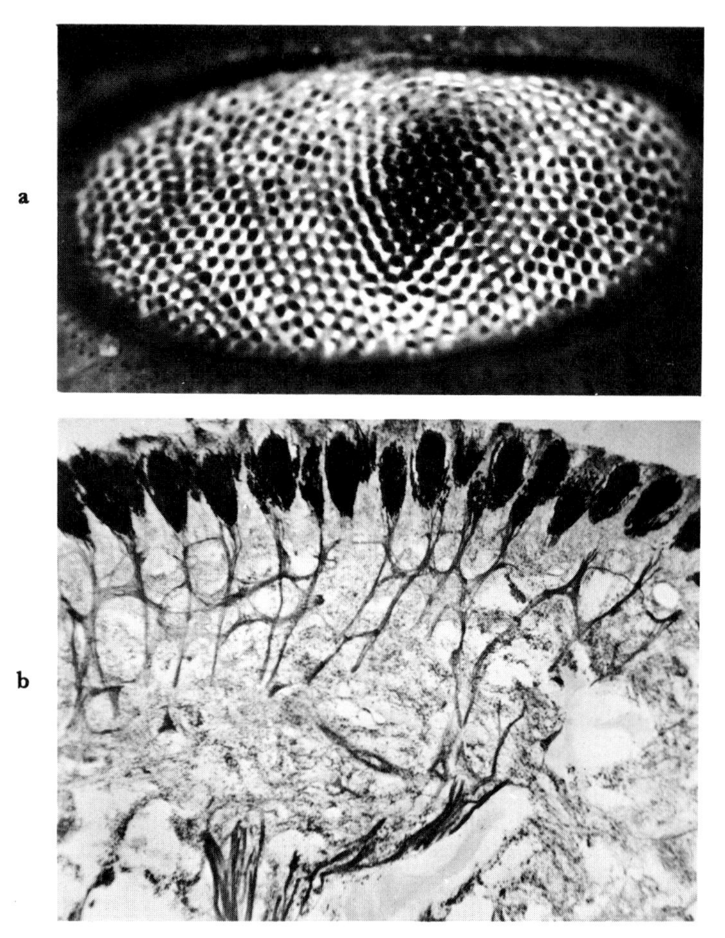

Figure 3.24. *The lateral eye of the horseshoe crab* Limulus. (a) *Corneal surface. In a medium-sized adult each eye forms an ellipsoidal bulge on the side of the carapace, about 12 mm long by 6 mm wide. The facets of the ommatidia are spaced approximately 0.3 mm apart, center to center, on the surface of the eye. The optical axes of the ommatidia diverge, so that the visual fields of all those in one eye taken together cover approximately a hemisphere. The optical axes of the ommatidia with the dark circular facets near the center of the eye are oriented in the direction of the camera.* (b) *Photomicrograph of a section of the compound eye of* Limulus *taken perpendicular to the plane of* (a) *at a slightly higher magnification. Samuel's silver stain. The cornea has been removed. The heavily pigmented sensory parts of the ommatidia are at the top of the micrograph. The silver-stained nerve fibers originating in the retinular cells and the eccentric cell of each ommatidium emerge as a bundle and join with similar bundles from other ommatidia to form the optic nerve. Small lateral branches of the nerve fibers form the network, or plexus, of interconnections immediately below the receptors. (Figure prepared by W. H. Miller; micrograph of section from Hartline, Wagner, and Ratliff, 1956).*

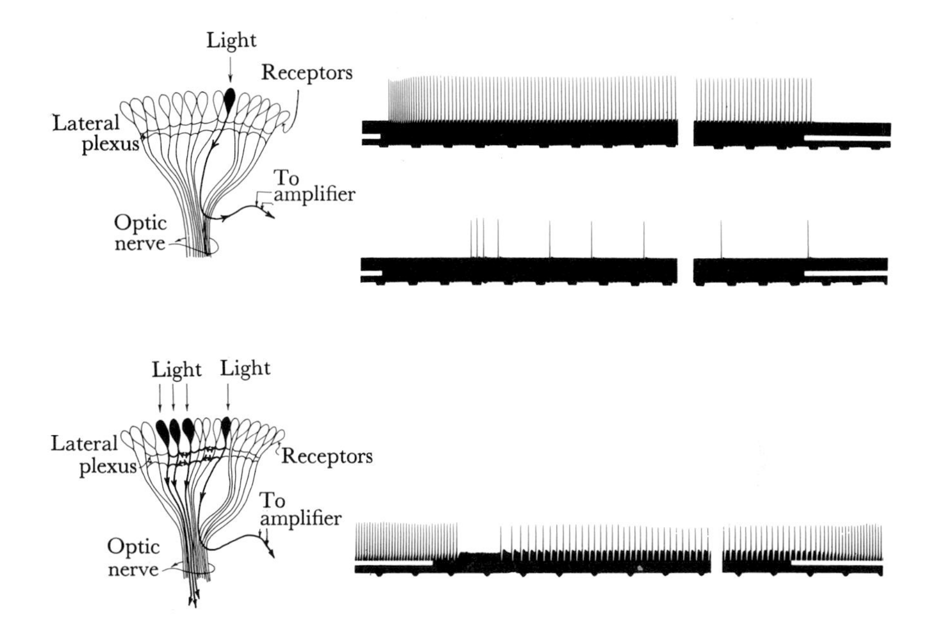

Figure 3.25. *Oscillograms of action potentials in single optic nerve fibers of* Limulus. *The experimental arrangements are indicated in the schematic diagrams.* (a) *Response to steady illumination of a single ommatidium. For the upper record the intensity of the stimulating light was 10,000 times that used to obtain the lower record. The signal of exposure to light blackens out the white line above the 1/5 second time marks. Each record interrupted for approximately 7 seconds. Records from Hartline, Wagner, and MacNichol (1952).* (b) *Inhibition of the activity of a steadily illuminated ommatidium produced by illumination of a number of other ommatidia near it. The blackening of the white line above the 1/5 second time marks signals the illumination of the neighboring ommatidia. Record from Hartline, Wagner, and Ratliff (1956).*

activity at various points within the ommatidia and along the nerve fibers arising from them, it is possible to study directly the functional properties of the neural network.

By using the technique of microdissection developed by Adrian and Bronk (1928), a small bundle containing a single active fiber may be separated from the main trunk of the optic nerve and placed on electrodes to record the electrical signs of the nerve impulses (Hartline and Graham, 1932).* Figure 3.25a illustrates the activity recorded from one of these

* Hartline, Wagner, and MacNichol (1952) and Waterman and Wiersma (1954) have shown that the impulses recorded from this preparation arise from the so-called "eccentric cell"—a bipolar neuron whose proximal process forms an axon in the optic nerve and whose distal process extends into the photosensitive rhabdom formed by

fibers in response to stimulation of the ommatidium from which it arises. Weak stimulation (lower record) produces a low frequency with a long initial latent period; strong stimulation (upper record) causes a high frequency response with a short latent period. Illumination of neighboring ommatidia (Fig. 3.25b) produces a similar discharge in their eccentric cell axons (not recorded) and a concomitant purely inhibitory effect on the discharge of nerve impulses from the nearby ommatidium under observation (Hartline, 1949).

The inhibitory influences are exerted mutually among the ommatidia so that each inhibits, and is inhibited by, its near neighbors. Unlike the models described above, however, the magnitude of the inhibition exerted on a particular element depends upon the response of neighboring elements rather than upon the stimulus to them. In physiological terms, the inhibition is recurrent, that is, it is exerted back on the site of generation of impulses in the elements affected.* Impulses are not first generated by the excitatory influence and then, at some point much farther along in the pathway, suppressed by the inhibitory influences. The opposing excitatory and inhibitory influences act simultaneously at or near the same point, and must therefore be described with simultaneous equations.

Consider just two ommatidia (generally referred to hereafter as "receptors" or "receptor units"); the magnitude of the inhibition exerted on each one depends (approximately) linearly on the frequency of response of the other, once a threshold has been reached (Fig. 3.26). Thus the activity of each is the resultant of the excitatory influence from its respective light stimulus and the inhibitory influence exerted on it by the other. This may be expressed by a pair of simultaneous linear equations:

$$r_1 = e_1 - k_{1,2}(r_2 - r^0_{1,2})$$

$$r_2 = e_2 - k_{2,1}(r_1 - r^0_{2,1}).$$

The activity of the receptor unit, its response r, is to be measured by the frequency of discharge of impulses in its axon. This response is de-

---

the surrounding retinular cells (see Miller, 1957, for anatomical details). At the time of this publication, no propagated impulses have been recorded from single axons of the retinular cells or from the fibers of the plexus. Records of the compound action potential of the whole optic nerve, however, indicate that two different types of fibers may be active in the intact nerve (H. Gasser and W. H. Miller, 1955, personal communication). It may be that the excision of the eye and dissection of the nerve trunk selectively kills the retinular cell axons. In any event, responses of retinular cells are not seen in the experiments to be described.

* In this respect the inhibition in the eye of *Limulus* is similar to the so-called "recurrent" inhibition in the spinal cord (see Granit, Pascoe, and Steg, 1957; Brooks and Wilson, 1959), and for that reason the term is used in the same sense here.

termined by the excitation e supplied by the external stimulus to the receptor, diminished by whatever inhibitory influences may be acting upon the receptor as a result of the activity of neighboring receptors. (The excitation of a particular receptor is to be measured by its response when it is illuminated by itself, thus lumping together in e the physical parameters of the stimulus and the characteristics of the photo-excitatory mechanism of the receptor.) The "threshold" frequency that must be exceeded before a receptor can exert any inhibition is represented by r^0. It and the "inhibitory coefficient" k are labeled in each equation to identify the direction of the action: $r^0_{1,2}$ is the frequency of receptor two at which it begins to inhibit receptor one; $r^0_{2,1}$ is the reverse. In the same way, $k_{1,2}$ is the coefficient of the inhibitory action of receptor two on receptor one; $k_{2,1}$, the reverse.

It has been shown that the inhibitory influences from two groups of receptors, which are widely separated so that the two groups do not interact with one another, combine by simple addition when acting

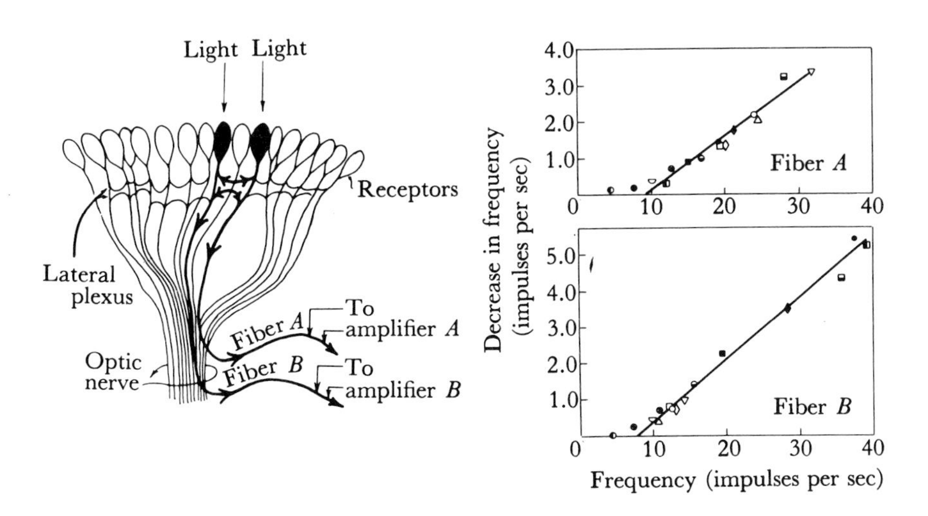

Figure 3.26. *Mutual inhibition of two receptor units in the lateral eye of* Limulus. *Action potentials were recorded simultaneously from two optic nerve fibers as indicated in the schematic. In each graph the magnitude of the inhibitory action (decrease in frequency of discharge) of one of the receptor units is plotted on the ordinate as a function of the degree of concurrent activity (frequency) of the other on the abscissa. The different points were obtained by using various intensities of illumination on receptor units A and B in various combinations. Data for points indicated by the same symbol were obtained simultaneously. The slope of the line gives the value of the inhibitory coefficient, the intercept with the x axis gives the value of the threshold. From Hartline and Ratliff (1957).*

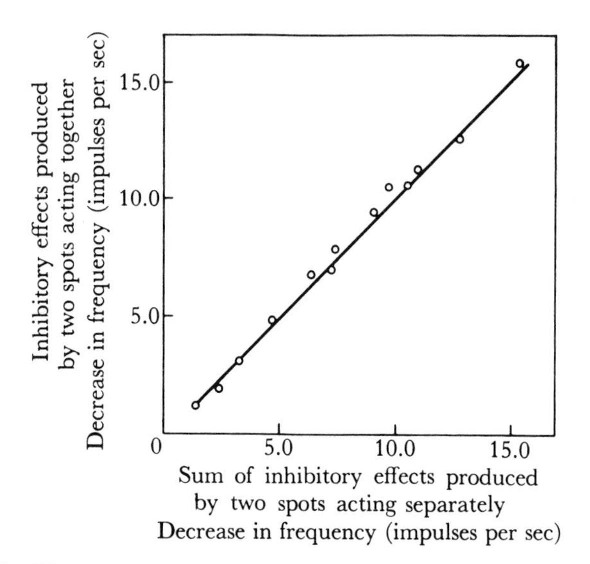

Figure 3.27. *The summation of inhibitory effects on a single receptor unit produced by spots of light illuminating two widely separated groups of receptors. The sum of the effects produced by each group acting separately is plotted as abscissa; the combined effect of the two groups acting simultaneously is plotted as ordinate. From Hartline and Ratliff (1958).*

simultaneously on an intermediate receptor. (See Fig. 3.27.) Consequently the activity of the n interacting receptor units may be described by a set of simultaneous linear equations, each with $n - 1$ inhibitory terms combined by simple addition

$$r_p = e_p - \sum_{j=1}^{n} k_{p,j}(r_j - r^0_{p,j})$$

where $p = 1, 2, \ldots, n$.*

Negative frequencies, of course, cannot occur; when the sum of the terms $k_{p,j}(r_j - r^0_{p,j})$ is greater than the excitation e_p the corresponding response r_p must be set equal to zero. Furthermore, when $(r_j - r^0_{p,j})$ is negative the inhibitory term must be dropped. Strictly speaking, then, the equations are not linear; they are only "piecewise linear." Also, as Figure 3.26 shows, the experimental points that correspond to the linear segments of the equations do not lie exactly on straight lines. The linear segments of the equations are only useful close approximations to the observed results.

* Terms for which $j = p$ are omitted, thus excluding possible "self inhibition" in this formal treatment. For a quantitative study of self inhibition in the lateral eye of *Limulus* see Stevens (1964).

The inhibitory influences diminish with increasing distance (Fig. 3.28); the threshold of inhibitory action increases and the coefficient of inhibitory action decreases. Thus, in the quantitative formulation above no special terms are required for distance effects; the diminution of the inhibitory effect with increasing distance may be ascribed simply to the combined effects of increasing thresholds ($r^0_{p,j}$) and decreasing inhibitory coefficients ($k_{p,j}$), both of which are already in the equations. A general function expressing the diminution of inhibitory influences with distance has not yet been determined directly, but on the basis of indirect evidence Kirschfeld and Reichardt (1964) have concluded that it is probably Gaussian.

The diminution of inhibition with distance introduces a topographic factor into the inhibitory interaction. As the previous models have shown, this is what gives the inhibitory interaction its special significance for spatial vision. In this network, as in the models described above, effects similar to Mach bands should appear in the pattern of neural responses. It is impractical, however, to record the response of every element in a real retina to determine a response curve similar to the response curves computed with a mathematical model. But an analogous curve can be obtained simply by measuring the response of just one element and then shifting the pattern of illumination between measurements so that this one element successively assumes a number of different positions with respect to the pattern. The responses to a simple gradient measured

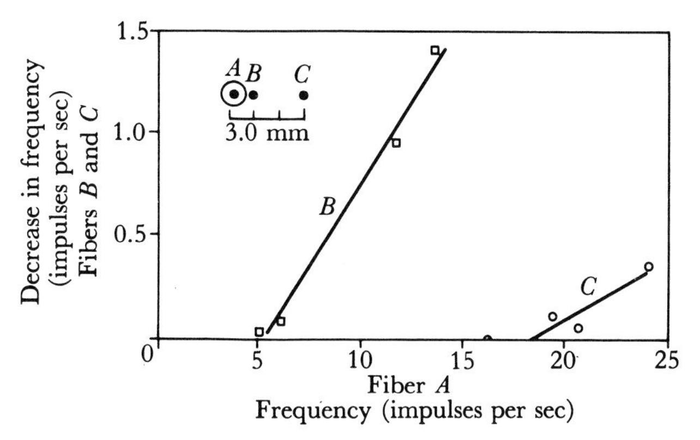

Figure 3.28. The diminution of the magnitude of inhibition with distance. The inhibition (decrease in frequency) exerted by a small group of receptor units (A) on two other receptor units (B and C) is plotted as ordinate. The concurrent frequency of discharge of impulses from one receptor in the center of the group A is plotted as abscissa. Configuration of the pattern of illumination on the eye is shown in the inset. From Ratliff and Hartline (1959).

in this way are shown in Figure 3.29. (For the responses to a step see Figure 4.17.) When a mask is placed over the eye so that only the one receptor unit "sees" the pattern, which is projected on the eye through a transilluminated slide with the density shown in the inset, then the responses, relative to independent control measurements, faithfully reproduce the stimulus distribution. When the mask is removed so that interaction among neighboring elements can take place, the expected maxima and minima then appear in the response curve. Similar effects also occur at the outer margins of the pattern, mainly outside of the boundaries of the figure shown, because the illuminated fields end on dark areas.

With certain spatial distributions, results that are apparently unique to recurrent inhibitory networks are obtained. For example, under some conditions the law of simple addition of inhibitory influences does not appear to hold. Sometimes the inhibitory effect produced by the combined influences of several groups of receptors acting together is *less* than the sum of the separate influences produced by the individual groups acting alone. But this is only an *apparent* failure of the law that results because the inhibition exerted by a receptor depends on its own activity. Since the amount of receptor activity in each of several groups close to one another is reduced by mutual inhibition when they are il-

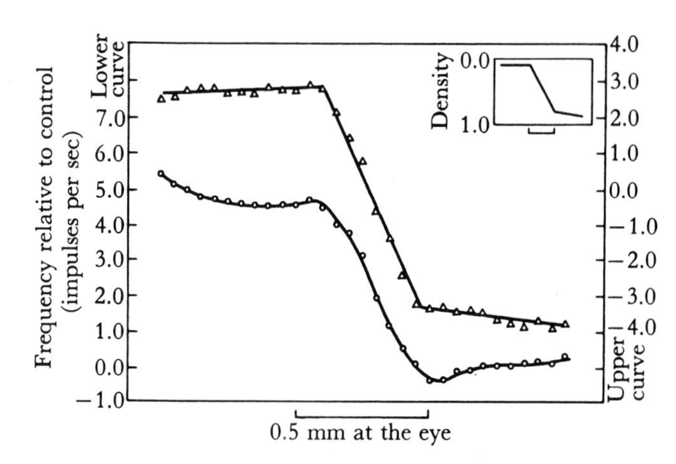

Figure 3.29. The discharge of impulses from a single receptor unit in response to a simple gradient of illumination moved in small steps across the retina. The upper curve (triangles) shows the form of the response of this receptor unit relative to control measurements when the illumination was occluded from the rest of the eye by a mask with a small aperture, thus preventing neighboring receptors from inhibiting the test receptor. The lower curve (open circles) is the response of the same receptor unit when the mask was removed from the eye and the test receptor was then inhibited by the activity of its neighbors. From Ratliff and Hartline (1959).

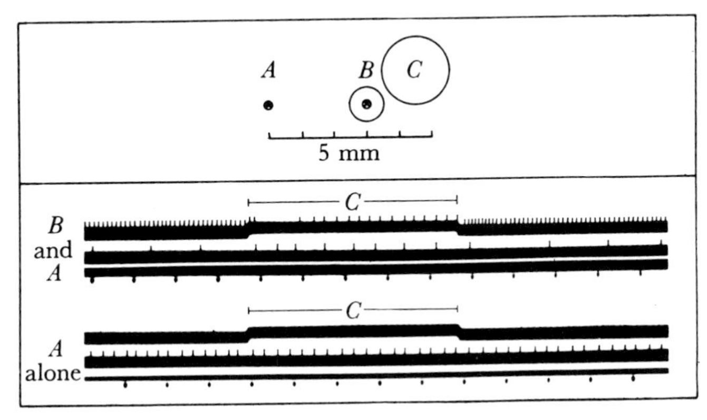

Figure 3.30. Oscillograms of the electrical activity of two optic nerve fibers showing disinhibition. The configuration of the pattern of illumination on the eye is sketched above the records. The lower record illustrates the activity of receptor unit A in the absence of illumination on B, showing that illumination of the large area C (signaled by the upward offset of the upper trace) had no perceptible effect. The upper record demonstrates the activity of receptor units A and B when both were illuminated, showing (1) lower frequency of discharge of A (as compared with lower record) resulting from activity of B, and (2) effect of illumination of C which caused a reduction in the frequency of discharge of B and concomitantly an increase in the frequency of discharge of A, as A was partially released from the inhibition exerted by B. Time marked in 1/5 seconds. The black band above the time-marks signals illumination on A and B, thin when A was illuminated alone and thick when A and B were illuminated together. Records from Hartline and Ratliff (1957).

luminated simultaneously, the total inhibition they exert when acting together should be less than the sum of the separate effects produced when acting alone. The additive law of spatial summation still holds; the reduction in the total effect is merely a consequence of the recurrent nature of the inhibition.

These "second-order" effects are shown clearly in the experiment illustrated in Figure 3.30. When additional receptors are illuminated in the vicinity of several interacting elements—too far from one receptor to affect it directly, but near enough to the others to inhibit them—the frequency of discharge of the one increases as it is partially released from the inhibition exerted on it by the others (Hartline and Ratliff, 1954, 1957).* Such disinhibition can occur in a single stage of a recurrent net-

* The idea for this experiment came from Pavlov's view of the supposed phenomenon of disinhibition in the brain, which he used to explain some of the results of his experiments on conditioned reflexes in dogs. As yet, disinhibition has not been observed in the brain, but effects attributed to disinhibition have recently been observed in electrophysiological experiments on the spinal cord of the cat by Wilson, Diecke, and Talbot (1960) and by Wilson and Burgess (1961).

work; it cannot take place in a single stage of a purely inhibitory non-recurrent network. (It will be shown later in this chapter, however, that both a single stage nonrecurrent system with certain additional excitatory influences and a nonrecurrent system with multiple stages can also produce second-order effects of this kind.)

Studies of the mechanism of the inhibition reveal the basis of the recurrent effects. In the above experiments electrical signs of propagated impulses were recorded from the axon of a specialized bipolar cell (eccentric cell) in the receptor unit (ommatidium). At rest this cell is polarized; there is a potential difference between the inside and the outside of the cell. Upon illumination of the receptor unit, this cell tends to be depolarized (Fig. 3.31a, upper record). This change in potential is sometimes referred to as a "generator potential" because the processes it reflects lead to the generation of impulses in the axon of the cell.* During steady illumination the magnitude of the depolarization increases approximately linearly with the logarithm of the light intensity and the discharge of impulses increases linearly with the depolarization (MacNichol, 1956). The same effect may be produced by passing a depolarizing current through the recording microelectrode. Conversely, increased polarization of the cell, which may be produced either by decreasing the intensity of illumination (Fig. 3.31a, lower record) or by passing current through the recording microelectrode, slows the discharge of impulses. Similarly, inhibitory influences exerted on a discharging cell produce an increase in polarization and, concomitantly, a slowing down or complete suppression of the discharge (Fig. 3.31b). For a detailed study of the mechanisms of the interplay of excitatory and inhibitory influences in the lateral eye of *Limulus* see Purple (1964). Extensive accounts of studies on the mechanisms underlying inhibitory phenomena may be found in the report of a symposium edited by Florey (1961) and in a book by Eccles (1964).

The inhibitory influences are not exerted instantaneously (Fig. 3.32). Following a burst of impulses in one element, an appreciable time elapses before the activity of a neighboring element is slowed (Ratliff, Hartline, and Miller, 1963). As a first approximation, these temporal properties may be included in the steady-state equations with the following modification:

$$r_p(t) = e_p(t) - \sum_{j=1}^{n} [k_{p,j} r_j(t - T_{p,j}) - r^0_{p,j}].$$

* Strictly speaking, the observed changes in polarization result from changes in the *conductance* across the membrane of the eccentric cell. See Tomita (1958), Fuortes (1959), and Purple (1964).

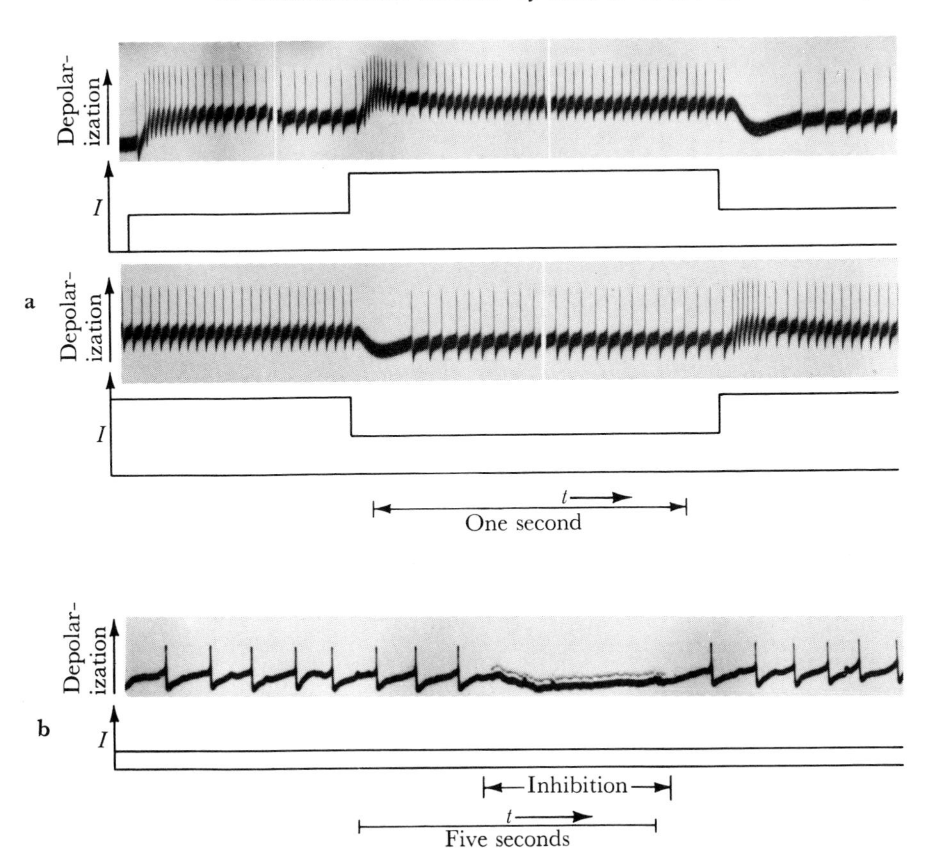

Figure 3.31. *Slow generator potentials and propagated action potentials recorded from the eccentric cell of an ommatidium in the eye of* Limulus. *The response to an increment (upper record) and a decrement (lower record) in illumination is shown in* (a). *The response to steady illumination and inhibition exerted by the activity of neighboring units produced by antidromic stimulation of optic nerve (signalled by small shock artifacts on record) is shown in* (b). *Record* (b) *from Ratliff, Hartline, and Miller, (1963).*

In these equations the response r_p of a particular element at any time t is determined by the level of excitation e_p of the element at that same time, diminished by the summated inhibitory influences exerted on it by the other elements j. These influences, however, are the ones initiated by the elements j at some earlier time $t - T_{p,j}$, where $T_{p,j}$ is the time lag of the action of any particular element j on the element p as defined above. (The restrictions on the equations mentioned earlier also apply here.)

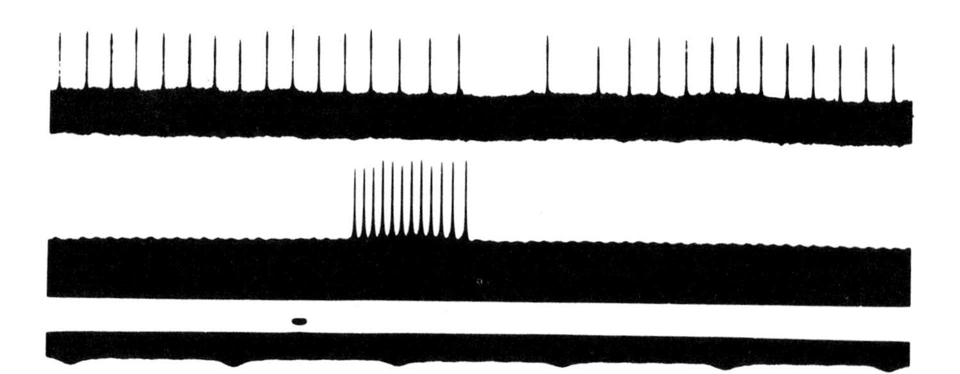

Figure 3.32. Transient inhibition of the discharge from a steadily illuminated receptor unit (upper trace) by a burst of impulses discharged from a second receptor unit nearby (bottom trace) in response to a 0.01 second flash of light (signaled by the black dot in the white band above the 1/5 second time marks). From Hartline, Ratliff, and Miller (1961).

It should be noted that this quantitative formulation of the temporal properties of the inhibition is only a rough first approximation in which a number of important details are omitted. In the first place it has been assumed that the inhibitory influence has no appreciable duration. That is, the inhibitory influence produced by r_j at the time $t - T_{p,j}$ is treated as if it were exerted on r_p only at the one instant of time t. Undoubtedly, the influence takes some time to build up and to decay. Second, there may be a natural transient in the initial phases of any prolonged inhibitory influence in addition to that which might be attributed to the initial high-frequency burst of impulses (Tomita 1958; Hartline, Ratliff and Miller 1961). Third, some experiments indicate that the inhibitory coefficients may not be constant in time as has been assumed here. It has been found, for example, that the second of two identical short bursts of impulses, spaced 1.0 sec apart, may produce a greater inhibitory effect than the first. Fourth, the time delay of the action may not be the same at all levels of frequency. Furthermore, there is a small overshoot, or "post-inhibitory rebound," following inhibition, which is neglected in the present treatment. Further experimental study is needed to elucidate these points and to incorporate a description of them in the model.* Some aspects of the dynamics of an electronic model of a pair of neurons hav-

* A comprehensive experimental and theoretical analysis of the dynamics of lateral inhibition in the compound eye of *Limulus* has since been carried out by Lange (1965). The essence of his formulation is the assumption that uniform amounts of inhibitory

ing both self- and mutual-inhibition are described in a recent article by Harmon (1964). The theory of rhythmic behavior due to reciprocal inhibition in small nerve nets and its simulation by electronic models is described by Reiss (1962). For a review of work dealing with real-time electronic neural analogs, see Harmon (1962). The significance of the temporal properties of the inhibition and of other aspects of the dynamic behavior of the retina will be discussed later in Chapter 4.

In general, the observed properties of this real neural network are quite similar to the properties of the various hypothetical neural networks: stimulation of any particular point on the receptor mosaic produces local excitatory influences and surrounding additive inhibitory influences that diminish with distance. In detail, however, there are important differences: the inhibition exerted by an element depends upon its response, rather than the stimulus to it; there is a threshold below which the response produces no inhibition; and there is an appreciable delay between any response and the inhibitory effect it produces.

TAYLOR (1956)—RECURRENT INHIBITION

The model formulated by Taylor (1956) was based on electrophysiological experiments on the integrative action of the vertebrate retina. It had been shown previously (Hartline, 1938b, 1941) that the discharge of im-

---

transmitter are produced by each nerve impulse. The transmitter is assumed to decay, or inactivate, along an exponential time course. The post-synaptic inhibitory potential is assumed to be linearly related to the transmitter concentration that exceeds a threshold value. This threshold is imposed locally (i.e., there is no subliminal interaction among units or between self- and lateral-inhibition). Time delay is then explained in terms of the time for summed influences to reach threshold. Potentiation of the inhibitory effect of one burst of impulses by a preceding burst appears to be due to a sub-threshold residium of transmitter. Post inhibitory rebound results from distortion of the exponential "tail" of lateral inhibition when it falls below threshold. (It is assumed that the self inhibition has no threshold.) Formally, the dynamic equations proposed by Ratliff, Hartline, and Miller (1963) thus become

$$r_p(t) = e_p(t) - \sum_j^n K_{j,p}\left(\frac{1}{\tau}\int_0^t \exp\left[(t' - t)/\tau\right] r_j(t')dt' - r_{j,p}^0\right)$$

where τ is the time constant of exponential decay of the hypothetical transmitter and $K_{j,p}/\tau$ is the amplitude of the corresponding inhibitory potential in units of frequency change. A simplification which seems to be justified is that $r_{j,p}^0 = C_p/K_{j,p}$. This makes the threshold term, when multiplied by the inhibitory constant, a function of p only. This leads to a prediction of a common intercept on the ordinate of plots of the inhibition exerted on a particular unit by various single neighbors (Fig. 3.37). The dynamic integral equation proposed by Lange reduces to the Hartline-Ratliff steady state equations when t approaches infinity and all frequencies become constant. In the case of no lateral inhibition (i.e., when the summation includes only the pth term) Lange's dynamic integral equation reduces to the equation for self inhibition proposed by Stevens (1964).

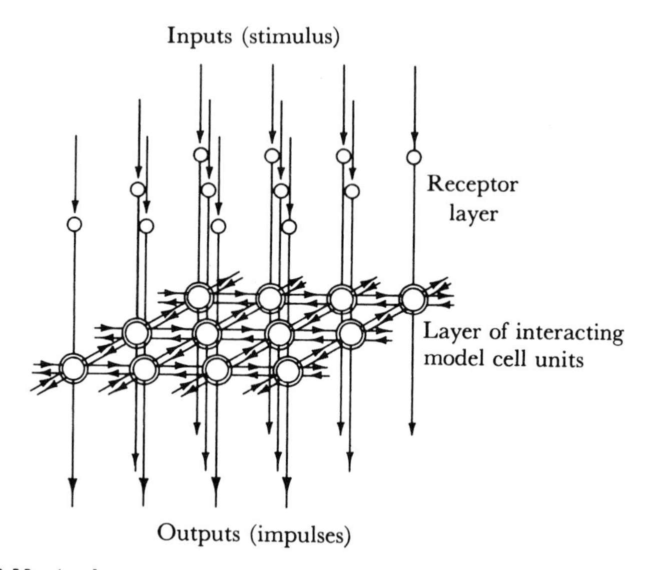

Figure 3.33. A schema of the receptor layer and interacting layer, with arrowheads indicating the direction of conduction of impulses. From Taylor (1956).

pulses in single axons of the vertebrate optic nerve depended on the summed effects of interacting pathways converging on the ganglion cells from which these axons arise. In general, the pattern of response appears to be determined by the net effects produced by opposed excitatory and inhibitory influences (see Chap. 4).

Taylor's model treats a specific one of the several types of ganglion cells in the cat retina described by Kuffler (1953)—the one with a so-called "on" center, "off" surround receptive field. (Receptive fields are discussed in detail in Chapter 4.) Taylor assumed that this receptive field—that is, the area of the receptor mosaic that must be illuminated to cause a discharge of impulses—has a sensitive central excitatory region surrounded by a less sensitive inhibitory region. The schematic network in Figure 3.33 represents the average trend of the interconnections. It is assumed that the interaction can be specified by two parameters, k and s, which denote the average magnitude and spread of the interaction, respectively. It was further assumed that the relationship between the logarithm of light intensity and the frequency of response (in the absence of interaction) is approximately linear as in the eye of the horseshoe crab *Limulus*.

Based on these assumptions the interaction of the opposed influences in the neural network may be expressed by a set of simultaneous equations, one for each of the units. Consider a single row of units, infinitely long so that end-effects can be neglected. The response r_p of a particular unit is then given by the equation

$$r_p = e_p + k \sum_{p-s}^{p+s} r_j.$$

The gain of each unit is normalized to unity so that if $k = 0$ the response r_p is equal to the excitation e_p resulting from the illumination on the receptor. To simplify, it is assumed that the coefficient of the action of each element j on a particular element p is uniform over the distance $\pm s$ from p or, in the two-dimensional case, within the circle of radius s centered on p. Taylor notes, however, that in any real neural network the coefficient is probably some function of the distance s or of the frequency of response r.

To account for a summation of excitatory influences that has been observed at low intensities of illumination (Beitel, 1936), Taylor suggests that the sign of the coefficient might change with intensity. At low intensity k could be positive and thus lead to summative excitatory effects; at a higher intensity it would become zero, and at a still higher intensity it would become negative so that inhibition would result. Thus the equations would be linear in segments, but nonlinear when the entire range of operation is considered. Note that the inhibition is assumed to be response-dependent, or recurrent.

Figure 3.34 shows responses to various patterns of illumination cal-

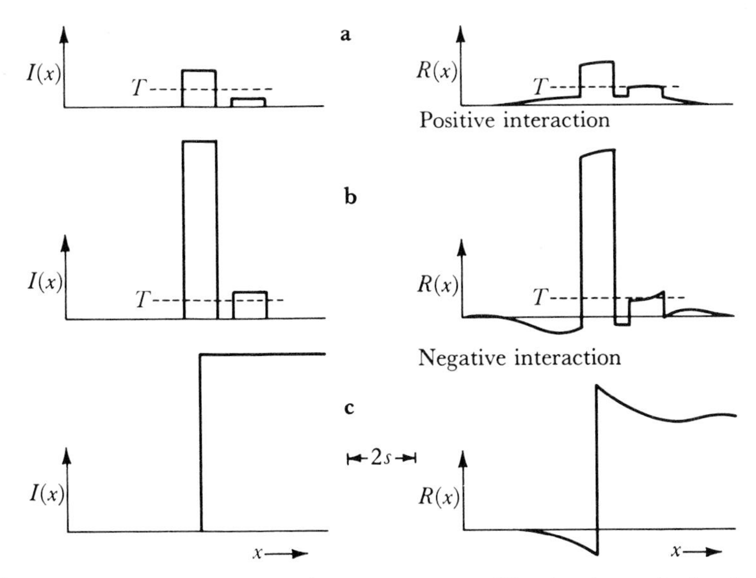

Figure 3.34. Responses to various patterns of illumination calculated with Taylor's equations. Redrawn after Taylor (1956).

culated with this model. In (a) the stimulus intensities $I(x)$ are weak, the coefficient is positive, and the responses $R(x)$ to both stimuli are elevated slightly. Thus a stimulus which would be below the threshold of visibility (T) without interaction might be raised to this threshold with positive interaction. Similarly, at higher intensities (b) where k is assumed to become negative, a stimulus which would be above the threshold of visibility without interaction might be suppressed below this threshold with negative (inhibitory) interaction. The inhibitory interaction also shows the expected edge-effects (c).

The above model applies to steady-state conditions only. In a later development, Taylor (1958) considered two temporal effects, adaptation and post inhibitory rebound, in a proposed explanation of some phenomenal movements that are seen when one observes a stationary grating or other striated pattern. These effects were not included in the mathematical model itself, however, and need not be considered here (see Chap. 4).

The basic properties of this mathematical model are similar to those of all the others: central excitatory influences are opposed by surrounding inhibitory influences, these inhibitory influences are additive, and they diminish to zero with distance. But, in agreement with the Hartline-Ratliff model, Taylor's version differs from the others in that the inhibition is response-dependent rather than stimulus-dependent. Furthermore, the explicit assumption that coefficients of interaction may become positive at low intensities is unique to this particular model.

SIX MODELS—OR ONE?

Reduced to their bare essentials, the six models are really one and the same, since the same basic neural processes—excitatory influences opposed by surrounding inhibitory influences—merely masquerade in slightly different mathematical forms in each of the several models. These simple processes alone seem adequate to account for the gross features of the Mach bands, and the fact that several diverse attempts to reach an understanding of the phenomena all point to essentially the same basic processes is reassuring. But as Mach once remarked, "We shall never ascertain what these processes are if, from the very beginning, we conceive of them in too simple a manner." Visual phenomena are complex, the retina is complex, and doubtless the processes that relate the two are equally complex.

Of course no mathematical model can represent each and every detail of a complex neural process; to simplify them many similar details must be embodied in a single expression. Indeed, as will be shown later, the behavior of the entire neural network from stimulus to response conceivably might be represented in a purely mathematical model by a single transfer function. The aim of a mathematical-*neural* model, however, is to represent individually at least some of the component neural processes that intervene between stimulus and response; thus each mathematical term should correspond to some physiological process, either known or hypothetical. Furthermore, the number and variety of terms in the mathematical expressions should be sufficient to account properly for all important details of the observed phenomena as well as the gross features, and they should be physiologically sound as well as mathematically succinct. It is in the varied treatment of all these details that a single basic model of opposed excitatory and inhibitory influences becomes six different models.

In reexamining the principal distinguishing features of the several models, an attempt will be made to reconcile the differences in detail among them, and, wherever appropriate, see how they might be further elaborated without sacrificing their basic simplicity to include various fundamental processes that probably would occur in any real neural network.

Continuous versus discrete forms Some models represent the excitatory and inhibitory influences by superimposable continuous weighting functions; others by the additive contributions of discrete elements in the network. It is easy to see that the two forms are not dissimilar. Indeed, if the discrete elements in a neural network are very small and numerous then representations in discrete and in continuous forms would be practically indistinguishable. In fact all of the above models may be represented about equally well in either form (Fig. 3.35).

To make this identity of the two forms of representation clear, consider as an example the simple weighting function used by Huggins and Licklider. If the weighting function is centered on the receptor associated with a particular element p, then the ordinate erected on that receptor multiplied by the stimulus intensity at that point gives the direct excitatory influence on that element.

Ordinates erected on any neighboring receptor m multiplied by the corresponding points on the stimulus distribution give its excitatory or inhibitory contribution to the responses of the element p. That is, the ordinates of the continuous function correspond to the coefficients of interaction in the discrete form of the neural network; positive ordinates are excitatory coefficients, negative ordinates are inhibitory coefficients, and their sign and magnitude depend on their distance from p. Note that in the models proposed by Mach and by Fry the excitatory and inhibitory influences must be kept separate; the *ratio* of the absolute

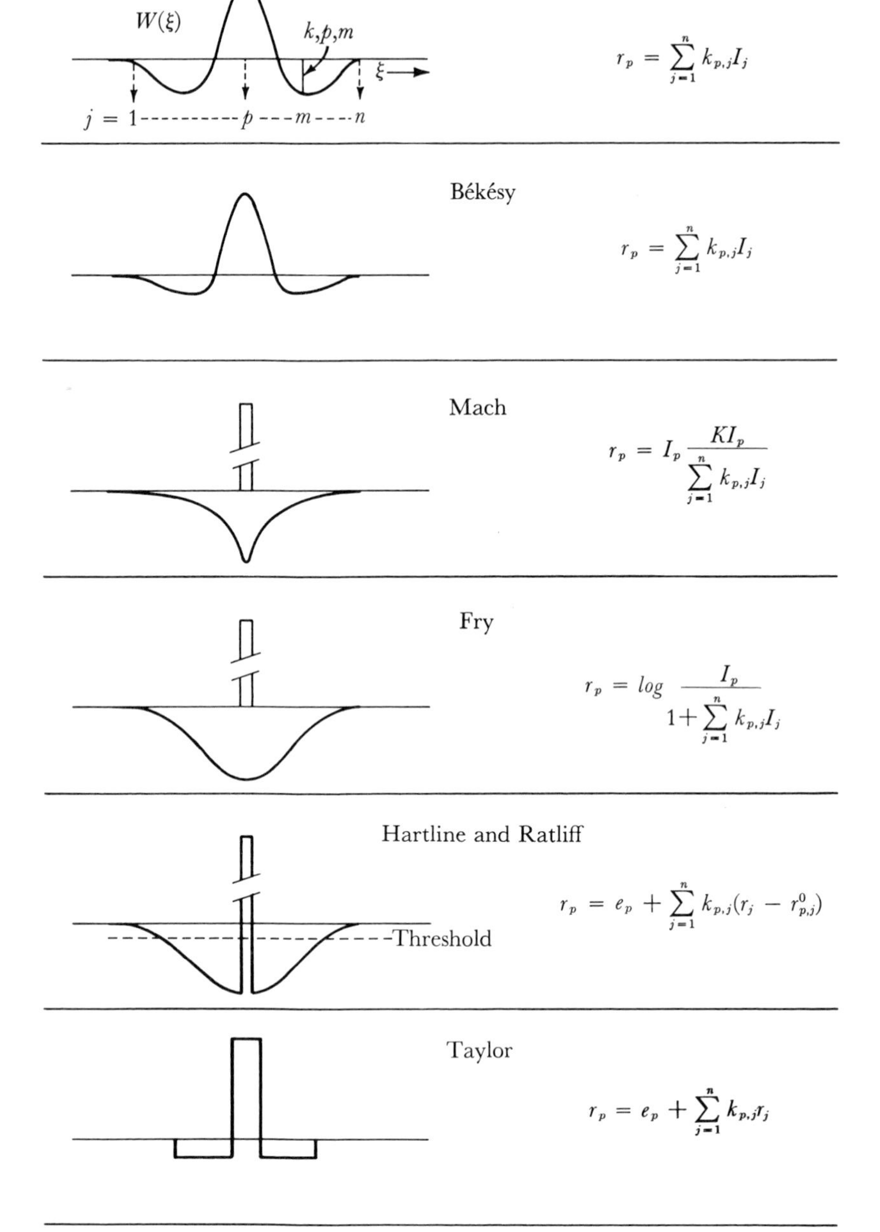

Figure 3.35. Graphical and mathematical representations of the six models of inhibitory networks.

values of the separate sums of the opposing influences, rather than the algebraic sum of the two, is to be determined. Note also that the weighting functions for recurrent models must be applied and reapplied until the results converge on the final solution (see below).

The essential identity of the discrete and continuous forms of a given model is intuitively clear, but Bliss and MacCurdy (1961) show rigorously that the inhibitory coefficients in a discrete linear model uniquely specify the form of the weighting function in an equivalent continuous model, and vice versa. On this basis they conclude that the Hartline-Ratliff model (discrete) and the Békésy model (continuous) are closely related. Their treatment, however, neglects thresholds and does not account fully for the recurrent effects in the Hartline-Ratliff model. The treatment of these effects in a continuous form, that is in terms of a weighting function, will be discussed in later sections of this chapter.

Some of the continuous forms of the models that are expressed differently actually turn out to be essentially identical when the integration is carried out. For example, the convolution integral used in the Huggins-Licklider model:

$$R(x) = K \int_{-\infty}^{+\infty} I(x - \xi) W(\xi)\, d\xi$$

and the superposition theorem used in the Békésy model:

$$R_0 = \int_{-\infty}^{+\infty} A_s(x - \xi) \cdot I'(\xi)\, d\xi$$

give the same results, provided that the weighting function in the Huggins-Licklider model and the neural unit in the Békésy model are the same.

If one applies integration by parts to Békésy's integral, then

$$R_0 = A_s(x - \xi) I(\xi) \Big|_{\xi=-\infty}^{\xi=+\infty} + \int_{-\infty}^{+\infty} A_s'(x - \xi) I(\xi)\, d\xi.$$

Since $A_s(x - \xi)$ is zero at plus and minus infinity the integrated part in the above equation is zero and from Figure 3.14 it can be seen that $A_s'(x)$ is indeed equal to the Békésy neural unit. Therefore, in the special case in which Békésy's neural unit and the weighting function in the Huggins-Licklider model have the same form, the two equations are identical.

Extent and relative magnitude of excitatory influences In some models the excitatory influences are treated as if they were confined to a single retinal element, while in others the influence is spread with diminishing effect over a small local region. This difference is more apparent than real and primarily arises because some models treat the distribution of intensity at the receptor mosaic, while others refer to the stimulus distribution external to the eye. If all models are considered from the latter point of view, it must be assumed that the light from any point in the external stimulus will generally not be imaged on a single receptor. Because of various optical imperfections, it is spread with decreasing intensity over a considerable distance on the retina. (This problem is discussed in some detail in Chap. 4.) Thus, if treated in terms of the external stimulus, all models should assume a blurring of the stimulus spatial distribution as the excitation distribution on the receptors. Fry (1963) has since taken this into account in his model, and Bliss and MacCurdy (1961) make use of it in a derivation of Békésy's neural unit.

Consider a model with a narrow excitatory component confined to one or a few receptors, and a surrounding inhibitory component that diminishes exponentially with distance (Fig. 3.36). A Gaussian blurring function (a) convolved with (that is, applied as a weighting function to) the original weighting function (b) yields a composite weighting function (c) which now resembles the continuous models proposed by Huggins and Licklider and by Békésy. Applying this composite weighting function to the external stimulus is equivalent to applying first the blurring function (a) to the stimulus and then applying the simple weighting function (b) to the blurred stimulus.

Considering these effects then, the excitatory influences in the several models become qualitatively similar, but some differences among the ex-

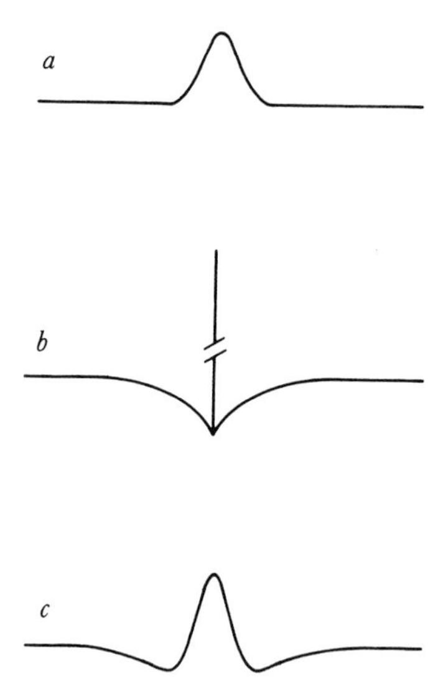

Figure 3.36. The composite weighting function (c) resulting from the convolution of a blurring function (a) with the function for an inhibitory network (b) having a narrow excitatory component.

citatory influences in various real retinas must not be overlooked. For example, evidence exists that there is a neural spread or "irradiation" of excitatory influences within the vertebrate retina, in addition to the optical blurring, but in the compound eye of the horseshoe crab all lateral neural influences appear to be purely inhibitory.

Extent and relative magnitude of inhibitory influences In all of the models it is assumed that the inhibitory influences diminish with distance. There are several lines of evidence to support this assumption. For example, Mach measured the extent of interaction among retinal points by gradually occluding a part of the illuminated field and determining at what point a dark Mach band was noticeably reduced in magnitude (Fig. 7, paper No. 6, Part Two). Under the particular conditions he used the band was not significantly affected by occlusion of points at a visual angle greater than 16 minutes from it. As points nearer the band were covered, the effect on the appearance of the band became more pronounced. Although the effects clearly diminish with distance, the exact shape of the distance function cannot be determined from these simple observations. Earlier, however, Mach had concluded that it was probably an exponential function, decreasing rapidly at first and then more slowly as illustrated in Figure 3.18 above.

For simplicity in calculation, Békésy and Taylor assume that the inhibitory zone is uniform throughout. Using this simple version of the inhibitory influence, calculated Mach bands are equal to the full width of the inhibitory zone. If such a model is approximately correct, then the real inhibitory zone should be equal to the width of real or observed Mach bands. On this basis Békésy determined that the half-width of the inhibitory zone in the retina (s in Fig. 3.7) must subtend a visual angle of about 10 or 15 minutes. Békésy notes, however, that because the width of the bands depends upon the intensity of illumination and other factors, the width of the inhibitory zone may not be constant (see below).

Similar calculations, based on the psychophysical experiments reported in the previous chapter, would yield inhibitory zones of about this same magnitude. Note, however, that the widths of the observed bright and dark bands are not the same. The width of the calculated inhibitory zone, therefore, depends upon which band is used for the calculations. Even so, the order of magnitude of these estimates agrees fairly well with the results of some completely different psychophysical experiments by Beitel (1936) on inhibitory effects in the human eye. According to these experiments—in which the inhibitory influence of a patch of light on threshold measurements in neighboring areas was determined—the inhibitory zone must decrease to zero at about 20 minutes of visual angle at the retina. It was on the basis of these experiments that Taylor assumed the half-width of the inhibitory zone in the graphical representation of his model to be 10 minutes of arc.

In some psychophysical experiments on contrast Fry found that the transient inhibitory effects produced by short flashes diminish with distance and disappear altogether at a distance of about 75 minutes. He assumed a Gaussian distribution in which the effect diminishes to about one-half the maximum value at a distance of approximately .13 mm on the retina. This corresponds to a visual angle of about 30 minutes of arc, and is substantially larger than the estimates made by Mach, Békésy, and Taylor. But the conditions of the experiments on which the various estimates were based are not strictly comparable. Mach and Békésy used two different measures of the Mach bands under steady-state conditions; Taylor used Beitel's measure of the influence of steady-state inhibition on the threshold of response to a flash of illumination; and Fry measured meta-contrast, that is, the transient inhibitory influence exerted by the response to one flash of light on the response to another. Not only were all of the measures different, but the results of each are strongly dependent on the particular conditions used.

This brings up the fundamental problem of what might cause the inhibitory zones to have different widths under different conditions. One possibility is the graded diminution of the inhibition with distance.* Because of this diminution with distance, the inhibitory influence could easily appear to shrink or expand with changes in the strength of the excitatory influence that produces it. One need only make the realistic assumption that there is a threshold which the inhibitory influence must exceed before it becomes effective. For example, the Hartline-Ratliff model showed that the diminution of inhibitory influences with distance may be represented as the resultant of two factors: a decrease in the inhibitory coefficient ($k_{p,j}$) and an increase in the threshold of inhibitory influence ($r^0_{p,j}$).

Changes in the effective size of an inhibitory zone caused by this combination of factors in a discrete linear model can be shown more clearly in the equivalent continuous linear weighting function model. Assume that the inhibitory influences have a Gaussian distribution, something like the function illustrated in Figure 3.37a. Ordinates of this function at specific points thus represent the coefficients of the inhibitory action of the central element on those points (or vice versa, since the inhibition is generally assumed to be about equal in the two directions). The magni-

* The uniform inhibitory zones assumed by Békésy and Taylor are simplified approximations intended for purposes of calculation only and are not intended to be realistic representations of the inhibitory influence.

tude of the inhibition exerted at any point is given simply by multiplying the response of the central element (or the stimulus intensity in a stimulus dependent system) times the ordinate (that is, the inhibitory coefficient) at the appropriate point.

These products for every point on the weighting function are shown in (b) for two intensities of illumination at the point where the function is centered. A low intensity on the central element yields a weak response and weak surrounding inhibitory influences (solid line); a high intensity yields a strong response and strong surrounding inhibitory influences (broken line). Now assume that there is a threshold that the inhibitory influences must reach in order to be effective. Because of this threshold, the effective field of inhibitory influence would shrink or expand as the response of the element exerting the influence decreased or increased.

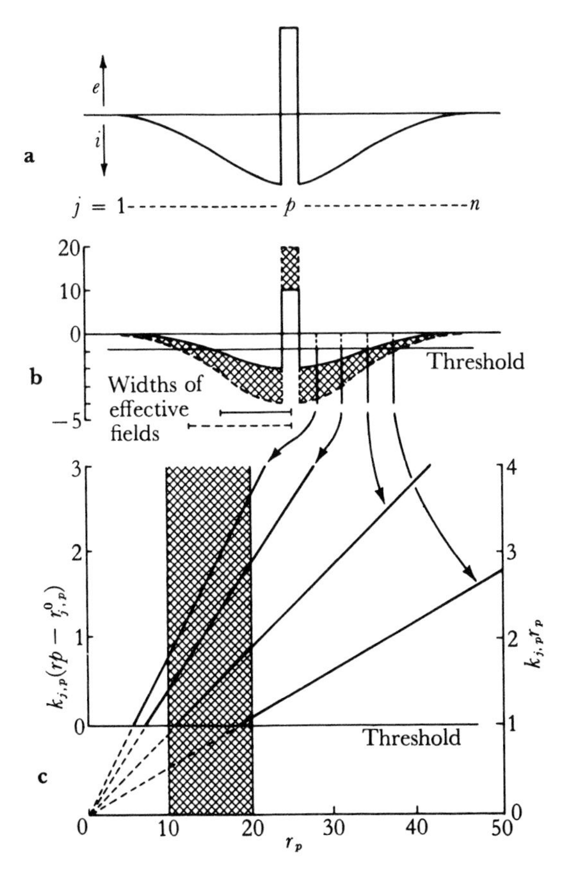

Figure 3.37. *Dependence of the size of the effective field of inhibition on the threshold of inhibition.*

(These changes may partly account for the marked asymmetry observed in the Mach bands.)

For the discrete form of the model, ordinates of the weighting function at various distances from the center are equivalent to the coefficient of inhibitory action $k_{j,p}$ of the central element p on the elements j at various points, or vice versa, if the influence is assumed to be about the same in both directions. As shown in (c) the inhibitory influence at any point is thus given by the product of the response r_p of the central element and the appropriate inhibitory coefficient $k_{j,p}$, according to the scale on the right-hand ordinate.

Based on the above assumption that there is a fixed threshold which the inhibitory influence exerted by any particular element on another must exceed to become effective, one finds that the corresponding threshold of response ($r_{j,p}^0$) which produces sufficient inhibition to reach this threshold increases with distance. That portion of the family of curves above the threshold shown by the solid lines only would be given by the product $k_{j,p}$ ($r_p - r_{j,p}^0$) represented on the left-hand ordinate. These functions very closely resemble the decrease in inhibitory coefficients ($k_{j,p}$) that were directly observed in the retina of the horseshoe crab (Fig. 3.28). Subthreshold influences exerted by different elements are assumed not to be additive; that is, several overlapping subthreshold influences cannot sum with one another to produce a suprathreshold influence. Only those subthreshold influences exerted by the same element can add up to reach the threshold. Of course, the influences from all elements which individually exceed the threshold are additive.

Thus, with these few assumptions, it is a relatively simple matter to include the threshold phenomena in any of the models, and they may be represented equally well in either the continuous or the discrete forms.

Linearity The classification of the models as linear or nonlinear was based on two general methods of expressing the inhibitory influences. In the so-called linear models the inhibitory influences are additive and their sum is *subtracted* directly from the excitatory influences to determine the response. A constant and suprathreshold inhibitory influence has a constant effect on the response of the element affected, no matter whether it acts alone or is added to other influences of any amount. Thus the inhibitory effect, the decrease in frequency of impulses generated, is a linear function of the sum of the separate inhibitory influences. In the so-called nonlinear models the separate inhibitory influences are also additive but the excitatory influences are *divided* by the sum of the inhibitory influences. Thus a constant inhibitory influence exerted by a particular element in a nonlinear system may frequently produce different inhibitory effects, depending upon whether it acts alone or in conjunction with other influences. Furthermore, the magnitude of the effect depends upon the magnitude of the response of the element affected, since the effect is produced by division.

Whether the inhibitory influences are treated in terms of subtraction or division, however, is not necessarily a distinguishing feature of a particular type of network. Indeed, the processes of multiplication and division may be turned into the simpler processes of addition and subtraction by use of exponents, for $a^m/a^n = a^{m-n}$ and $a^m \cdot a^n = a^{m+n}$. In general, such exponential expressions are available in a neural network, for logarithms *are* exponents, and often the relation between external stimulus and neural response is approximately logarithmic. Addition and subtraction of these logarithmic transformations, for example, the linear depolarization or hyperpolarization of a cell as log I increases or decreases, are thus equivalent to direct multiplication and division. Therefore, the same network can sometimes be described equally well in either of these two ways. Thus far, the choice of one form or the other has usually been more or less arbitrary; the final choice must await decisive experimental evidence.

In any event, classification of the models as linear or nonlinear is not very definitive, for even the so-called linear models are not strictly linear. First of all, the excitatory influences and the responses they produce in any particular element must have some realistic lower and upper limits. Below a certain threshold, which generally depends on the state of adaptation of the eye, a stimulus may produce no neural response at all. Above this threshold responses usually increase with increasing intensity, but not indefinitely, of course; there is some upper limit. Similarly, thresholds of inhibitory influence and possibly some upper "saturation" points further limit the range over which the inhibitory components of a neural network can operate.

Because of these limits, especially the thresholds of inhibitory action, it is a formidable task to find a general analytic expression adequate to account fully for the behavior of a complex neural network under any and all conditions. Indeed, the problem of expressing the interactions among three elements in a recurrent system with thresholds is reminiscent of the famous "three-body problem" in astronomy.* But if these

* One of the most celebrated of all dynamical problems is the three-body problem, which has been posed as follows: "*Three particles attract each other according to the Newtonian law, so that between each pair of particles there is an attractive force which is proportional to the product of the masses of the particles and the inverse square of their distance apart: they are free to move in space, and are initially supposed to be moving in any given manner; to determine their subsequent motion.*

"The practical importance of this problem arises from its application to Celestial Mechanics: the bodies which constitute the solar system attract each other according kinds of limitations are not placed on the several models, results that are physiologically absurd—such as negative frequencies or infinite values of frequencies—are certain to occur. If it is realistic, then no model can be strictly linear over its entire range of operation; it can be only segmentally, or piecewise linear, and at best even these linear segments are likely to be only reasonable first approximations to the actual behavior of a real neural network. Furthermore, recurrent effects in strictly linear segments of a system can yield inhibitory influences such as the disinhibition described above that appear to be nonlinear when expressed in terms of the stimuli, rather than the responses, that produce them.

Recurrent inhibition and disinhibition In the Hartline-Ratliff model, based on electrophysiological observations of the inhibitory network in the compound eye of *Limulus,* the strength of the inhibitory influence exerted by one receptor unit on another (assuming only two elements to be illuminated) is determined by its level of activity which, in turn, is the resultant of the excitatory stimulus to that receptor and the inhibitory influences exerted back on it from the other (Fig. 3.38a). Both the excitatory influences and the inhibitory influences operate at or ahead of the site of generation of impulses (marked x in the figure). The inhibitory influences exerted by an element thus depend on its ultimate response, rather than on the stimulus to it; that is, the inhibition is recurrent. Taylor's model for the vertebrate retina also assumes a similar recurrent or response-dependent type of inhibition.

The inhibitory influences in all of the other models described above are stimulus-dependent; that is, the inhibition is nonrecurrent. The strength of the inhibitory influence exerted by each unit upon the others depends upon its level of activity ahead of the site at which inhibitory influences from others are exerted upon it (Fig. 3.38b).* The inhibitory influences are exerted at some point in the network beyond the site of the generation of impulses.

---

to the Newtonian law, and (as they have approximately the form of spheres, whose dimensions are very small compared with the distances which separate them) it is usual to consider the problem of determining their motion in an ideal form, in which the bodies are replaced by particles of masses equal to the masses of the respective bodies and occupying the positions of their centers of gravity.

"The problem of three bodies cannot be solved in finite terms by means of any of the functions at present known to analysis. This difficulty has stimulated research to such an extent, that since the year 1750 over 800 memoirs, many of them bearing the names of the greatest mathematicians, have been published on the subject." Whittaker (1959, page 339). For a history of the problem see Whittaker (1899).

* Reichardt (1961) and Varju (1962) have called these two forms of inhibition *Vorwärtsinhibition* and *Rückwärtsinhibition.* The equivalent terms in English—forward inhibition and backward inhibition—generally refer to the temporal properties of inhibitory phenomena, and to avoid confusion will be used only in this latter sense.

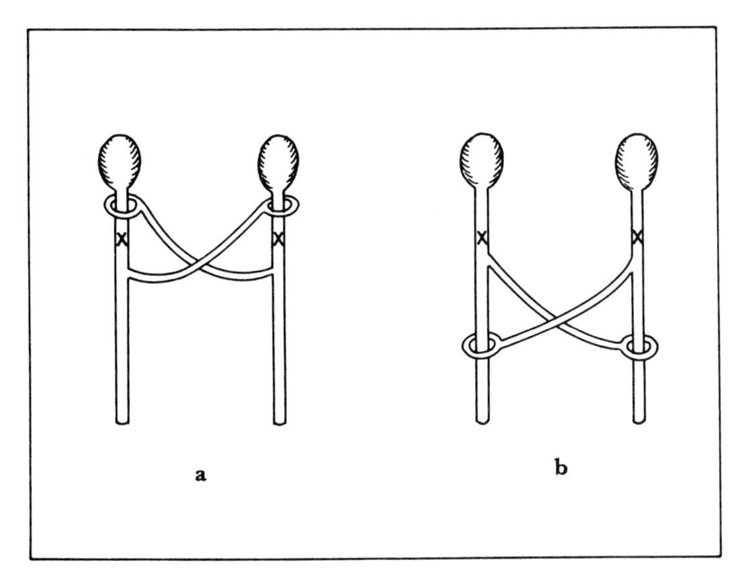

Figure 3.38. *Schematic diagram of* (a) *recurrent and* (b) *nonrecurrent inhibitory systems. In both systems the magnitude of the inhibitory influence exerted by each unit on the other depends upon the level of activity generated at the site* x *ahead of the interconnecting branches. In the recurrent system* (a) *each unit exerts inhibitory influences back upon the other at or ahead of the site* x *at which impulses are generated and which is also ahead of the lateral branches. In the nonrecurrent system* (b), *each unit exerts influences on the other at some point below the lateral branches, presumably at the next synapse in the system (see Fig. 3.41). From Ratliff, Hartline, and Miller (1963).*

The difference between these two forms of inhibition is important. As was shown above, in the recurrent system influences are not only exerted on neighbors, but also indirectly on others by way of those affected directly. The inhibition that one receptor exerts on another may thus be diminished by the activity of still other receptors that are in a position to inhibit the first. Such disinhibition resembles facilitation.

Alpern and David (1959) and Mackavey, Bartley, and Casella (1962) have obtained evidence of a similar disinhibition in the human visual system. They interpreted these results as indicating that inhibitory influences in the human retina are recurrent. The evidence is not conclusive, however, for Varju (1962) has shown that a multiple stage nonrecurrent network can produce disinhibition similar to that produced in a single-state recurrent network (see also Ratliff, Hartline, and Miller, 1963). Therefore, if the possibility of repeated stages of the inhibitory network cannot be excluded, the demonstration of disinhibition or of apparent nonadditive properties of inhibition is not conclusive proof that

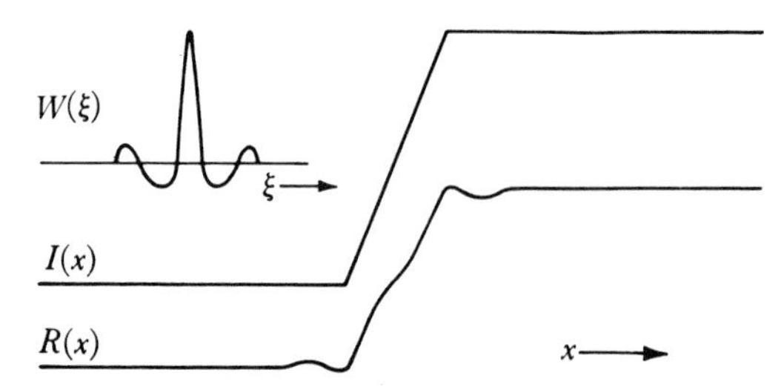

Figure 3.39. *The second-order effect in the response of a single stage network in which the inhibitory zone is surrounded by a weak excitatory zone.*

a network is recurrent. These facts show a way to reconcile to some extent the differences between the recurrent and nonrecurrent forms of inhibition. Actually, there are two ways to produce disinhibition in nonrecurrent networks, one in a single stage, the other in multiple stages. Both are physiologically realistic and within the realm of possibility.

The first to be considered is based on the fact that since disinhibition resembles facilitation it may be represented simply and directly as such. Assume, as in all the other models, that there is a central excitatory region surrounded by a zone of inhibitory influences. In a true recurrent network, because of the diminished responses they cause, these inhibitory influences would reduce the inhibition that the affected elements exert on more distant neighbors. This disinhibition may be represented as an outer zone of weak excitatory influences, as shown in Figure 3.39. (To be exact, diminishing higher order zones of inhibition and excitation should be represented also.) The same figure shows that the application of such a weighting function to a typical Mach pattern produces second-order effects similar to those produced by an ordinary recurrent system. In essence it is merely a simplification of the familiar function of the form sin x/x which when convolved with a step function as shown (Fig. 3.40)

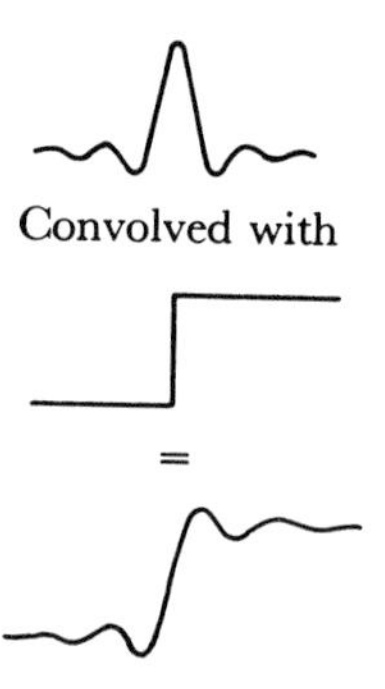

Figure 3.40. *The convolution of sin x/x function with a step function.*

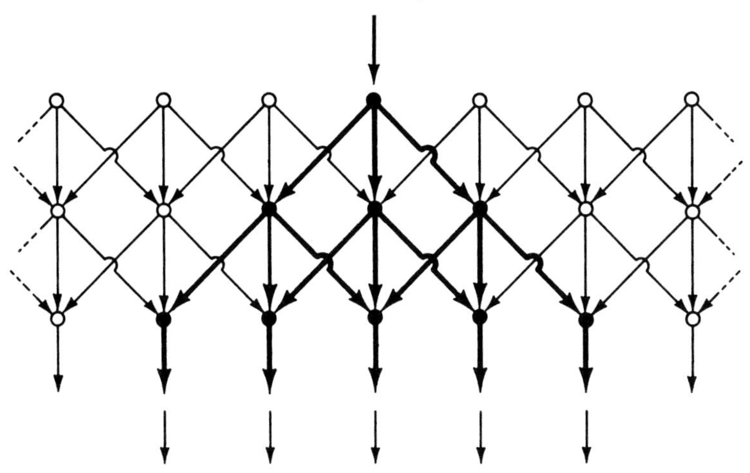

Figure 3.41. *Two stages of nonrecurrent inhibitory networks.*

yields a function with maxima and minima that resemble the Mach bands.* The undershoot and overshoot are the so-called Gibbs phenomenon and are inherent to the function. The overshoot and undershoot become very narrow if the function sin x/x that is used in the convolution extends out to very large values of x, but their amplitudes are always nine percent. It is said that when A. A. Michelson observed these overshoots in the output of his mechanical wave analyzer he thought at first that they were due to a fault in the machine (Jennison, 1961).

The second method, which achieves the effects of recurrent inhibition by using multiple stages of nonrecurrent inhibitory networks, has been treated in great detail by Varju (1962). Basically it is very simple, and requires only a succession of similar stages in the network (Fig. 3.41). (The possibility of such repetition is certainly provided by the several layers of interconnected neural elements in the vertebrate retina.) Although any one receptor in the diagram affects directly only its immediate neighbors, it can exert effects indirectly, as shown by the heavy lines, on the responses of elements far removed from it in the network.

These multiple stages are represented mathematically by successive applications of the same nonrecurrent weighting function (Békésy, 1960b). It is applied first to the stimulus distribution to obtain the response at the end of the first stage; next, to this response (which is the stimulus to the second stage); then to the response thus obtained (which is the stimulus for the third stage); and so on for whatever number of stages are in the network. Expressed in the form of discrete nonrecurrent equations,

* The author is indebted to Robert L. Schoenfeld who pointed out the similarity between this method of representing inhibition and the sin x/x function.

the response r at any point p for each of s stages would be given by the following iteration

$$r_p^{[1]} = \sum_{j=1}^{n} k_{p,j} I_j$$

$$r_p^{[2]} = \sum_{j=1}^{n} k_{p,j} r_j^{[1]}$$

$$\vdots$$

$$r_p^{[s]} = \sum_{j=1}^{n} k_{p,j} r_j^{[s-1]}$$

where $j = 1 \ldots p \ldots n$, and $k_{p,j}$ can be either positive or negative depending on the location of j. The response r_p at all (or representative) points along the stimulus distribution $I(x)$ would yield the corresponding response distributions $R(x)$ for each of the successive stages.

As shown in Figure 3.42, the second application of a weighting function representing a nonrecurrent network yields second-order or disinhibition effects similar to those that might appear in a single-stage recurrent system. The weighting function was designed so that the sum of the excitatory influences minus the sum of the inhibitory influences equals one. Thus the response to uniform fields did not increase or decrease with successive applications of the weighting function. (The succeeding curves in the figure are displaced downward so that they do not overlap.) In this particular example, however, the maxima and minima change rapidly

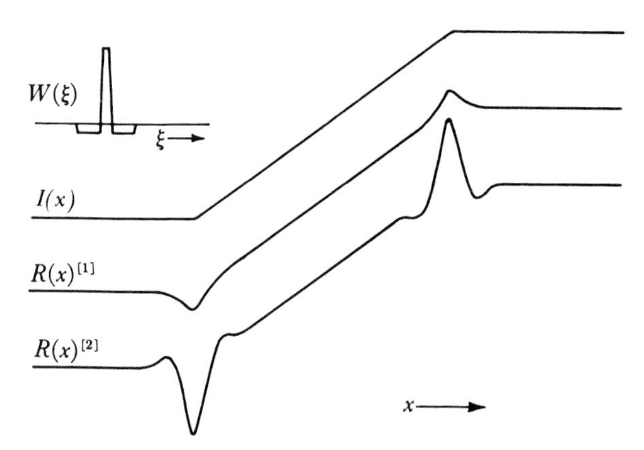

Figure 3.42. The two-stage application of a weighting function representing a nonrecurrent network. The weighting function is first applied to the stimulus distribution $I(x)$ and then to the response $R(x)^{[1]}$ to obtain the final response $R(x)^{[2]}$.

with successive stages and would finally diverge to infinity. Even so, it is possible to represent, at least approximately, the main features of single stage recurrent inhibition in multiple stages of nonrecurrent networks. Indeed, with the proper choice of inhibitory coefficients, any particular recurrent network can be duplicated fairly exactly with two (or more) stages of a nonrecurrent network.*

It is a well-known result of Fourier Analysis that a continuous function of position $f(x)$ may be expressed as a sum of complex sinusoidal waves $\exp(i\ k\ x)$:

$$f(x) = \int dkC(k) \exp (i\ k\ x).$$

Similarly, a given function f_p having values at only discrete points may be expressed as a superposition of "discrete complex waves"

$$f_p = \sum_q C_q \exp (i\ q\ p)$$

where p labels the pth point. The effect of linear manipulations on a set of numbers f_p may thus be induced from the effect of the same manipulations on a complex wave form $\exp (i\ j\ p)$.

For a uniform, linear, nonrecurring network of neural interconnections arranged one-dimensionally, the impulse rate at the $(s + 1)$st stage is given from that at the sth by

$$r_p^{[s+1]} = \sum_j A_{p-j} r_j^{[s]}.$$

Letting

$$r_p^{[s]} = \exp (i\ q\ p)$$

gives

$$\begin{aligned} r_p^{[s+1]} &= \sum_j A_{p-j} \exp (i\ q\ j) \\ &= \sum_j A_{p-j} \exp \{-i\ q\ [(p - j) - p]\} \\ &= \sum_j A_{p-j} \exp [-i\ q\ (p - j)] \exp (i\ q\ p) \\ &= \Big[\sum_m A_m \exp (-i\ q\ m)\Big] \exp (i\ q\ p) \\ &= \Big[\sum_m A_m \exp (-i\ q\ m)\Big]\, r_p^{[s]}. \end{aligned}$$

If there are two identical layers in the system, then evidently

$$r_p^{[2]} = \Big(\sum_m A_m \exp (-i\ q\ m)\Big)^2 r_p^{[0]}.$$

* The author wishes to express his appreciation to Bruce Knight for the analysis which follows (pp. 135-137).

For a recurrent system, on the other hand,

$$r_p = e_p - \sum_j K_{p-j} r_j,$$

and letting

$$r_p = \exp (i\ q\ p)$$

leads in the same way to

$$r_p = \frac{1}{1 + \left(\sum_m K_m \exp (-i\ q\ m)\right)} e_p.$$

Thus a two-step nonrecurrent network may be made to duplicate the output of the recurrent network to the degree of precision with which the relation

$$\left(\sum_m A_m \exp (-i\ q\ m)\right)^2 = \frac{1}{1 + \left(\sum_m K_m \exp (-i\ q\ m)\right)}$$

may be satisfied by shrewd choice of the network interconnection strengths A_m. To make this choice intelligently, one must know what values to expect from the number

$$X = \sum_m K_m \exp (-i\ q\ m).$$

If the neural plexus is symmetric, then

$$K_m = K_{-m}$$

which, with the preceding equation, gives an X that is a real number. If all conditions are inhibitory, then all the K_m are positive, giving

$$\sum_m K_m \geqq |X|.$$

In practical fact, for realistic choices of the inhibitory interaction K_m it turns out that

$$1 \geqq \sum_m K_m \geqq X \geqq 0.$$

It may be seen that when $1 \geqq X \geqq 0$, then

$$\frac{1}{1 + X} \cong \left\{1 - \left(1 - \frac{1}{\sqrt{2}}\right) X\right\}^2$$

to within less than 10 percent, as the following table shows:

X	$\left\{1 - \left(1 - \frac{1}{\sqrt{2}}\right) X\right\}^2$	$\frac{1}{1 + X}$	difference
1	.500	.500	.000
.8	.585	.555	.030
.6	.680	.628	.060
.4	.778	.715	.063
.2	.885	.834	.051
0	1.000	1.000	.000

The equation

$$\left(\sum_m A_m \exp(-i\ q\ m)\right)^2 = \frac{1}{1 + \left(\sum_m K_m \exp(-i\ q\ m)\right)}$$

will be satisfied with the same precision provided

$$A_m = \delta_m - \left(1 - \frac{1}{\sqrt{2}}\right) K_m$$

where

$$\delta_m = \begin{cases} 1 & \text{if } m = 0 \\ 0 & \text{otherwise.} \end{cases}$$

The choice A_m in fact does indeed yield excitation patterns everywhere within 10 percent of those of the recurrent network.

If the number of stages is unlimited and the same excitatory influence is available at every stage, it is possible to duplicate exactly a single-stage recurrent system. As a matter of fact, the iterative solution of a set of simultaneous equations—such as those that describe a recurrent system—is analogous to just this kind of successive processing by a large number of multiple stages. Let p represent any particular one of the n elements in the network and j all the others. Assume $e = kI$. The first step in the iteration is

$$r_p^{[1]} = e_p,$$

which gives the uninhibited response of any particular element in the network. The first approximation to the inhibited response—the second step in the iteration—uses these uninhibited responses to determine the inhibition on any particular element

$$r_p^{[2]} = e_p - \sum_{j=1}^{n} k_{p,j}(r_j^{[1]} - r_{p,j}^0).$$

Similarly, the third step in the iteration uses the inhibited responses determined in the second step in the iteration

$$r_p^{[3]} = e_p - \sum_{j=1}^{n} k_{p,j}(r_j^{[2]} - r_{p,j}^{0})$$

and so on to the sth step in the iteration

$$r_p^{[s]} = e_p \sum_{j=1}^{n} k_{p,j}(r_j^{[s-1]} - r_{p,j}^{0}).$$

The successive steps in a converging iterative solution are, of course, alternately over-estimates and under-estimates which gradually approach the final solution that is shown in Figure 3.43. (To simplify the figure, the thresholds have been omitted and negative frequencies allowed to occur.) In general, if the inhibitory coefficients are small, convergence is rapid; and if they are large, convergence is slow and the system may even be unstable (see Reichardt and MacGinitie, 1962). Although instability is a mathematical possibility, it is unlikely to occur in a real network. In the eye of *Limulus,* for example, the inhibitory coefficients are small, the system does converge, and is finally stable. Furthermore, the solutions, that is, the responses to a particular distribution of illumination, are unique (see Melzak, 1962).

Delayed inhibitory interaction It might appear awkward and cumbersome to represent recurrent inhibition by an iterative process, particularly if a large number of steps is required. But the successive steps

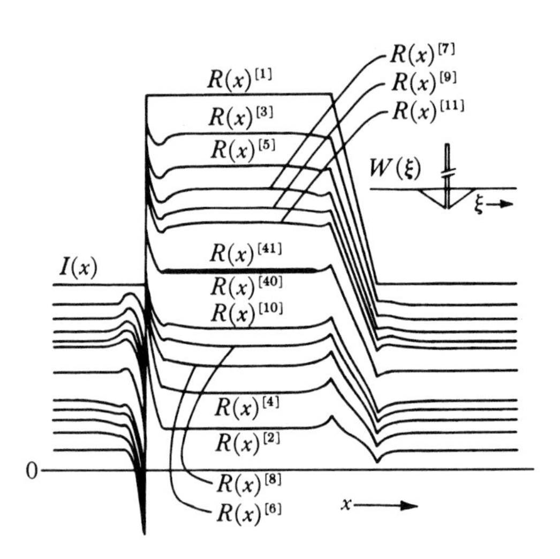

Figure 3.43. *A graphical representation of the successive steps in the iterative solution of the response of a recurrent network to a rectilinear stimulus distribution. Only the results of the first 10 and the 40th and 41st steps are shown. In the computation the two ends of the stimulus distribution were extended a great distance to the right and left so that no edge effects would appear in the figure. Note that* $R(x)^{[1]}$ *equals* $I(x)$*, the top line in the graph.*

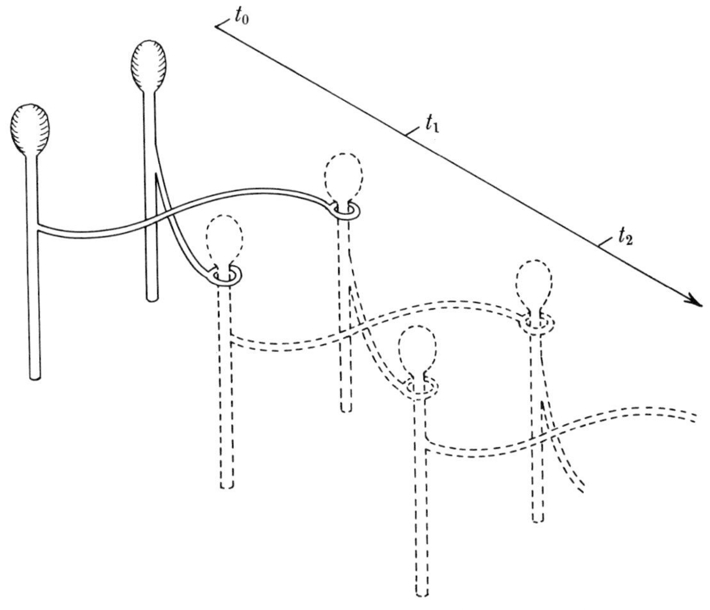

Figure 3.44. A highly schematic diagram of the temporal sequence of the mutual inhibitory influences exerted between a pair of interacting elements. From Ratliff, Hartline, and Miller (1963).

in the solution bear a close resemblance to the successive action and reaction of elements on one another that actually takes place in the real single-stage recurrent neural network in the eye of *Limulus*. These successive actions and reactions occur because of the delays in the inhibitory action of one element on another that were described above and illustrated in Figure 3.32.

Because of the delays, the dynamic response of the recurrent network may be regarded as nonrecurrent in time; that is, the successive states of a pair of interacting elements may be represented as linked in time as shown in Figure 3.44. Neither element affects the other immediately at t_0; each affects the response of the other at some later time, t_1. The modified response of each then affects the other at a still later time, t_2, and so on. With constant illumination, of course, the excitatory influences remain approximately constant throughout.

These delays are of no significance in the steady state, but they are important in the dynamic response of the inhibitory network. It is intuitively clear that they are likely to lead to damped oscillations in the response following any change in stimulus intensity. And, indeed, such oscillations are observed (Fig. 3.45). In this experiment a small group of

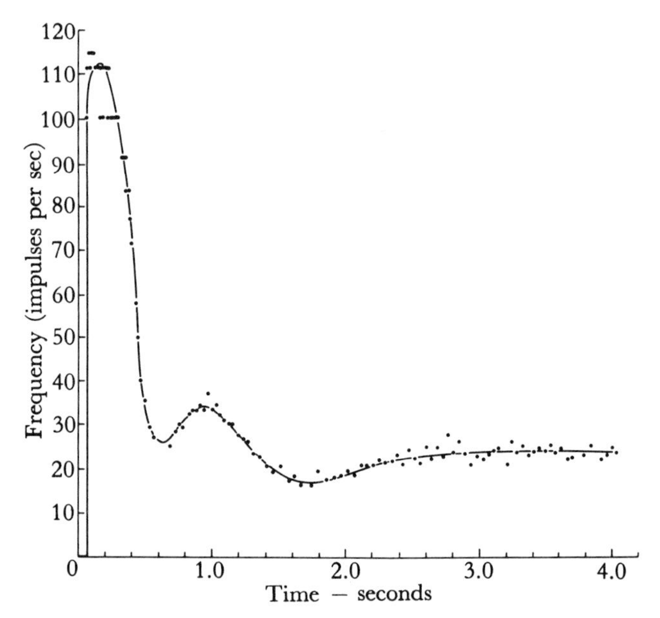

Figure 3.45. Plot of the time course of the frequency of discharge of an ommatidium illuminated together with several nearby ommatidia, showing a damped oscillation resulting from the time delay in the action of the mutual inhibitory influence. From Hartline, Ratliff, and Miller (1961).

receptor units in the eye of *Limulus* was illuminated and the frequency of response of one in the center of the group was recorded. Following an abrupt onset at $t = 0.0$, the illumination was constant throughout the period shown. The strong initial responses of the elements in the group produce strong mutual inhibitory influences among them which at a later time diminish their responses. They then exert weaker mutual inhibitory influences and subsequently their responses are somewhat stronger. These stronger responses produce stronger inhibitory influences, so the subsequent responses are again weaker, and so on. The inhibitory coefficients in the eye of *Limulus* are not very large and, as might be expected, the oscillations are strongly damped.*

The analogy with the iterative mathematical solution of the simultaneous equations outlined above is obvious. The response of the real network passes through several maxima and minima before converging on

* The change in frequency is not entirely due to the inhibitory action, however; adaptation and other receptor properties are partly responsible. That is to say, the excitatory mechanism itself doubtless undergoes changes in time. But the inhibitory interaction contributes a great deal to the effect as can be shown by increasing (or decreasing) the area of illumination; thus changing the number of elements in the group increases (or decreases) the amplitude of the oscillations.

the steady state, as does the iterative solution. In the recurrent inhibitory network, nature has designed a very simple and economical way to solve simultaneous equations.

A few words of caution It would be tempting to conclude that the Mach bands have now been "explained" in terms of the integrative action of the retina either described or postulated in the various mathematical models described in this chapter. It is indeed true that the principal feature of the several models—opposed excitatory and inhibitory influences—has been shown to be sound physiologically and to be adequate in accounting for at least the gross features of the phenomena. But even the most cursory examination of the details of the Mach bands and of the corresponding features of any of the models that purport to explain them reveals obvious discrepancies too numerous to mention here. Furthermore, most of the models are narrowly based on these phenomena alone and for this reason are almost certain to be incorrect. Opposed excitatory and inhibitory influences play many roles in vision; the more of these that can be considered, the fuller will be our understanding of both the nature and significance of integrative processes in the retina and elsewhere in the nervous system. The mere fact that these shortcomings of the models can be recognized, however, is itself an essential step in the process of improving them. Indeed, since some models are deficient in one respect, and others in other respects, it might now be possible to combine the best features of all and to construct a "master model" which would give a much more complete and satisfactory theoretical account of the Mach bands. But from a purely empirical neurophysiological point of view, such a model might seem to be little more than a mathematical *tour de force,* in which, according to this view, processes which ought to be demonstrated are only postulated.

What do mathematical models contribute to the direct experimental analysis of the function of the nervous system? They help to solve one of the major problems facing neurophysiology: how to reduce, analyze, and comprehend the enormous amounts of data that can now be obtained. It is now a simple technical matter to record the activity of individual neurons simultaneously at several different points in the nervous system and to accumulate in a few seconds a permanent record of several hundred, or even several thousand, essentially identical nerve impulses. But describing the function of the nervous system in terms of a great multiplicity of essentially identical unitary processes is not unlike attempting to mete out "the heavens with a span" or to comprehend "the dust of the earth in a measure." The greatest contribution any mathematical description of, or theorizing about, the function of the nervous system is likely to make is to increase the width of our "span" and the volume of our "measure."

That is, mathematically useful and physiologically meaningful ways of measuring and comprehending the enormously complex interactions among the myriad elements of the great populations of neurons that make up the nervous system will almost certainly grow out of the attempts to describe these interactions in a rigorous and quantitative manner—whether the actual mechanisms of interaction be directly observed or deduced from the behavior of the whole system. Nevertheless, it is always worth remembering that the explanations we seek are ultimately to be found in the facts of vision and in the physiology of the visual system rather than in hypothetical models. As Mach pointed out, "We err if we expect more enlightenment from an hypothesis than from the facts themselves."

In general, opposition appears as an obstruction, but when it represents polarity within a comprehensive whole, it has also its useful and important functions. The oppositions of heaven and earth, spirit and nature, man and woman, when reconciled, bring about the creation and reproduction of life. In the world of visible things, the principle of opposites makes possible the differentiation by categories through which order is brought into the world. From a commentary on *The I Ching or Book of Changes* (Wilhelm-Baynes translation)

CHAPTER FOUR *The functional significance of inhibitory interaction*

The process of seeing is a process of abstraction, for in a very real sense the visual system schematizes and caricatures. From the immense detail in the retinal image the eye selects mainly that information which is of significance to the organism, enhances it at the expense of less significant information, and then transmits this schema to the central nervous system.

Among the most significant features of a pattern of illumination are the loci of the transitions, either in space or time, from one condition to another. For example, the transitions from one intensity to another or from one color to another in a pattern of illumination are perhaps more significant than the particular intensities and colors themselves. Everyday experience shows that this is so. The ability to see and recognize objects is little affected by tremendous changes in both color and intensity such as those that take place from early dawn to high noon. The sudden alterations in color and intensity that result when one puts on a pair of tinted sunglasses produce no serious impairment of vision. The elimination of natural spectral colors altogether, as in oriental paintings in black ink on a white background, in black and white photography, in motion pictures, and in television, is hardly noticed. Indeed, both intensity and color can be radically altered in countless ways and if the contours alone are preserved in their original configuration, such as in a line drawing or cartoon, much of the essential information in the original pattern is retained.

Artists who endeavor to portray the essence of real things seem to recognize almost instinctively that outline and contour are of paramount importance. The primitive artist, limited by crude methods, seems content to show only what is of utmost significance to him. The figures of the thunderbird and archer in the American Indian pictographs illustrated in Figure 4.1, for example, were drawn by laboriously chipping away the dark weathered surface of the rock to expose the lighter interior color. The single contour bounding each silhouette thus formed suffices to convey the intended meaning. Indeed, one frequently finds petroglyphs in which only this single line is incised in the rock. The more sophisticated artist, who is less hampered by limitations of technique, not only selects and represents the significant contours, but sometimes goes further and enhances their appearance by heavy lines or exaggerated contrast. Seurat's drawings and paintings are especially notable in the latter respect. In *The Black Bow,* reproduced in Figure 4.2, form and contour are boldly accentuated by an intentional exaggeration of the contrasting light and

Figure 4.1. *American Indian pictograph of a thunderbird and an archer located in the vicinity of Rattlesnake Buttes, Colorado. An approximate scale is provided by the cigar held near the figure of the archer. The author is indebted to R. D. Mutz, who discovered this pictograph.*

Figure 4.2. The Black Bow, *by Georges Seurat. From Rewald (1954).* © *SPADEM, 1954, by French Reproduction Rights, Inc.*

shade.* All in all, the artist is less concerned with the accuracy of representation than with its significance.

* Homer (1964) gives a detailed account of the scientific influences on Georges Seurat's theory of art and the application of this theory in his major paintings.

In the same way, the eye itself sacrifices accuracy about information of little consequence, such as the absolute levels of illumination, in order to enhance features that are more significant, such as contours and edges. The functional significance of inhibitory interaction in the retina is at least partly to be found in the roles it plays in the preservation and enhancement of this kind of information.

The Mach bands themselves give an indication of the nature of one of these roles. As Chapter 3 illustrated, graded transitions from one level of intensity to another in the retinal image become steeper and the flections are pointed up in the corresponding response of the inhibitory network. Boundaries, edges, and contours are thus accentuated. But this process of accentuation may be, at the same time, an equally important process of rectification which partially serves to compensate for blur in the retinal image. The inhibitory interaction may play other roles that are more subtle, and in the author's view, perhaps more important. These have to do with the generation of specialized neural responses to complex spatial and temporal patterns of illumination on the retina. Certain psychophysical and neurophysiological experiments on simple stationary contours will be considered before the more complex spatial and temporal patterns are discussed.

THE ACCENTUATION OF SIMPLE STATIONARY CONTOURS

Psychophysical studies on the human visual system Because of its imperfections the dioptric apparatus of the eye (cornea, lens, vitreous and aqueous humors) degrades the sharpness of the image it forms on the retina. The blur is considerable, as has been shown by mathematical calculation of the effects of diffraction, chromatic and spherical aberrations, and so forth, and by more or less direct measurements on excised eyes. (For a review of work on this general problem see Westheimer, 1963.) Recently, Westheimer and Campbell (1962) and Krauskopf (1962) have obtained estimates of the blur or "line spread function" in the intact living human eye. They based their calculations on measurements of the energy distribution in the aerial image formed by light from a bright vertical line first imaged on the retina and then subsequently reflected out of the eye essentially along the same path by which it entered. Estimates of the spread functions of a long line object for an eye in best focus, with various pupil diameters, are shown in Figure 4.3.

In the special case of a point (or narrow line) source, the spread function directly shows how the light from that point is spread out along one dimension of the retina. In the general case, that of extended objects

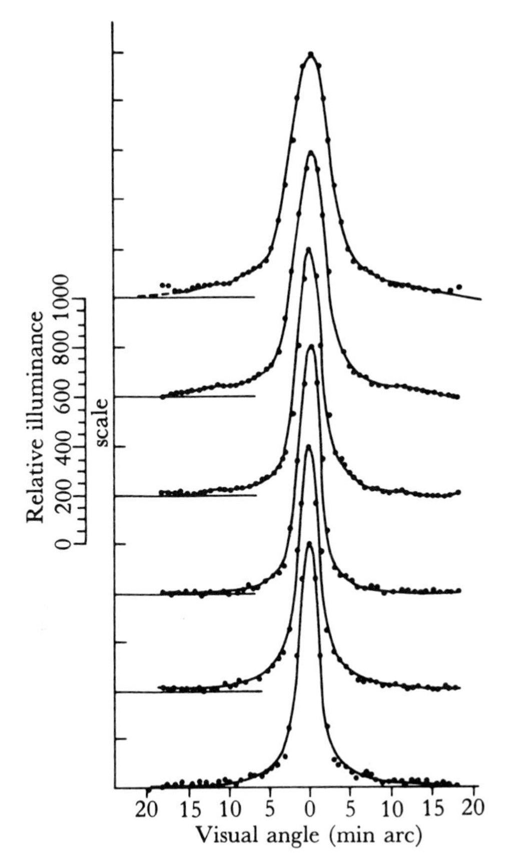

Figure 4.3. *Reconstructed retinal images of bright vertical line target (1.6 seconds wide) for various pupil diameters. Ordinates are displaced in equal vertical steps with pupil diameters 3, 4, 5, 6, 7, and 8 mm from bottom to top. From Krauskopf (1962).*

with many points of various intensities, the distribution of intensity $I_i(x)$ in the image space is determined by convolution of the line spread function $W(\xi)$ of the system with the intensity distribution $I_o(x)$ in the object space

$$I_i(x) = \int_{-\infty}^{+\infty} I_o(\xi - x) W(\xi)\, d\xi.$$

The curves in Figure 4.3 may be regarded as close approximations to the ideal line spread functions that would be obtained using an infinitesimally narrow bright line. As Figure 4.4(a) shows, when such a spread function is applied to an object intensity distribution $I_o(x)$ with a fairly abrupt step (solid line), it yields an image distribution $I_i(x)$ which is

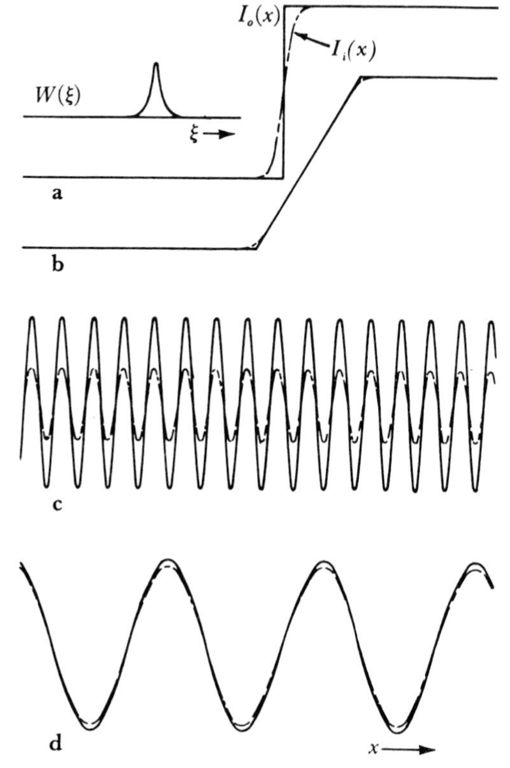

Figure 4.4. *Results of convolution of line spread function with various intensity distributions. (See also Fig. 3.3.)*

considerably blurred (broken line). Note, however, that when the spread function is applied to an intensity distribution with a less steep gradient (b) there is much less blurring. Similarly, when applied to a sinusoidal object distribution with a high spatial frequency (c) there is a significant reduction in the amplitude of the corresponding image distribution, but when applied to a sinusoidal distribution with a low spatial frequency (d) there is little reduction in amplitude. The sharper the flection, the greater the blurring; the higher the spatial frequency, the greater the attenuation. These two effects are mathematically one and the same. Their essential equivalence provides the key to the analyses that will be discussed shortly.

Practically every investigator who has studied the Mach bands, beginning with Mach himself in 1865, has considered the possibility that neural mechanisms in the retina might serve to rectify optical blur and thus restore the partially effaced contours in the retinal image. The possible contribution of an inhibitory network in such a process is obvious: the effects produced by inhibition occur in the same locations as do the blur errors, but they have the opposite sign. (See Figure 3.3 above, for example.)

It is not yet possible to observe directly the operation of these neural mechanisms in the human retina, but since the light curve, the sensation curve, and the blurring function of the optical elements of the eye may all be measured independently, it is possible to estimate indirectly by mathematical calculations what the contribution of the neural network to the behavior of the visual system as a whole may be. The Fourier methods that are now being applied to the study of the transmission characteristics of optical systems and to the analyses of optical images are used to make such calculations.

As Mach pointed out in 1866 (Part Two, Paper 3) a unidimensional pattern of illumination may be analyzed into component spatial frequencies, that is, sinusoidal patterns, in the same way that a complex sound wave may be analyzed into its component temporal frequencies. Therefore lenses may be regarded as devices which "transfer" spatial frequencies from object space to image space (see Duffieux, 1946). But, as Figure 4.4 showed, the transmission by any real lens is imperfect; all spatial frequencies are not transmitted equally well. In effect, every lens is a "filter"; some spatial frequencies may be transmitted almost perfectly, others may be attenuated somewhat, and still others may be filtered out almost entirely. The image formed by a lens can thus be determined by making a Fourier analysis of the spatial frequencies (ν) that make up the object pattern, multiplying these by the optical transfer function of the lens system, which is simply the modulation and phase shift of the various frequencies, and then summing the results to obtain the image distribution. For a general treatment of Fourier methods see Jennison (1961).

The optical transfer function $\mathcal{W}(\nu)$ is itself the Fourier transform of the line spread function $W(\xi)$. Therefore

$$\mathcal{W}(\nu) = |\mathcal{W}(\nu)| \exp [i\theta(\nu)] = \int_{-\infty}^{+\infty} W(\xi) \exp [-2\pi i\nu\xi] \, d\xi,$$

in which ξ is a spatial coordinate, ν is the spatial frequency of the component wave in sine cycles per minute of visual angle, and θ is the phase shift (in radians) of the component wave from its geometric image. If the line spread function is symmetrical, as is assumed here, there is no phase shift ($\theta = 0$) and the transfer function may be expressed in the simpler cosine form:

$$\mathcal{W}(\nu) = |\mathcal{W}(\nu)| = \int_{-\infty}^{+\infty} W(\xi) \cos 2\pi\nu\xi \, d\xi.$$

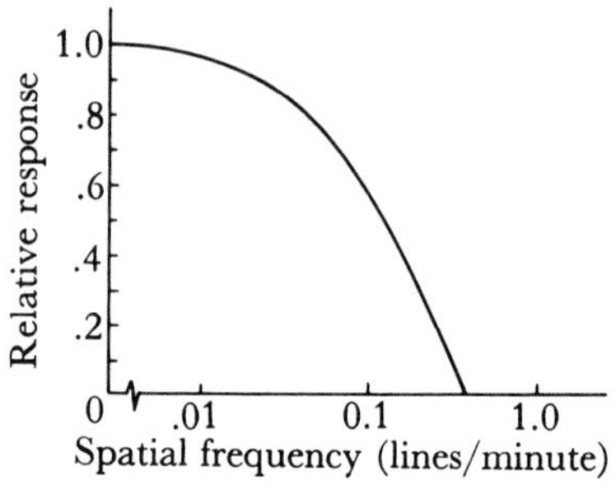

Figure 4.5. *Optical transfer function for the human eye (5 mm pupil). From Krauskopf (1962).*

Since the line spread function for the optical media of the human eye is known, at least to a good first approximation, the equivalent optical transfer function may be determined. (See Krauskopf, 1962, for example.) The exact form of the function depends, of course, on the particular estimate of the line spread function from which it is derived, but all are something like the curve illustrated in Figure 4.5. That is, high frequencies are attenuated more than low frequencies with the optical media of the eye forming a low pass filter. The image forming characteristics of the eye as a whole, however, are determined by both the optical and the neural components of the system. If the assumption is made that the action of each of these components is linear, which is reasonable for the lens but somewhat questionable for the neural network, then the whole system may be treated in terms of a cascade of transfer functions.

Let $\mathcal{W}(\nu)$ be the composite transfer function for the whole visual system from object to subjective image, $\mathcal{W}_1(\nu)$ the optical transfer function relating the object to the retinal image (as defined above), and $\mathcal{W}_2(\nu)$ the neural transfer function relating the retinal image to the subjective image seen by the observer. The transfer function of a system of cascaded elements acting as a whole is simply the product of the transfer functions of the individual elements with

$$\mathcal{W}(\nu) = \mathcal{W}_1(\nu) \cdot \mathcal{W}_2(\nu).$$

Therefore, since the transfer function for the optical component is already known, it would be a simple matter to calculate the function for the remaining (presumably neural) component *if* the composite function could be determined precisely and *if* the assumption of linearity were justified.

Unfortunately, as Chapter 2 illustrated, it is extremely difficult to make precise determinations of the sharp flections, that is, the high spatial frequencies, in the subjective image distribution. For this reason, the higher the spatial frequency, the less confidence may be placed in the evaluation of the composite transfer function. It is also extremely difficult to evaluate accurately the transfer function for the optical media of the intact human eye, particularly for the higher spatial frequencies which are transmitted poorly. Finally, as Marimont (1963) has pointed out, the human visual system is evidently nonlinear because the bright and dark bands in the subjective images are not symmetrical in the forms in which they are usually expressed.

In spite of all these difficulties, several attempts have been made to evaluate the composite transfer function for the human visual system and to relate it to the Mach bands and the underlying optical and neural mechanisms.* Although these experiments cannot be expected to be definitive, they are nonetheless worthy of attention because they yield some useful approximations that help to interpret the function of neural networks in the complex human retina, which cannot be studied directly as yet, and they introduce a method of analysis which is applicable to the simpler, partially linear network in the retina of *Limulus*, which can be studied directly.

Menzel (1959) evaluated the composite transfer function for the human eye by measuring the relative visibility of several sinusoidal distributions of illumination with different spatial frequencies, such as those illustrated in Figure 4.4 above. (The basic assumption here is that the relative visibility of various spatial frequencies of equal amplitude in the object space is inversely related to their attenuation by the visual system.) The results, which are an average for five observers, are shown in Figure 4.6.

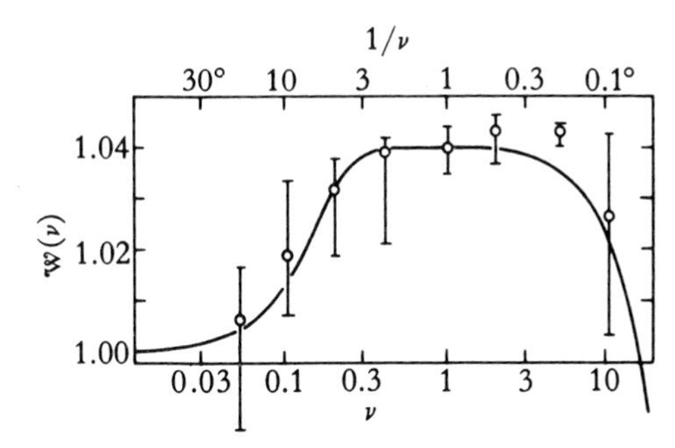

Figure 4.6. *Composite transfer function for the human eye. Note that the visual angle is expressed in degrees. The mean values (open circles) and the extremes (vertical lines) of the measurements for five observers are plotted. Redrawn after Menzel (1959).*

* Some earlier work by Schade (1956) and by Ooue (1959) on the so-called sine-wave response of the eye is worthy of mention, but it is not reported in detail here because it does not bear directly on the problem of the Mach bands.

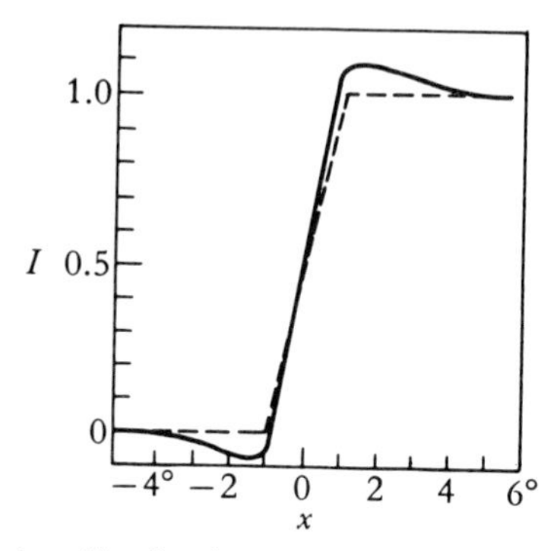

Figure 4.7. *Subjective distribution (solid line) calculated from objective distribution (broken line) using the transfer function shown in Figure 4.6. Redrawn after Menzel (1959).*

Note that the function increases rapidly with increasing spatial frequency up to about 0.5 cycle per degree of visual angle, remains at a high level until about 2.0 cycles per degree, but above that level it falls rapidly. As would be expected, very high frequencies are transmitted quite poorly—the eye cannot resolve extremely fine and closely spaced lines.

Using the composite transfer function $\mathcal{W}(\nu)$ determined in this way, Menzel then calculated the subjective distribution $I_s(x)$ that would result from the objective distribution $I_o(x)$ in a typical Mach pattern. The two distributions are shown in Figure 4.7. Qualitatively, the calculated results agree with the distribution actually seen in the Mach pattern, with the maxima and minima appearing as expected. This one test therefore indicates that the estimate of the transfer function is at least a fair approximation, but there are two important discrepancies: the calculated widths of the Mach bands are much larger than those observed, and the calculated bands are symmetrical, while the observed bands are not (see Fig. 2.12). Nevertheless, as a later discussion will show, the general forms of the various estimates of the composite transfer function $\mathcal{W}(\nu)$ give a meaningful indication of the probable form of the transfer function $\mathcal{W}_2(\nu)$ for the neural component of the system, and of the nature of the neural mechanisms involved.

Lowry and DePalma (1961) approached this same problem from a different direction. Instead of making measurements on sinusoidal distributions, they began by measuring the objective luminance distributions $I_o(x)$ in various Mach patterns and the corresponding subjective distributions $I_s(x)$ seen by the observer. An analysis of the spatial frequencies contained in these two distributions then provided the basis for the calculation of the composite transfer function.

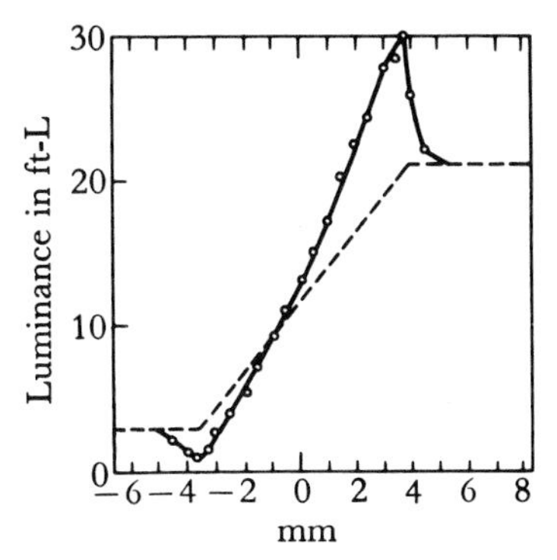

Figure 4.8. *Luminance distribution in foot-lamberts across a test pattern (broken line) and the corresponding subjective distribution (open circles and solid line). The pattern was viewed from a distance of 14 inches. Redrawn after Lowry and DePalma (1961).*

As Figure 4.5 graphically shows, a transfer function is simply an expression of the ratio of the amplitudes of each and every spatial frequency in the entire Fourier spectrum before and after transmission by the system that the function represents. Let $\mathcal{I}_s(\nu)$ represent the Fourier spectrum of the subjective image distribution $I_s(x)$, and $\mathcal{I}_o(\nu)$ the spectrum of the objective intensity distribution $I_o(x)$. If these spectra can be determined, the composite transfer function can easily be calculated by

$$\mathcal{W}(\nu) = \frac{\mathcal{I}_s(\nu)}{\mathcal{I}_o(\nu)}.$$

Figure 4.8 shows the object distribution and the subjective image distribution for one of the test patterns used. Harmonic analyses of the spatial frequencies in several patterns with different slopes were carried

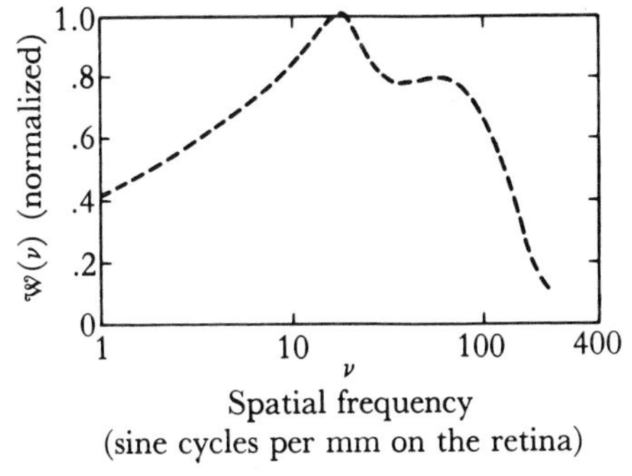

Figure 4.9. *Composite transfer function for the whole visual system. For comparison with other figures note that 0.3 mm on the retina subtends approximately 1.0° of visual angle. Redrawn after Lowry and De Palma (1961).*

out and the corresponding transfer functions were calculated. The results were similar, but not identical, for all patterns. An average composite transfer function $\mathcal{W}(\nu)$ for the whole visual system, based on these results, is shown in Figure 4.9. The general form of the transfer function resembles the one calculated by Menzel, but the correspondence between the two functions is far from exact.

In still another approach to this problem, Bryngdahl (1964a, 1964b) made an effort to minimize some of the difficulties that the previous investigators had encountered in their experiments. His innovation was to use intensity distributions composed of low spatial frequencies (upper curve Figure 4.10). The corresponding subjective distributions, which have no sharp flections, can thus be measured more exactly. Also, the optical media of the eye appear to transmit low spatial frequencies with little or no attenuation. Therefore, the difference between the intensity distribution and the subjective distribution (the lower curve in Figure 4.10) may be ascribed entirely to the action of the subsequent stages in the visual process, which are presumably neural. In addition, Bryngdahl found that expression of the stimulus distribution in terms of the logarithm of the luminance, rather than in units of luminance, yielded a better agreement among transfer functions determined for different patterns. His estimate of a portion of the composite transfer function, based on results obtained from three different patterns of illumination, is shown in Figure 4.11. Over the short range that was measured, the transfer function increased with increasing spatial frequencies.

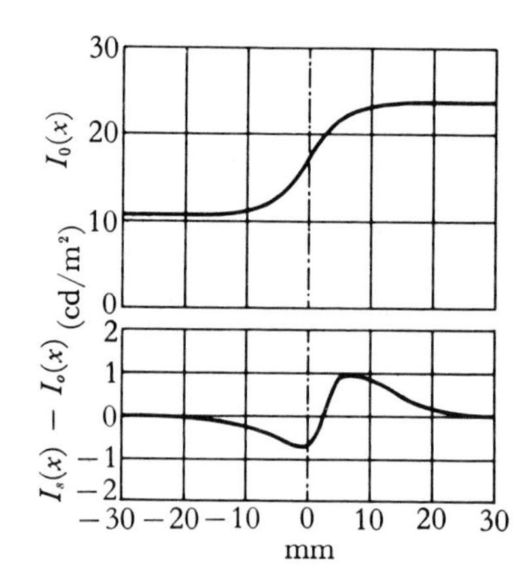

Figure 4.10. *Objective distribution of a luminance gradient (upper graph) and the difference between the subjective distribution and the objective distribution (lower graph). The ordinate shows candles per sq. meter; the abscissa, distance from center of pattern in mm. The pattern was viewed from a distance of 50 cm. From Bryngdahl (1964b).*

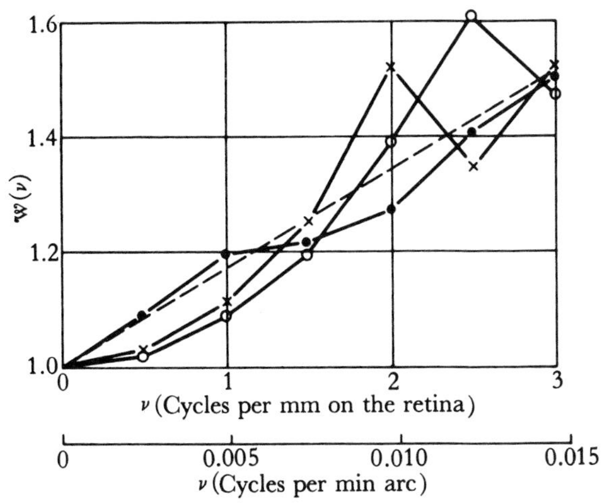

Figure 4.11. *Low frequency portions of composite transfer functions of the visual system obtained for three different luminance distributions, expressed in terms of the* logarithm *of the luminance. Solid circles show the function obtained from the stimulus distribution in Figure 4.10. The other two functions were obtained from Gaussian distributions. From Bryngdahl (1964b).*

On the basis of the evidence from these three experiments and keeping in mind all the difficulties involved in the application of Fourier methods to this particular problem, the tentative conclusion is that the composite transfer function $\mathcal{W}(\nu)$ for the human visual system gradually increases with increasing spatial frequencies, passes through a maximum, and then gradually decreases to near zero at higher frequencies. This finding is in accordance with the facts of vision. Shallow gradients and greatly rounded curvatures in a distribution of illumination (mainly low spatial frequencies) are seen as nearly uniform; moderate curvatures (mainly intermediate frequencies) are seen distinctly; and very sharp and closely spaced curvatures (mainly very high frequencies) cannot be resolved. As a matter of fact, the general form of the composite transfer function (*at threshold*) can be seen more or less directly in a sinusoidal pattern of illumination in which both the spatial frequency and the modulation of the amplitude are varied (Fig. 4.12). The fact that there is a threshold, however, means that the system is not linear, or—at best—that it is only piecewise linear. Moreover, the same figure shows that the transfer function is not the same under all conditions. (See Campbell and Robson, 1964.)

The results of diverse independent experiments show that the transfer function $\mathcal{W}_1(\nu)$ for the dioptric apparatus of the eye gradually decreases with increasing frequency, falling to near zero somewhere in the neighborhood of 0.5 cycle per minute (Fig. 4.5). Since in this mathematical repre-

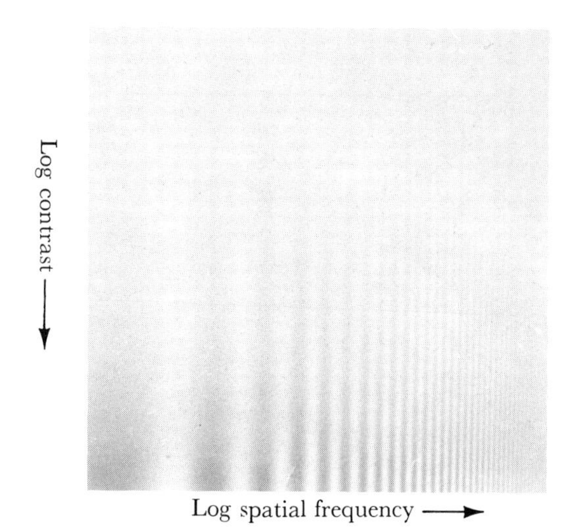

Figure 4.12. *Modulation threshold as a function of log contrast and log spatial frequency. The photograph should be viewed from about 50 cm (arm's length). The spatial modulation is sinusoidal; the contrast varies logarithmically from 30% to 0.2%, approximately. Note that the intermediate spatial frequencies may generally be seen at lower contrasts than the very low or very high frequencies, that is, the dark lines appear taller in the center of the figure than at the sides. The effects of changes in luminance, adaptation, viewing distance, and sharpness of focus are easily demonstrated. Photograph courtesy of F. W. Campbell and J. G. Robson, Physiological Laboratory, Cambridge, England.*

sentation the composite function $\mathcal{W}(\nu) = \mathcal{W}_1(\nu) \cdot \mathcal{W}_2(\nu)$, one should now be able to evaluate the unknown transfer function $\mathcal{W}_2(\nu)$ for the neural component of the system. But with all the uncertainties that exist in determining the composite and optical transfer functions, particularly at the higher frequencies, it would be foolhardy to place much confidence in an exact numerical evaluation. This much can be said, however: to be compatible with the existing measurements, the transfer function $\mathcal{W}_2(\nu)$ for the neural component must generally increase with increasing frequency. That is, the relative attenuation of the spectrum of spatial frequencies by the neural component is generally the reverse of the relative attenuation by the optical media. In this way, the neural component partially compensates for the defective transmission by the optical component.

The next question to be considered is what role inhibitory interaction may play in this admittedly imperfect but nevertheless significant rectification of the blurred retinal image. In other words, how does the transfer function for an inhibitory network compare with the general form of the transfer function for the neural network that may be deduced from the above experiments? To simplify the problem, assume that the inhibitory network is linear, nonrecurrent, and that the field of inhibitory influence is Gaussian with a width of the order of magnitude suggested by the psychophysical experiments cited in Chapters 2 and 3. Assume further that the central excitatory component of the network is very narrow.

As a rough first approximation, the narrow excitatory component may be considered as a simple positive delta function, the Fourier transform of which is a straight line of a constant amplitude (Fig. 4.13). Thus, the excitatory component may be regarded as the positive gain or amplifying factor in the neural system. In this transformation, however, the scale of

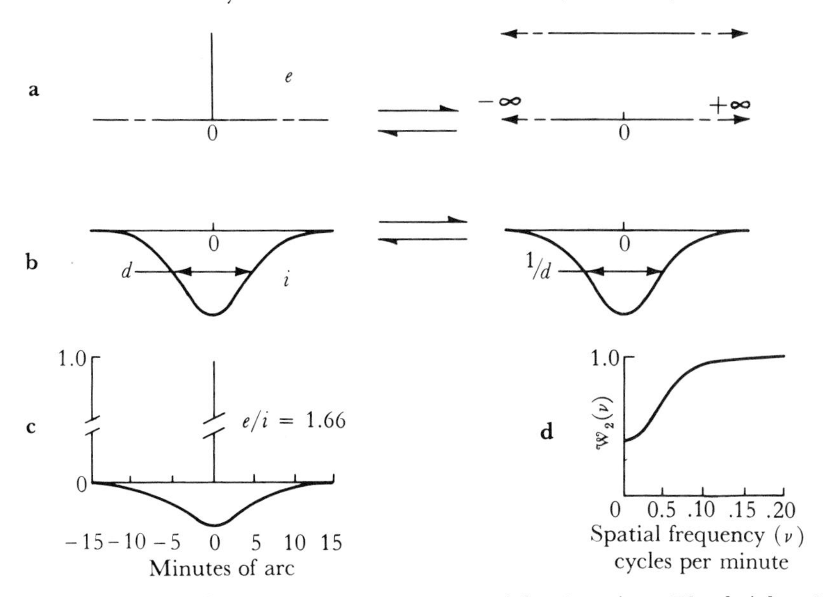

Figure 4.13. (a) *The Fourier transform of a delta function. The height of the continuous spectrum of spatial frequencies in the transform on the right is proportional to the area of the delta function (unity) represented by the line on the left.* (b) *The Fourier transform of a Gaussian distribution with a half-width d is another Gaussian with a half width 1/d.* (c) *An ideal representation of an inhibitory network consisting of a delta function (excitatory) and a negative Gaussian function (inhibitory). The ratio of the areas of the two functions e/i = 1.66. The half-width* d *of the inhibitory distribution is 10 minutes of visual angle.* (d) *The transfer function representing the idealized inhibitory network in* (c) *is the sum of the Fourier transforms of the excitatory component (positive delta function) and of the inhibitory component (negative Gaussian distribution) from 0 to +∞. Negative spatial frequencies are omitted since they have no physiological meaning in the present context.*

measurement of amplitude must be changed from some measure of light intensity in the retinal image to some measure of neural activity. Therefore, it is meaningful to speak only of the relative amplification or attenuation of the various spatial frequencies. To make these different scales comparable in what follows, all are normalized to a scale ranging from zero to plus or minus one.

The transfer function of the inhibitory component of the network alone is simply the Fourier transform of the Gaussian inhibitory (negative) function. Since the Fourier transform of a Gaussian distribution with a half width d is itself a Gaussian distribution with a half width $1/d$, one need go no further. The desired transfer function is also a Gaussian curve, or rather, the half of the curve relating to spatial frequencies from 0 to plus ∞ (Fig. 4.13b). It is similar in shape to the Fourier transform of the line spread function of the lens and, accordingly, also attenuates high frequencies more than low ones. Because the inhibitory transfer function is negative, the polarity of the transmitted waves is inverted so that positive amplitudes become negative, and negative amplitudes become positive.

Since the action of the network as a whole (Fig. 4.13c) is the *sum* of the positive (excitatory) and negative (inhibitory) effects, and since the positive gain is uniform and the negative gain is greatest at low frequencies, the result is that the over-all gain of the network increases with increasing frequency (Fig. 4.13d).

The transfer function of the dioptric apparatus (Fig. 4.5) and the hypothetical transfer function of the neural network (Fig. 4.13d) acting together yield a composite transfer function (Fig. 4.14) with the general

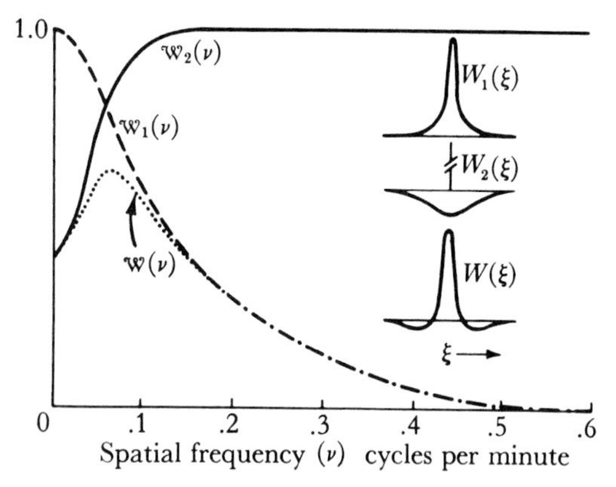

Figure 4.14. *An idealized composite transfer function (dotted line) for the whole visual system. The composite function is the product of the transfer function for the dioptric apparatus (broken line) and the transfer function for the inhibitory network (solid line). The corresponding spread functions (or weighting functions) are shown at the right of the graph. (Compare with* ***Figure 4.12.****)*

properties indicated by the results of the above psychophysical experiments.* In addition, the line spread function for the optical system convolved with the spread function for the neural network yields a composite spread function very much like the theoretical ones in the mathematical models described in the previous chapter (see Figs. 3.35 and 3.36). Thus this interpretation of the Fourier analyses of psychophysical experiments on the human visual system is compatible with the view that inhibitory interaction plays a fundamental role in the rectification of blurred contours. The direct electrophysiological observations available, which will be considered shortly, lend further support to this view.

In the light of one very important experimental fact, however, the above interpretation must be tempered somewhat. This is the fact—revealed in one way or another in each of the three psychophysical experiments cited above—that some component of the visual system (evidently the neural component) must be nonlinear. The most obvious indication of this nonlinearity is the asymmetry of the Mach bands themselves, which differs considerably from the symmetrical response that would be predicted by a cascade of linear transfer functions—even though the predicted and observed bands are grossly similar. Furthermore, differences between the forms of the supposed transfer functions measured under different conditions also indicate that the system is nonlinear and that—strictly speaking—the functions are not transfer functions after all.

As Bryngdahl and Riseberg (1964) have pointed out, there is now a compelling need to detect and measure the nonlinearities and to determine to what extent one may rigorously apply Fourier methods to the analysis of the human visual system and what approximations are necessary. At the time of this writing, sufficient evidence on this point is not available to permit any general conclusions to be drawn or to form the basis for any alternative mathematical approach. (Some relevant work by Campbell and Robson, 1964, and by Bryngdahl, 1964d, has been reported—but as yet is available only in the form of brief abstracts.) In any event, the fact that the nonlinearities *do* exist, and that no linear approximations are completely justified until the extent of the nonlinearities has been determined, must always be kept in mind. Of course, whether Fourier methods of analysis are applicable or not has no bearing on the validity of the experimental observations themselves.

Electrophysiological experiments on border contrast in the eye of Limulus In the compound eye of *Limulus*, as in the vertebrate eye,

* See Hiwatashi, Watanabe, Mori, and Nagata (1964) for a similar analysis. Using test patterns with various exposure durations these investigators have deduced that the lateral inhibition in the human visual system follows excitation with a considerable time delay, and grows more or less linearly until it reaches the maximum value.

optical limitations and imperfections blur the image of the external stimulus and the neural network is left with the problem of how to rectify it, or in some way preserve or enhance the significant information that remains. The major cause of blur in the compound eye, however, is not the same as in the vertebrate eye. The blur results mainly because the eye *is* compound, that is, it is an aggregation of many individual small "eyes" (ommatidia), each with a sizeable visual field which partially overlaps that of its near neighbors.

Each of the 1,000 or so individual ommatidia in the eye of *Limulus* is oriented differently so that the visual field of the eye as a whole covers approximately a hemisphere (Fig. 3.24). The field is actually slightly larger than that indicated by the morphological axes of the ommatidia.

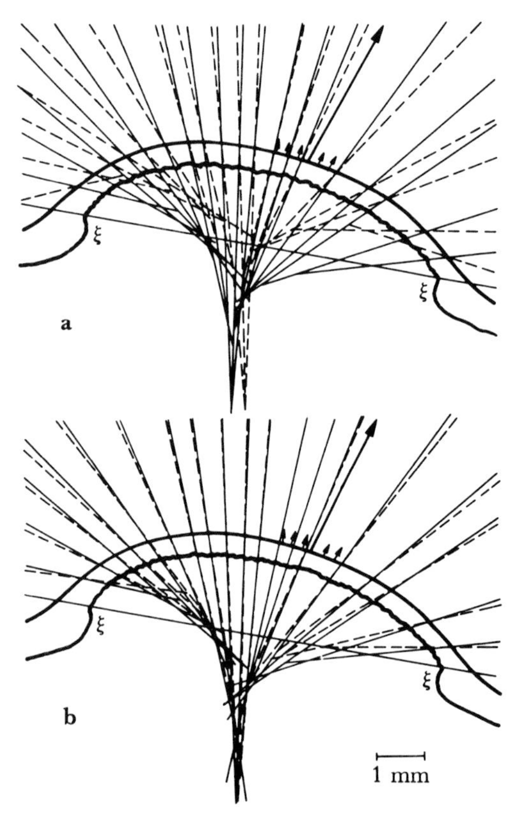

Figure 4.15. *Schema of representative optical axes (broken lines) and morphological axes (solid lines) of the ommatidia along a horizontal section of the lateral eye of* Limulus. (a) *In air;* (b) *in sea water. The axis ξ and the heavy arrow refer to some experimental arrangements which will be described shortly. From Kirschfeld and Reichardt (1964). See also Figures 3.24 and 4.17.*

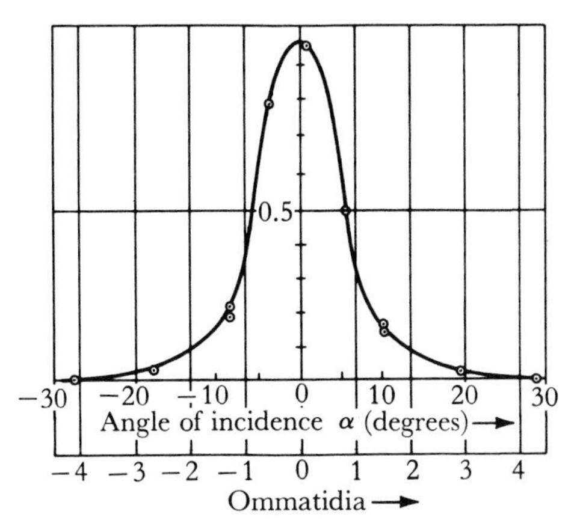

Figure 4.16. *The sensitivity distribution function of a single ommatidium in air with data points indicated by circles. The sensitivity is expressed on the ordinate as the reciprocal of the light intensity required to produce a steady discharge of 2.5 impulses per second from the ommatidium under investigation. On the abscissa is represented the angle of incidence α of the illumination on the test ommatidium and (below) the corresponding number of ommatidia that the sensitivity distribution would cover. Redrawn after Kirschfeld and Reichardt (1964).*

The cornea is not everywhere perpendicular to these morphological axes, so the optical axes, especially near the margins of the eye, diverge laterally from them. Figure 4.15a shows representative optical and morphological axes (broken and solid lines respectively) when the eye is in air; Figure 4.15b shows the same axes with the eye in sea water. Although *Limulus* spends most of its life in the ocean, it spawns on shore, so the eye has to function both in air and water.

Because the visual field of each ommatidium covers an angle larger than the angles formed by the intersections of the optical axes of adjacent ommatidia, the visual fields of closely neighboring ommatidia overlap one another considerably. The extent of this overlap has been measured by observing the discharge of nerve impulses from one ommatidium in response to a point source of light moved across the visual field (Waterman 1954, Kirschfeld and Reichardt, 1964). The measurements by Kirschfeld and Reichardt (Fig. 4.16) avoided possible complications due to inhibition from neighboring ommatidia by perfusing the eye with ethyl alcohol, which abolishes inhibition (Bernhard and Skoglund, 1941; MacNichol and Benolken, 1956). The measurements, shown by the symbols and solid line, were made with the eye in air, as were the experiments described below. These distributions are analogous to the line spread functions for the human eye illustrated in Figure 4.3 above.

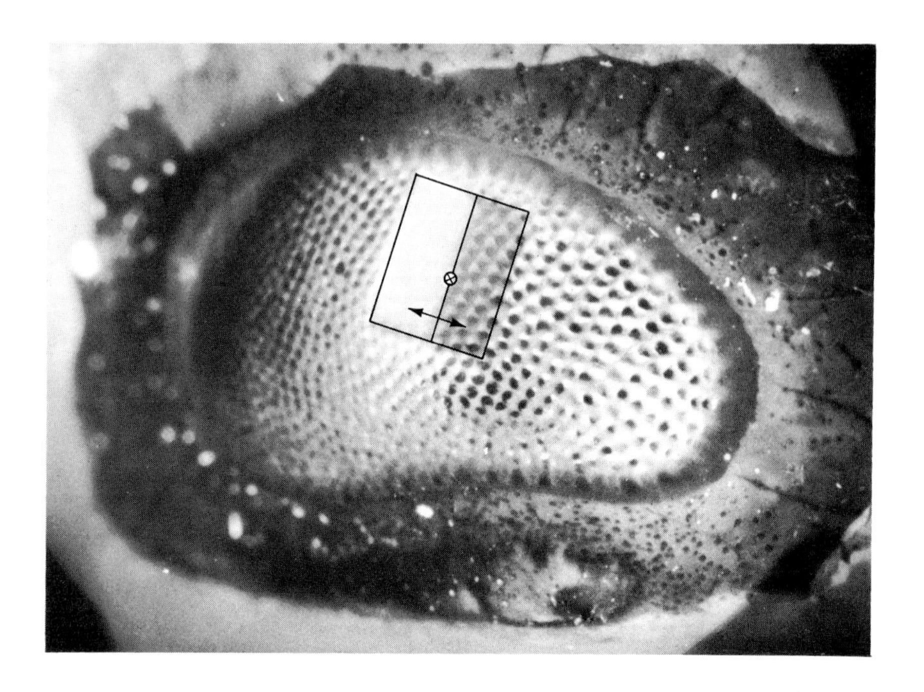

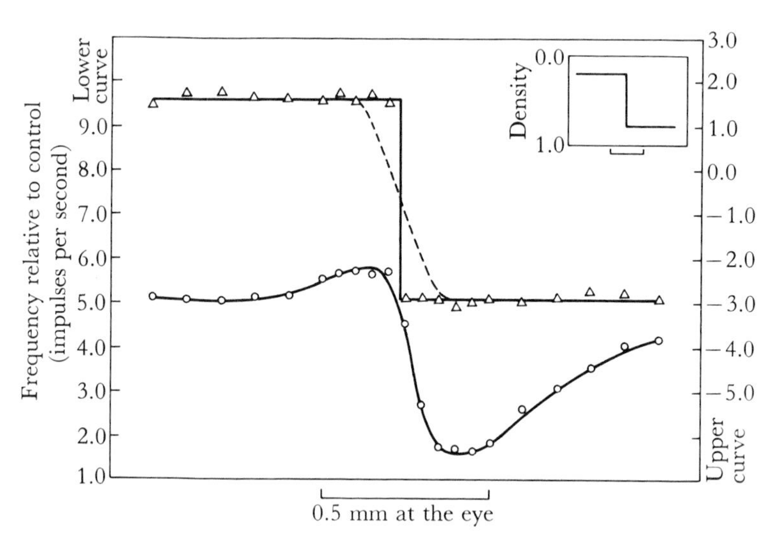

Figure 4.17. *The response of a single ommatidium to a simple step pattern of illumination. Double exposure photograph shows pattern centered on the test ommatidium (marked ⊗). Outlines of light and dark areas are shown by solid lines drawn on the photograph. Double headed arrow indicates direction of movement of test pattern. Graph shows response, relative to control, without*

The effects of the spread of illumination to several ommatidia from a particular point in the object plane may be eliminated almost entirely by sharply focussing the object distribution on the receptor plane with auxiliary lenses. Thus, light from a pinhole aperture in the object plane of the auxiliary optical system, focussed on the corneal surface, stimulates only the single ommatidium directly beneath the image of the stop, if scatter within the optical system and the eye is negligible. (Alternatively, the pinhole aperture may be placed in the image plane at the cornea.) Similarly, all points on an extended object (wide aperture in the object plane) are focussed on corresponding points on the corneal surface and stimulate only the receptors beneath those points; the part of the extended image seen by a particular ommatidium is thus determined only by its aperture (about .2 or .25 mm in diameter in the eye of a large adult).

In the experiment illustrated in Figure 4.17 (Ratliff and Hartline, 1959), a simple step pattern of illumination—bright on the left and dim on the right—was sharply focussed on the eye, thus eliminating or at least reducing the effects of the excitatory spread function. A mask with a very small aperture was placed against the surface of the cornea and centered on the facet of one ommatidium near the center of the eye. The small aperture of the mask—rather than the much larger aperture of the ommatidium—was the limiting stop in the system, and thus the blurring effect of the normally large aperture was also practically eliminated. Furthermore, since only one ommatidium was illuminated, no inhibitory influences were exerted on it by its neighbors. (See also Fig. 3.29.)

The pattern of illumination was next moved laterally in small steps and the steady-state frequency of response of this one ommatidium (indicated by the symbol in the photograph) was measured at each step. (It is impractical to record the activity of several receptors in a row across the pattern, but by recording from one and moving the pattern, the single receptor assumes successively the positions of several receptors in a row with respect to the pattern.) Since the major causes of blur and the inhibitory influences from neighboring ommatidia were both eliminated, the frequency of response, which was approximately linear with log I, was a fairly good replication (Fig. 4.17, upper curve) of the distribution of intensity in the pattern (Fig. 4.17, inset). Thus, this one ommatidium with its artificial small aperture served as a "physiological microphotome-

---

inhibition (triangles) and with inhibition (circles). The position of the zero point on each ordinate was chosen arbitrarily. See text for details. The pattern of illumination was produced by focussing the demagnified image of a transilluminated photographic plate on the eye. The inset shows the relative density of the plate across its width. Graph from Ratliff and Hartline (1959).

ter" with which the pattern of illumination could be measured fairly accurately in terms of the frequency of discharge of nerve impulses. (The broken line shows the calculated blurred response that would have resulted with a normal aperture, about 0.25 mm in this eye.)

In the final stage of the experiment the mask was removed, the pattern again moved across the eye, and the neural responses measured as before (Fig. 4.17, lower curve). Now, when neighboring ommatidia were illuminated and the inhibitory influences were allowed to come into play, a maximum and a minimum that were not in the stimulus pattern appeared in the response pattern. One cannot say that the blurred response has been fully rectified because the slope of the gradient is only slightly steeper, and the sharp corners are not restored; nevertheless, the maxima and minima contain significant information about the magnitude and location of the contour. Furthermore, this is not the whole story—this experiment merely shows what the inhibition can accomplish under steady-state conditions. The inhibitory influences that result from temporal changes are much more pronounced, as will be discussed in a later section of this chapter.

How do the directly observed responses of the inhibitory network in the eye of *Limulus* compare with those calculated by Fourier methods from the results of psychophysical experiments on humans? Some experiments by Kirschfeld and Reichardt (1964), in which the results were expressed in terms of transfer functions, answer this question. Their method was basically similar to the one just described, but instead of focussing an image on the receptors, the eye viewed the step pattern of illumination directly. The pattern was provided by a sheet of translucent material (opal Plexiglas) with a diffusing front surface which was placed before the eye and illuminated from behind. A step filter (Fig. 4.18a), formed by an exposed strip of photographic film, was inserted between the light source and the diffusing material.

The intensity of the transmitted light from any small element of area ΔA on the surface of a perfect diffuser follows Lambert's cosine law; that is, the luminous intensity ΔI_θ of any ray emerging at the angle θ from the normal ray (with intensity ΔI) is given by the equation

$$\Delta I_\theta = \Delta I \cos \theta.$$

The projection of any small element of surface area ΔA onto a plane perpendicular to any ray ΔI_θ also follows a cosine law

$$\Delta A_\theta = \Delta A \cos \theta.$$

But since the *luminance L* is given by the intensity per unit of projected area, it is therefore independent of the angle θ

$$L = \frac{\Delta I_\theta}{A_\theta} = \frac{\Delta I \cos \theta}{A \cos \theta} = \text{a constant.}$$

The above relations explain why a luminous sphere, such as the sun, appears to be a uniformly bright disc even though the edges are viewed tangentially and the center perpendicularly. For the same reason, ommatidia oriented in quite different directions, but toward the same half of the bipartite diffusing surface used in this experiment, were *approximately* equally illuminated. (Some deviations from the Lambert cosine law were noted (Fig. 4.18b) and taken into account in the calculations of results.) In addition to providing nearly uniform illumination on differently oriented ommatidia (over a range of plus or minus 20°), the method also had the advantage that when the eye was placed close to the screen practically the entire receptor mosaic was illuminated. Thus any extraneous effects that might have been produced by the outer edges of a focussed pattern, such as the one shown in Figure 4.17, were reduced.

The eye was mounted on slides so that it could be moved in two directions—along a line parallel to the pattern and toward or away from

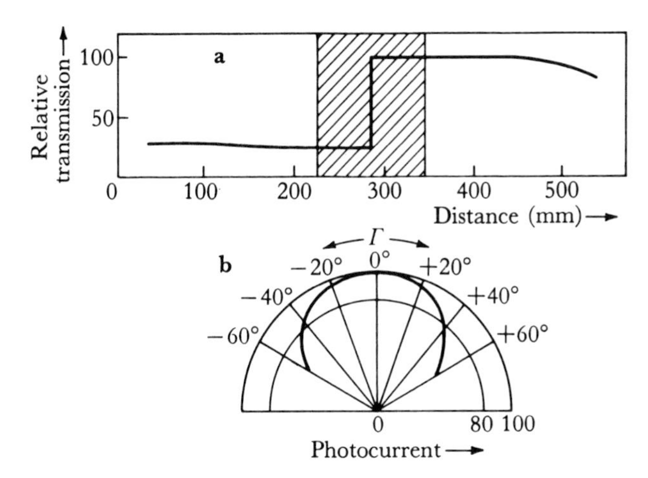

Figure 4.18. (a) *The relative transmission of light (ordinate) through the film used to provide the step pattern of illumination (solid line). Distance in millimeters from left-hand edge of film shown on abscissa. During the experiment the eye was moved laterally across the step within the range indicated by the shaded area.* (b) *The directional characteristics of the diffusing material placed on the surface of the film. The measurements (heavy line) were made with a photocell which had a small angular aperture and which could be swung about the point 0 so as to "view" the surface from any direction. The half circle drawn about 0 with a radius of 100 gives the relation between photocurrent and angle of view for an ideal Lambert surface. From Kirschfeld and Reichardt (1964).*

the pattern. With the eye fixed in a particular position, the steady discharge of nerve impulses was recorded from one centrally located ommatidium (heavy arrow in Fig. 4.15). The eye was then moved to a new position along the axis ξ (Fig. 4.15), and the discharge of impulses, always coming from the same ommatidium, was recorded again, and so on.

In the experiment shown in Figure 4.19 the eye was placed in direct contact with the pattern and measurements made across a wide range of lateral positions. The effects of overlap of the visual fields of adjacent ommatidia were thus reduced to a minimum, since the whole pattern was practically on the surface of the cornea. Two abscissae are shown in the figure: one is the position in millimeters with respect to the step in the pattern; the other is the position in terms of number of ommatidia illuminated by the pattern. The latter was calculated on the basis of the orientation of the ommatidia, which was determined after the experiment by sectioning the eye in the horizontal plane.

Assuming the system to be linear and assuming that responses were all above the threshold of inhibition, a theoretical function relating the inhibitory coefficients to distance along the abscissa could be chosen which in calculating would yield a good approximation to the measured impulse frequency.* The inset in Figure 4.19 shows that calculations

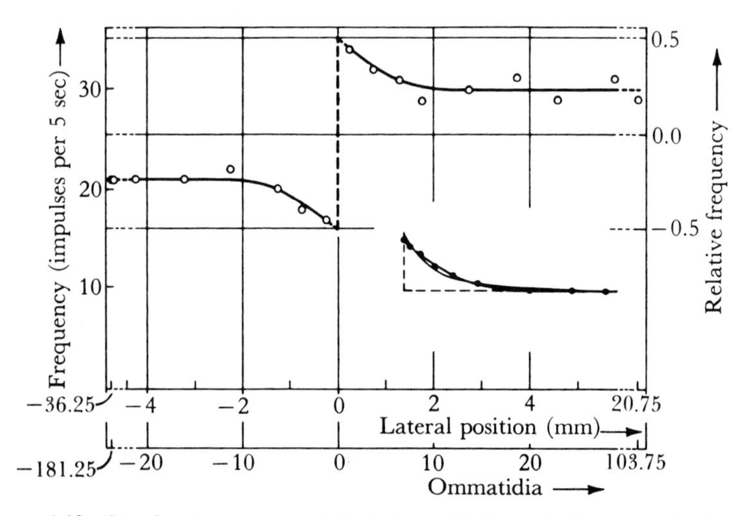

Figure 4.19. Steady frequency of impulses discharged from a single ommatidium in response to a step pattern of illumination. The eye was placed in direct contact with the transilluminated film. From Kirschfeld and Reichardt (1964).

* Inhibitory coefficients determined in this way are, on the average, much smaller than those observed directly by measuring the mutual interaction of two neighboring

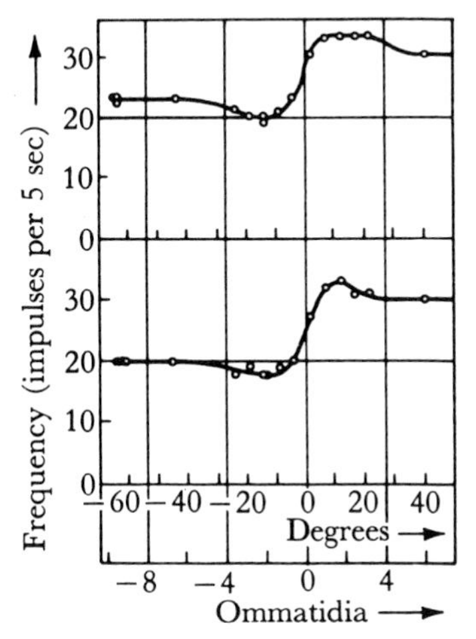

Figure 4.20. Frequency of impulses discharged from a single ommatidium when the eye was 30.5 mm from the pattern of illumination. From Kirschfeld and Reichardt (1964).

based on an exponential function do not fit the data as well as those which utilized a Gaussian function. (Constants were selected by finding those which gave the best fit to the experimental data.)

Impulse frequencies were also measured with the eye at greater distances from the pattern. Figure 4.20 shows the results for a distance of 30.5 mm. The upper curve was obtained just before the curve in Figure 4.19; the lower curve was obtained just after it. Measurements made at this and greater distances are essentially identical when converted from the linear scale to a scale in degrees or number of ommatidia.

At this point in the experiment the.following information was available: (1) The theoretical Gaussian function relating inhibitory coefficients to distance (calculated from the experimental results in Fig. 4.19); (2) the excitatory spread function (determined experimentally, Fig. 4.16); (3) the distribution of illumination in the step pattern (Fig. 4.18); and (4) the response to this step distribution of illumination (determined experimentally, Fig. 4.20). With these data, the calculations shown in Figure

---

ommatidia (as in Fig. 3.26 above) although the results of the two types of experiments are qualitatively similar. The quantitative discrepancies have not yet been fully explained. They may result in part from a biased selection of the more strongly interacting pairs of ommatidia in the direct experiments and in part from neglect of the effects of thresholds in the indirect experiments. In addition, there may be some possible effects due to occlusion (that is, diminished inhibitory influences resulting from several ommatidia sharing common pathways) that are not taken into account in either type of experiment.

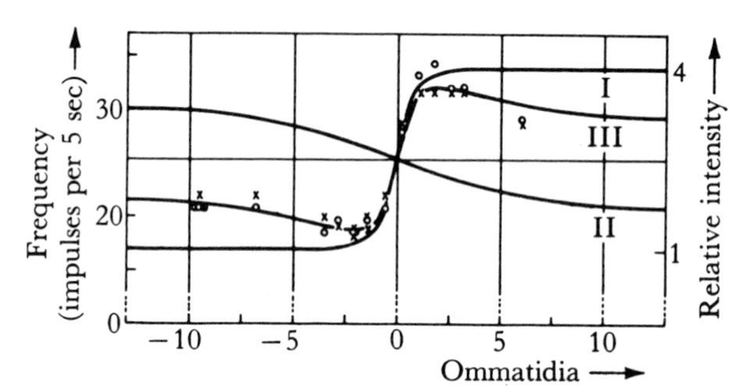

Figure 4.21. A comparison of the calculated and the observed response to a step pattern of illumination. From Kirschfeld and Reichardt (1964).

4.21 were made. Curve I, which was calculated using the known distribution of illumination in the pattern and the experimentally determined spread function, is the distribution of illumination on the receptor mosaic when the eye was at a distance of 30.5 mm from the pattern. Curve II is the calculated effect of inhibition based on the theoretical Gaussian distance function of the inhibitory coefficients determined from Figure 4.19. Curve III is the calculated frequency of neural response to the intensity distribution in curve I; that is, curve I plus the effects of inhibition represented in curve II. The symbols are the observed neural responses, open circles from the upper curve in Figure 4.20, *x*'s from the lower curve in Figure 4.20.

Using these data, Kirschfeld and Reichardt calculated the Fourier spatial frequency transfer function for the *Limulus* eye (Fig. 4.22). The broken line, shown full extent in the inset, is the transfer function for the excitatory spread function alone. The solid line is the transfer function of the inhibitory network alone. The dotted line is the composite

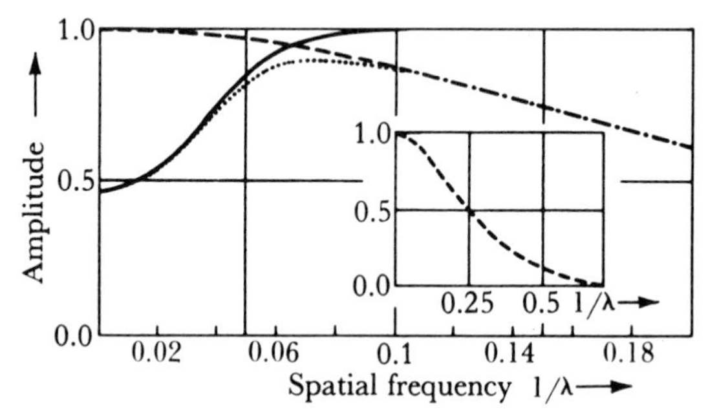

Figure 4.22. The component and composite transfer functions for the eye of Limulus. *Units of λ = average separation of ommatidia, center to center. From Kirschfeld and Reichardt (1964).*

transfer function for the whole system, that is, the product of the two component functions.

The similarity between the results of this analysis and those of the preceding analyses of the experiments on the human visual system is obvious and one may reason by analogy that some form of lateral inhibition similar to that observed directly in the *Limulus* retina probably occurs in the human visual system. But this line of reasoning should not be carried too far because the retinas of vertebrates and the retinas of arthropods are obviously of different orders of complexity in both structure and function. Furthermore, the two sets of experiments described above are not strictly comparable: the experiments on the *Limulus* retina were all carried out under steady-state conditions, but those on the human visual system only seemed to be. It is true that the stimulus distributions were stationary, but the observer's *eyes* were free to move, and did so, while he observed the stimulus. This seemingly minor difference between the two sets of experiments must not be neglected because it conceals the most striking feature of the functional organization of the vertebrate retina—a pronounced specialized sensitivity to temporal changes in illumination.

THE DYNAMICS OF THE INTEGRATIVE ACTION OF THE RETINA

The most common natural cause of temporal changes in the pattern of illumination on the retina is *motion,* and these changes are of special significance for vision, because, as Ulysses remarked when upbraiding Achilles for his inaction, "Things in motion sooner catch the eye than what stirs not" (Shakespeare, *Troilus and Cressida,* III, iii). But motion is relative. To produce movement of the retinal image with respect to the receptor mosaic, the thing that moves can be either the object viewed or the eye itself. Indeed, as has already been shown (Fig. 2.19), the human eye is in continual motion even when one attempts to maintain steady fixation. Thus, there is always considerable movement of the retinal image whether the object moves or not. The visual significance of this ever present motion will be considered first, and then the underlying neural mechanisms in the retina that make use of it are discussed.

Stabilized retinal images The importance of retinal image motion for human vision has been demonstrated in experiments in which the effects of eye movements are cancelled by means of a simple optical device. The optical lever provided by light reflected from a mirror on a contact lens tightly fitted to the eye (Ratliff and Riggs, 1950) is used as part of a projection system. A pattern of illumination projected on a screen by way of the mirror on the contact lens moves as the eye moves. The light reflected from a mirror, however, turns through twice the angle of rotation of the mirror so that the angular motion of the projected pattern is twice the angular motion of the eye about its center of rotation. To compensate for this fact, the screen on which the pattern is projected is viewed through a system of mirrors (Fig. 4.23) such that the viewing path is twice the distance from the eye to the screen (Ditchburn and Ginsborg, 1952; Riggs, Ratliff, Cornsweet, and Cornsweet, 1953). Under these conditions the image projected on the screen is effectively moved twice as far away, and its angular motion, measured by way of this longer path, is halved so that it now equals the angular motion of the eye. Viewed along this path, the motion of the image as seen by the observer is the same as the motion of his eye and the retinal image is stationary on the receptor mosaic. All details of patterns of illumination that are viewed in this way appear sharp and clear at first, but they gradually fade out. Usually within a few seconds all contrast and form disappears and the stationary image on the retina appears uniform no matter what may be the physical distribution of illumination in it.

These phenomena are not artifacts caused by the attachments to the eye. If the image that has disappeared is flickered (Cornsweet, 1956) or is caused to move on the retina (Krauskopf, 1957), it immediately reappears. Furthermore, one can produce stationary images on the retina without direct attachments to the eye. The entoptic phenomena known

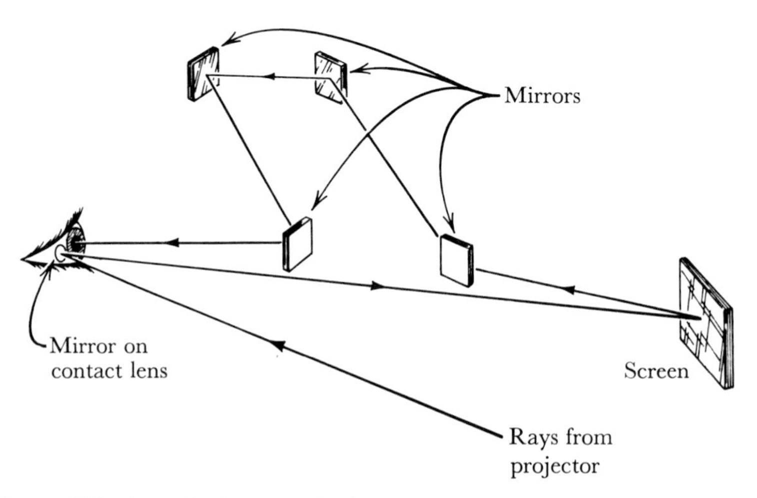

Figure 4.23. *A method for producing a stationary image on the retina even though the eye itself is not stationary. Redrawn after Riggs, Ratliff, Cornsweet, and Cornsweet (1953). See also Ditchburn and Ginsborg (1952).*

as "Haidinger's brushes," for example, are stationary images under certain conditions (Ratliff, 1958). By observing these phenomena the reader may see for himself the effects of stabilizing a retinal image. The brushes may be seen simply by looking through a polarizer at a field of blue light. They are dark images, shaped somewhat like an hour glass and centered on the fovea, with their longest dimension perpendicular to the plane of polarization of the incident light. (See also Cornsweet, 1962.)

The generally accepted interpretation of the phenomenon (first suggested by Helmholtz) is that some of the molecules in the macula lutea are oriented with radial symmetry about the fovea, and those which are parallel to the plane of polarization absorb more of the light than those oriented in other directions. The fixed symmetrical distribution of the macular pigment about the fovea insures that the brushes will remain centered on the fovea whatever their orientation. This orientation is determined by the relative orientations of the polarizer in front of the eye and the analyzer, or molecules of macular pigment, within the eye. If the orientation of the polarizer is fixed, then the orientation of the brushes on the retina will change only if the orientation of the analyzer is changed; that is, only if the eye rolls about an antero-posterior axis. Since appreciable rolling of the eye takes place only with large oblique movements, the brushes remain fixed on the retina during the small involuntary eye movements that occur during fixation; consequently, the brushes gradually disappear from view just as do retinal images stabilized by other means. (This naturally occurring stabilization of the image accounts for the transient character of the Haidinger brushes, which is usually remarked on by all who observe them.) The brushes immediately reappear if they are turned about their center by rotating the polarizer in front of the eye, just as images stabilized by other means immediately reappear if they are slightly displaced on the retina.

An analogous effect, the so-called fixation-blindness, is also produced without attachments to the eye. If one stares fixedly at a blurred shadow, or at very dimly lit objects, contours at first seen clearly gradually fade away. Apparently, intensity changes that result from normal eye movements under these conditions are inadequate to produce a neural response sufficient to reach the threshold of vision. (This effect is a possible source of error in psychophysical experiments which require prolonged steady fixation of graded or blurred patterns such as those that exhibit the Mach bands.)

The relative importance of various frequencies and amplitudes of motion were investigated by Ditchburn, Fender, and Mayne (1959). In these experiments an image of a line was first stabilized on the retina and then controlled motions were introduced by deflecting the beam

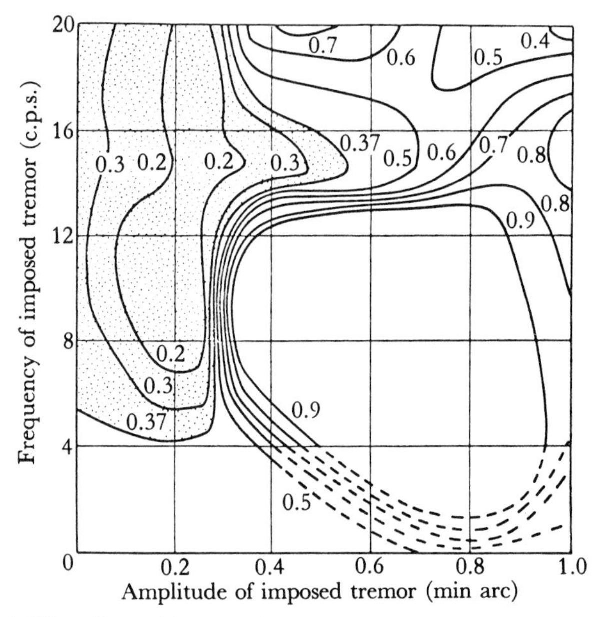

Figure 4.24. The effect of imposed tremor motion on the visibility of a stabilized retinal image as a function of both amplitude and frequency. From Ditchburn, Fender, and Mayne (1959).

reflected from the mirror on the contact lens. The results are shown as a contour map in Figure 4.24. The numbers on the contours indicate relative visibility of the image as a function of the amplitude and frequency of the imposed movement. (No measurements were made below 4 cycles per second; the broken lines are conjectural.)

A plateau of good visibility, shown in the lower right quadrant, extends over a range of frequencies from about 4 to 10 cycles per second and amplitudes of about .4 to 1.0 minute of arc. Minute rapid frequencies (shaded area in upper left quadrant) decrease the relative visibility of the image. It is evident that frequencies in the general range of 4 to 10 cycles per second are most efficient in maintaining vision under these particular conditions. Fourier analysis of the irregular component of the normal tremor of the eye (Fender and Nye, 1961) shows that a high proportion of the power is approximately in this same range.

These results and the results on oscillating Mach bands (Fig. 2.20 above) are in general agreement as far as the efficacy of various frequencies of motion are concerned. Visibility of a graded field of illumination such as the Mach pattern, however, depends not only on the frequency and extent of motion, but also on the important factor of the slope of gradient. The point to be emphasized here is that motion of the eye can in effect steepen such gradients and thus change low *spatial* frequencies into higher ones, relative to the receptor mosaic. This might partly account for the fact that the neural network in the human visual system seems to "regenerate" high spatial frequencies that are filtered out by the lens (see Fig. 4.9).

In any event, these experiments on eye movements definitely indicate that transient effects are essential for the maintenance of clear vision. Therefore it is important to ask how and what kind of neural responses the transients generate. Answering these questions requires a further analysis of the behavior of neural networks, which ultimately returns to the main topic of inhibitory interaction.

Transient responses in the vertebrate retina Practically all sensory systems exhibit marked transient responses to sudden changes in stimulus intensity, but the visual system is probably the most highly specialized of all in this respect. Indeed, only a very small proportion of the retinal ganglion cell axons that form a vertebrate optic nerve typically yield a steady discharge of impulses in response to steady illumination. The majority are either quiescent or discharge very slowly under steady-state conditions, but respond vigorously when the illumination is changed (Hartline, 1938b). Some yield a burst of impulses when the light is turned on, and another burst when the light is turned off. Others remain completely inactive during maintained illumination and then respond with a burst of activity when the light is turned off. On the basis of these specialized responses Hartline called these three types of ganglion cells "on," "on-off," and "off," respectively. (As will become apparent in a later section of this chapter, there are many complex variations of and elaborations on these three fundamental response "types.")

Typical responses of an "on-off" ganglion cell in the frog retina are illustrated in Figure 4.25. In this particular cell impulses could be generated either by turning a stationary pattern of illumination on and off (a), or by moving a pattern of illumination back and forth across the receptor mosaic, rapidly in (b) and slowly in (c) as indicated by the slopes of the diagonal lines. This type of ganglion cell responds primarily to a *change* in illumination, no matter how it is produced, and the vigor of the response depends primarily on the magnitude and abruptness of the change. Such "on-off" mechanisms must be of great significance for vision because they, or some variant of them, are found at one level or another in virtually all well-developed visual systems in both vertebrates and invertebrates that have been studied to date.

The responses of single fibers of the vertebrate optic nerve, such as

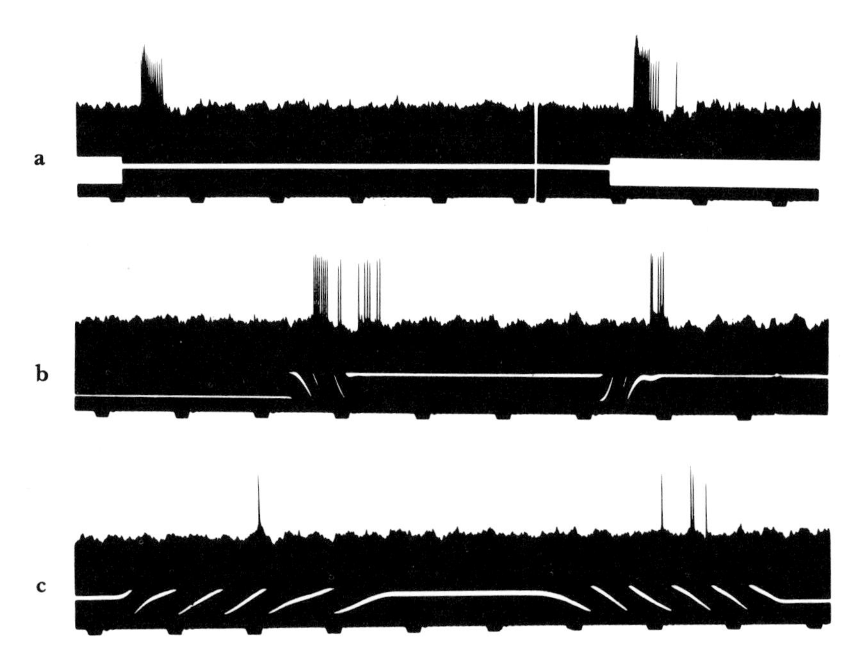

Figure 4.25. *Discharge of impulses from an "on-off" ganglion cell in the retina of the frog in response to a spot of light 50μ in diameter on the retina being turned on and off* (a), *or moved back and forth rapidly in* (b) *and slowly in* (c). *The signal marking the period of illumination blackens the white strip above the 1/5 second time marks. Movements of the spot on the retina are signalled by narrow diagonal white lines appearing above the time marks, each line corresponding to 7μ on the retina. From Hartline (1940).*

those illustrated in Figure 4.25, are not simple manifestations of the activity of single receptors. Retinal ganglion cells are third-order neurons and presumably can be activated by the stimulation of any of the large number of receptors with which they have anatomical connections. These so-called receptive fields of ganglion cells are generally quite large, compared with the dimensions of the photoreceptors, and there is considerable overlap of neighboring fields; thus, any one particular region of the receptor mosaic does not belong exclusively to any one particular ganglion cell (see Fig. 4.26).

In the retina of the frog, the type of response elicited in a ganglion cell is more or less the same no matter what part of the receptive field one stimulates. In other species the response of a particular ganglion cell may be an admixture of several types, with the particular type of response depending largely upon which part or combination of parts of the receptive field is stimulated. For example, the receptive field of a

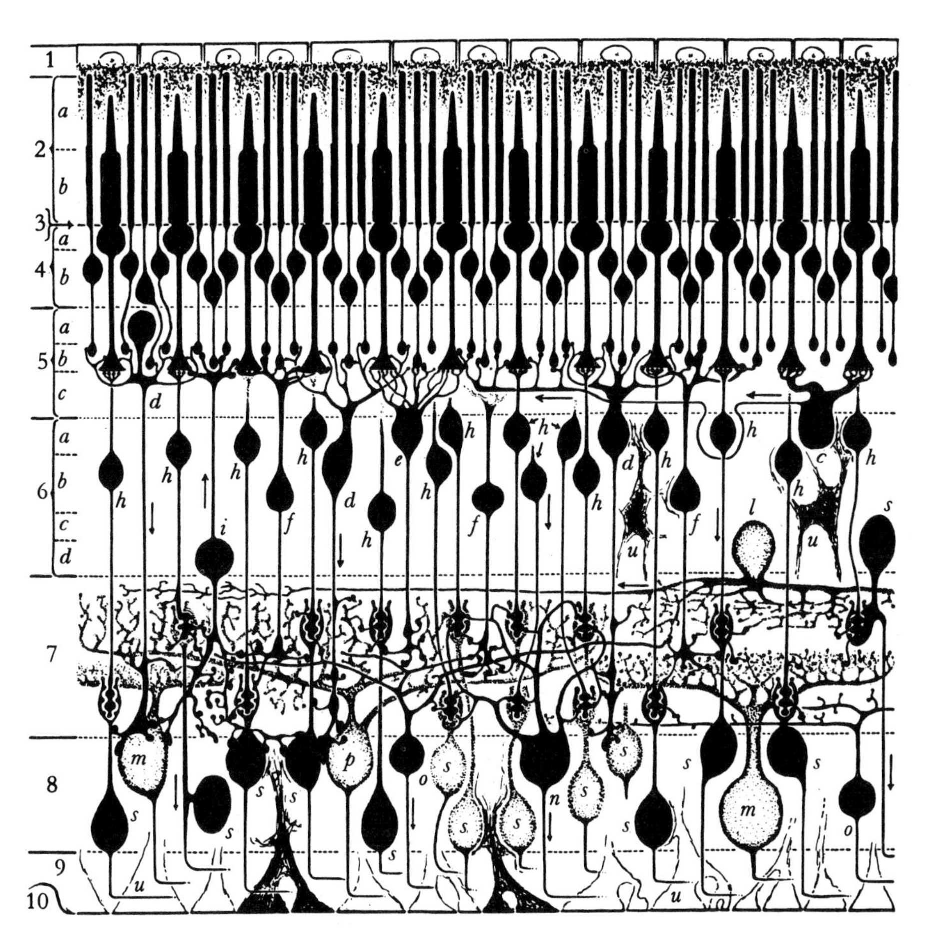

Figure 4.26. *Schema of the structures of the primate retina as revealed by the method of Golgi. The designation of the layers and the zones: (1) pigment layer; (2a) outer zone; (2b) inner zone of the rod and cone layer; (3) outer limiting membrane; (4a) outer zone; (4b) inner zone of the outer nuclear layer; (5a) outer zone; (5b) middle zone; (5c) inner zone of the outer plexiform layer; (6) inner nuclear layer with its four zones; (7) inner plexiform layer; (8) layer of the ganglion cells; (9) layer of the optic nerve fibers; (10) inner limiting membrane. The designation of the nerve cells: (a) rods; (b) cones; (c) horizontal cells; (d, e, f, h) bipolar cells; (i, l) so-called amacrine cells; (m, n, o, p, s) ganglion cells; (u) "radial fibers" of Müller.*

In this scheme the nervous elements are reduced to their essentials; however, the characteristic features of each variety are preserved—the location of the bodies, the size, the shape, and the spreading of the dendrites and of the axis cylinders. The synaptical contacts are presented fairly accurately. From Polyak (1941).

ganglion cell in the cat retina may have an "on" center and an "off" periphery with an intermediate "on-off" zone (Kuffler, 1953). Since the responses of these different parts of the receptive field all converge on and share a final common path—the axon of the ganglion cell—it is evident that the intensity, the color, and the spatial and temporal configuration of the pattern of illumination falling on the receptive field may all be significant factors in determining the ultimate pattern of impulses which the cell discharges.

An experiment by Baumgartner (1961a) on a so-called "on" center "off" surround retinal ganglion cell in the eye of the cat illustrates one aspect of these several factors. This experiment is of special interest here because it utilized simple step patterns of illumination similar to those in the experiments discussed earlier in this chapter.* The eye was immobilized and the stimulus pattern, which was a bright central field flanked by dark fields, was exposed in a fixed position for a short period. The impulses generated in response to the first 500 milliseconds of this exposure were counted and recorded. The stimulus pattern was then moved to a new position, exposed briefly, and the number of impulses counted as before. This process was repeated until the responses to all parts of the pattern had been sampled (Fig. 4.27). The maximal response appeared when the center of the receptive field was located just inside the border of the bright field. Note that the responses throughout the entire extent of the narrow bright field were significantly greater than the responses to a greatly extended uniform field of the same intensity (indicated by the broken line).

As was mentioned above, these results were obtained from an "on" center "off" surround type of retinal ganglion cell. Results obtained from "off" center "on" surround types of cells generally were the negative of those shown in the figure. In combination, these two types of retinal ganglion cells yield a complex distribution of neural responses with maxima and minima adjacent to the points that correspond to the steps in the pattern of illumination. Because these results are in many respects similar to the results obtained in the experiments on the inhibitory network in the eye of *Limulus* (Figs. 4.17 and 4.20 above), they lend some support to the view that neural responses to steps and gradients of illumination on the vertebrate retina are similarly accentuated by lateral inhibitory influences. But it must be remembered that the results illustrated represent the behavior of *one* particular type of ganglion cell in the retina of *one* particular species under *one* particular set of stimu-

* For some related experiments on contrast effects in the carp retina see Motokawa, Yamashita, and Ogawa (1961). For studies on border contrast at the level of the visual cortex see Jung (1961) and Baumgartner (1961b and 1965.)

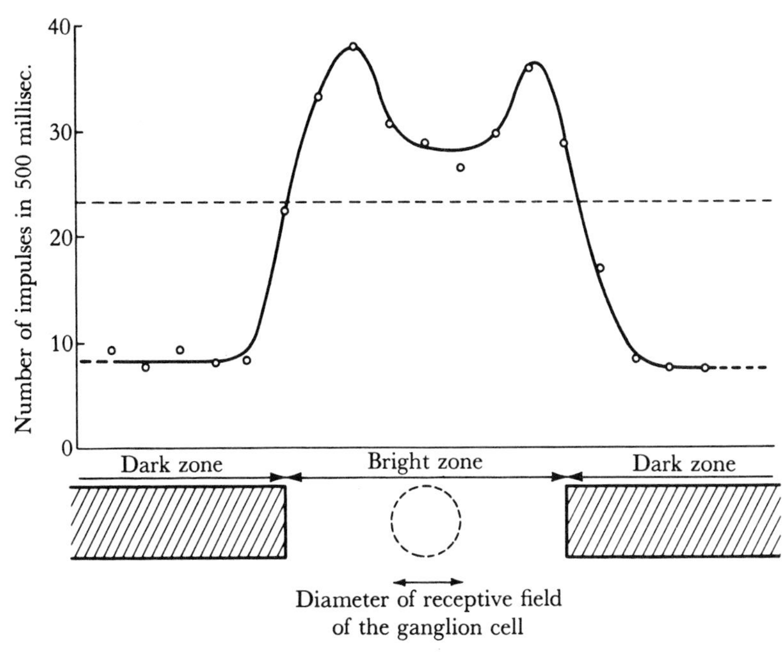

Figure 4.27. *Discharge of impulses from retinal ganglion cell of cat in response to a step pattern of illumination. Open circles represent data points. Solid curve fitted by inspection. Width of narrow bright zone 5°41′ of visual angle. Broken line shows response to an extended field with same intensity as narrow bright zone. Redrawn after Baumgartner (1961a).*

lus conditions, rather than typifying the behavior of vertebrate retinal ganglion cells in general.

Under the conditions of this experiment the transient "on" and "off" responses actually resulted from turning the illumination on and off, rather than from the normal movement of the eye that might have occurred during steady fixation of the pattern. In this case the results might not have been much different if the transients had been produced by motion of the eye or of the pattern, because motion itself effectively results in the illumination on various receptors being turned on and off as the retinal image moves from one place to another. As Figure 4.25 above illustrated, some ganglion cells respond about equally well to either type of transient, although in other cases an actual change in the *location* of the pattern of illumination on the retina, not just the intensity change it produces, seems to be required to generate a response. Grüsser-Cornehls, Grüsser, and Bullock (1963) have observed ganglion cells of this type in the retina of the frog. These cells respond little or

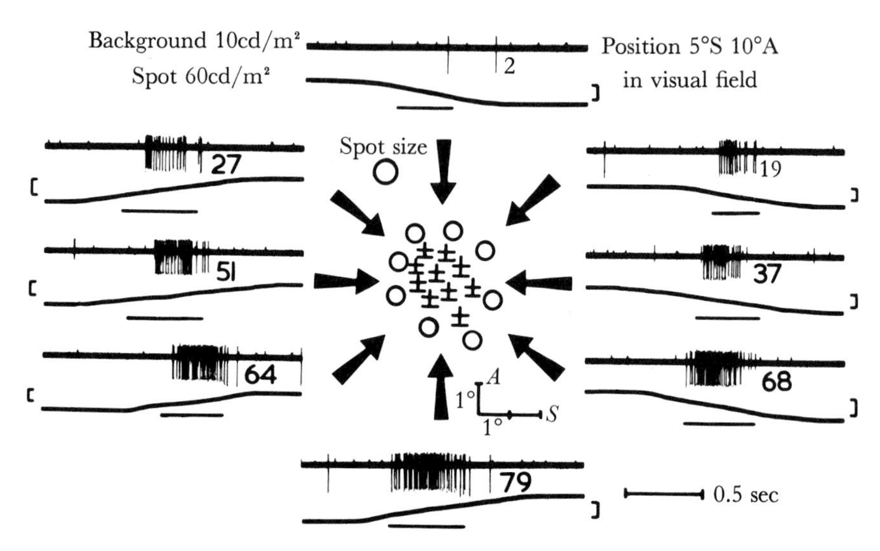

Figure 4.28. *A directionally selective unit. The map of the receptive field is shown in the center. The following symbols are used: + for responses at "on"; − for responses at "off"; ± for responses at "on" and "off"; 0 for no response. The orientation of horizontal and vertical meridians of the visual field is also shown: A is anterior; S is superior. Calibration marks, degrees of visual angle. Each record is the response to movement of a spot of light entirely across the receptive field in the direction of the adjacent arrow. The upper trace is a recording from an axon in the layer of nerve fibers with a tungsten microelectrode; the lower trace is a signal representing displacement of the spot across the visual field, vertical calibration bar 5°. The time for which the spot was within the receptive field is indicated by the horizontal bar in each record. The number of spikes is shown immediately after each response. All records read from left to right; increasing positivity in action-potential traces causes a downward deflection. From Barlow, Hill, and Levick (1964).*

not at all to changes in illumination without movement, but do respond vigorously to changes in the location of the pattern of illumination. (Experiments with short flashes of light show that neither the illumination nor the movement needs to be continuous; a change in the location of two successive flashes is an adequate stimulus for this type of unit.)

The *configuration* of the stimulus, as well as a change in its intensity or location, is an important factor in determining the response of some units. Lettvin, Maturana, McCulloch, and Pitts (1959) found that a relatively large stimulus pattern with a straight edge might yield no response at all when moved into the receptive field of a particular type of ganglion cell in the eye of the frog, while a small circular stimulus might yield a vigorous response when moved into the same field. Curvature of the edge, rather than size, appears to be the adequate stimulus because these cells also respond strongly to a sharp corner of a large stimulus pattern. (Inhibitory networks respond similarly. See Fig. 4.45.)

Barlow and Hill (1963) and Barlow, Hill, and Levick (1964) have found that certain retinal ganglion cells in the rabbit retina are even more highly specialized and show a selective sensitivity to *direction* of movement. Impulses are discharged in response to a movement in one direction, but not in response to movement in the opposite direction (Fig. 4.28), with the "preferred" direction of motion generally being either horizontal or vertical. The same directional sensitivity holds over the whole receptive field of any particular ganglion cell, but may be different for different cells. Maturana and Frenk (1963) have observed ganglion cells with similar properties in the pigeon retina. Some of these cells would respond to any edge, curved or straight, moving in a particular direction, but others were selective not only with respect to direction but also to the configuration of the stimulus and would respond only to an extended horizontal edge moving vertically.

The effects of color add further complications to this already complex sketch of some of the salient features of the vertebrate retina. To cite

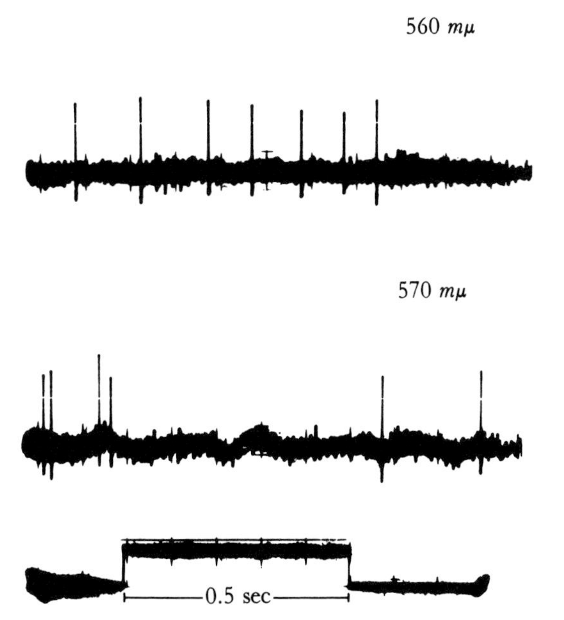

Figure 4.29. *A variation of ganglion cell response (goldfish retina) with a small change in wavelength of the stimulus. The duration of the stimulus is indicated by the step in the signal trace at the bottom of the figure. Spikes occurring before the onset of the stimulus are "off" responses from preceding stimuli. From Wagner, MacNichol, and Wolbarsht (1960).*

only one example, Wagner, MacNichol, and Wolbarsht (1960) have found that in the eye of the common goldfish some colors of illumination cause excitation and other colors inhibition of the same ganglion cell. The response that finally appears seems to depend upon the balance of these two opposed wavelength-dependent influences. In some cases the balance is so delicate that a shift of only 10 millimicrons in the wavelength of the stimulus can change the response from "on" to "off" (Fig. 4.29).

These various experiments on a wide variety of species illustrate some of the many complexities of the vertebrate retina. There are variations among different species, of course, and the diverse ganglion cell types described above should not be regarded as representative of the population of ganglion cells in any particular retina or in the vertebrate retina in general. Nevertheless, the general conclusion can be drawn that vertebrate retinal ganglion cells are very highly specialized, and although the pattern of impulses they discharge may depend to some extent on all of the spatial, temporal, and spectral characteristics of the pattern of illumination, it often depends mainly on only one or a few of them. If any one thing can be said to characterize all retinal ganglion cells, it is this special ability to respond *selectively* to some particular features of the stimulus pattern.

The mathematical models outlined in Chapter 3 emphasize only one aspect of this selectivity: the specialized responses to edges and contours. There are good reasons for this rather restricted character of the models. For one thing, most of them are based on the incorrect assumption that the human visual system operates under steady-state conditions when, as a matter of fact, the eye of the observer is in continual motion even during supposedly steady fixation. Secondly, most of the models are based on psychophysical experiments in which practically the entire visual system is involved so that it is difficult to parcel out and identify the many and diverse separate processes that must be taking place in the human retina (if one can safely extrapolate from the electrophysiological studies on lower animals). Despite these limitations, one major process can be identified in the results of the psychophysical experiments: each and every one of the models points to opposed excitatory and inhibitory influences as being one of the fundamental physiological mechanisms in the retina. If this deduction is correct, then this basic mechanism must be concealed somewhere in the whole assembly of mechanisms that underlies the generation of the complex transient responses in the axons of the retinal ganglion cells.

The origin of transient responses in the retina The point of view outlined above is neither new nor original. In their early studies on the electrophysiology of the retina and optic nerve, Adrian and Matthews (1928), Granit (1933), and Hartline (1938b) all attributed the complexity of the retinal responses to the integrated effects of excitatory and inhibitory influences exerted over retinal structures interposed between the ganglion cells and the photoreceptors, rather than to special properties of the photoreceptors themselves.

Several lines of evidence, including comparative studies on simpler eyes with structures more favorably arranged for experimental observations, strongly support this view. In the squid, for example, the retina is not inverted and axons arise from the receptors themselves, pass directly out of the back of the eye in numerous small nervules, and then travel some distance before entering the optic lobe of the central ganglion. Recently, MacNichol and Love (1960) succeeded in recording the simple maintained "on" type of discharge from these first-order neurons, apparently the only type of activity that they yield. The "off" responses, which occur at the next higher stage in the optic lobe of the central ganglion, apparently result from neural interactions mediated over the interconnections within the central ganglion.

The situation is similar in *Limulus*. The axon from which impulses can be recorded arises from the eccentric cell of the ommatidium, and although it is not a first-order neuron, it is in direct contact with the rhabdomeres of the retinular cells which are presumed to be the photoreceptors. As has already been shown (Fig. 3.25), these neurons ordinarily respond with a simple maintained "on" discharge. In the optic lobe of the central ganglion, however, "off" responses similar to those occurring in the third-order neurons of the vertebrate retina can be recorded (Wilska and Hartline, 1941; Oomura and Kuriyama, 1953). As in the squid, the interconnections within the central ganglion presumably provide the anatomical basis for interactions which give rise to the more complex responses. Indeed, where an optic ganglion closely apposed to the retina can be removed surgically, as Bernhard (1942) did in his experiments on the water beetle *Dytiscus,* then the formerly complex response exhibited in the gross retinal action potential becomes a simple "on" type.

In the pineal eye, which is found in some lower vertebrates, the retinal ganglion cells which give rise to the axons making up the optic nerve are second-order neurons. Miller and Wolbarsht (1962) found that these second-order neurons in the pineal eye of the American chameleon, *Anolis,* yield "on-off" or pure "off" responses similar to those observed in the more complex lateral eyes of vertebrates. Dodt and Heerd (1962) obtained similar results in their study on pineal nerve fibers in frogs. Although such observations alone do not prove that the more complex responses are the product of neural interactions in post-receptor levels of these retinas, they are compatible with such a view.

Turning now to third-order neurons, the retinal ganglion cells of the lateral eyes of vertebrates provide abundant evidence to support the view that the complex patterns of response observed in these cells result from the integrative action of the retinal network. As has already been shown, the response in a particular retinal ganglion cell may generally be produced by illuminating any part of a relatively large portion of the receptor mosaic. The integrated response resulting from the stimulation of different portions of this receptive field is not a mere summation of identical influences converging on a final common pathway, however, because the influences from neighboring regions often oppose one another. Hartline (1939) found that in the eye of the frog an "off" response elicited in a particular fiber by illuminating one group of receptors may be inhibited by illuminating another neighboring group of receptors in the same receptive field. Barlow (1953) observed a similar inhibition using stimuli outside of, but near, the receptive field. The role of antagonistic excitatory and inhibitory influences in shaping the response of a retinal ganglion cell may be seen even more clearly in experiments on the eye of the cat. As was mentioned earlier, Kuffler (1953) found that stimulating the center of some receptive fields in the cat retina might yield a pure "on" response, a surrounding zone an "on-off" response, and the periphery of the field a pure "off" response. The arrangement of the receptive fields of other retinal ganglion cells was similar, but with the relations reversed, so that the center would yield a pure "off" response, the intermediate area an "on-off" response, and the periphery a pure "on" response. The functions of the central and peripheral parts thus appear to be antagonistic.

This antagonism is demonstrated by the results of an experiment on an "on" center "off" surround type of ganglion cell which are illustrated in Figure 4.30. Separate short (0.33 sec.) flashes of light on the "on" center (a) and the "off" surround (b) yield the expected "on" and "off" responses. The greater the intensity, as indicated by the height of the stimulus signal, the greater the response. When the two spots of light were flashed simultaneously (a + b) the response in the final common path, the axon of the ganglion cell, was determined by the relative strengths of the opposing influences. In I the "off" response was completely suppressed, in II the "on" response was completely suppressed, and in III both were reduced, but not completely suppressed, thus yielding an "on-off" response. This fact suggests that the intermediate "on-off" zone, which can be mapped with a single spot of light, is simply the region where the pure "on" and pure "off" zones gradually shade into one another. It should be noted that these response types are rather labile; the patterns of response, dimensions of receptive fields, and so forth of any particular ganglion cell depend strongly on the general level of background illumination and state of adaptation of the eye, among other things (Barlow, FitzHugh, and Kuffler, 1957).

The different parts of a receptive field not only share in common the final pathway through the ganglion cell, but they also probably share a great many intermediate structures as well. Therefore, any long-lasting changes produced in these common structures by stimulating one region of the receptive field might alter the response produced by stimulating another part, even at some later time. Lipetz (1961) and (1962) has demonstrated two effects of this sort in the frog retina. First he showed that adapting one region of the receptive field to light affected the threshold of response not only of that region but also of neighboring regions which had not been illuminated. Subsequently he found that the spectral sensitivities of the neighboring regions were also altered by this procedure in an effect similar to the so-called Purkinje shift that occurs with light and dark adaptation in the human eye. Formerly, both these effects had generally been attributed entirely to changes in the receptors themselves. Of course, these experiments do not rule out the possibility that the receptors may be partly responsible for these changes in sensitivity, but nevertheless they do lead to the inescapable conclusion that some neural mechanism or mechanisms in the common pathway must share in this responsibility.

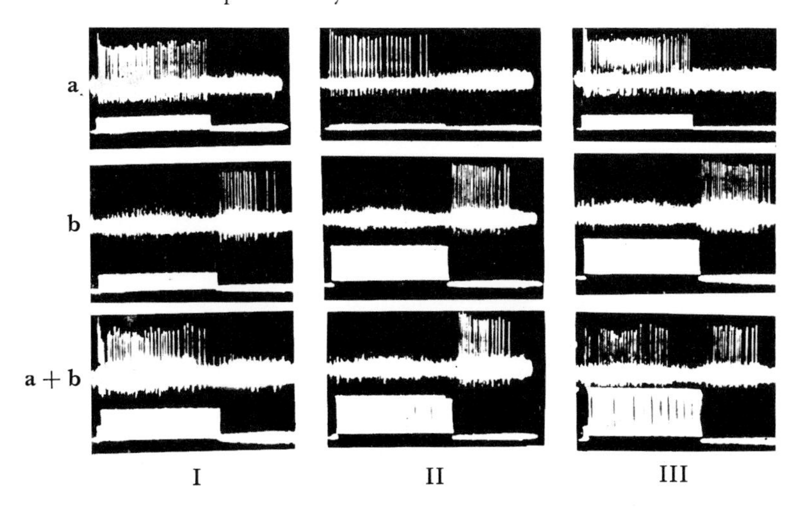

Figure 4.30. *The integration of opposing influences generated by two separate spots of light falling on different parts of the receptive field of a ganglion cell in the cat retina. From Kuffler (1953).*

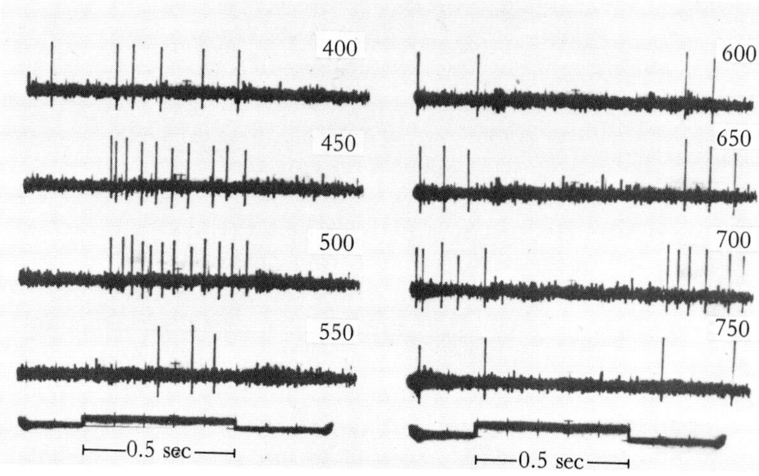

Figure 4.31. The impulses discharged from goldfish retinal ganglion cell in response to 0.5 second flashes of light. Wavelength in millimicrons indicated at the right-hand end of each record. From Wagner, MacNichol, and Wolbarsht (1960).

Practically all of the experiments on retinal ganglion cells cited above were concerned with the analysis of the interaction and integration of influences that result from stimulation of *different* parts of the receptive field. The dependence of the "on" and "off" character of the responses of some retinal ganglion cells on the wavelength of illumination (Fig. 4.29), demonstrated by Wagner, MacNichol, and Wolbarsht (1960, 1963), provides the basis for a new method of analysis by means of which it is possible to isolate and measure opposing influences that originate in the *same* part of the receptive field. This new and different approach leads to a fuller understanding of the nature of the organization of the receptive field.

The investigations were carried out on the retina of the common goldfish. Two general classes of ganglion cells showing wavelength dependent response patterns were observed. The cells in one class (Fig. 4.31) are maximally excited by short wavelength illumination and maximally inhibited by long wavelength illumination; in the other class these relations are reversed.* In all of these cells, stimulation with illumination of intermediate wavelengths can activate either the inhibitory process, or the excitatory process, or both, depending on the locus of the spot of illumination in the receptive field. The excitatory and inhibitory processes are so arranged that when the receptive fields are mapped with a

* Similar effects have since been observed in the lateral geniculate of the macaque by DeValois, Jacobs, and Abramov (1964).

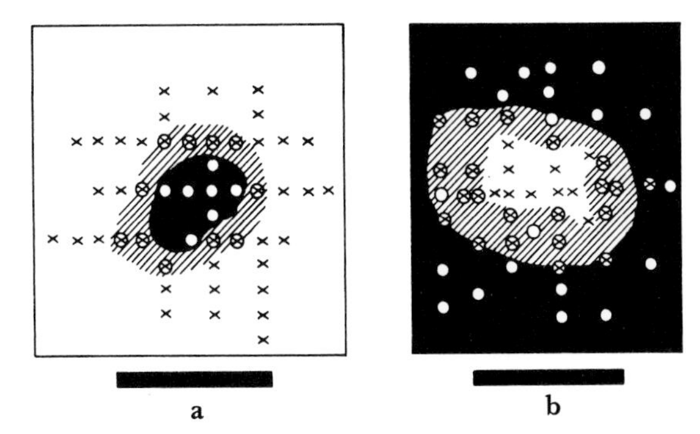

Figure 4.32. Receptive field response pattern of an "on"-center (a) *and an "off"-center* (b) *color-coded ganglion cell. Goldfish retina. The field* a *was mapped with a circular stimulus 300 μ in diameter, wavelength 550 mμ, exposed for 0.5 sec in each position. The field* b *was mapped with a circular stimulus 153 μ in diameter, wavelength 600 mμ. × = "off" response; o = "on" response. Pure "on" regions are shown in black, pure "off" regions in white, and "on-off" regions are hatched. The bars under each diagram represent 1 mm on the retina. From Wagner, MacNichol, and Wolbarsht (1963).*

spot of light of some intermediate wavelength, the opposed influences yield the familiar "on" center "off" surround type of pattern, or the converse (Fig. 4.32).

At first glance it might appear that the centers of these fields are purely excitatory (or inhibitory), the intermediate zones a mixture of the two influences, and the peripheral zones purely inhibitory (or ex-

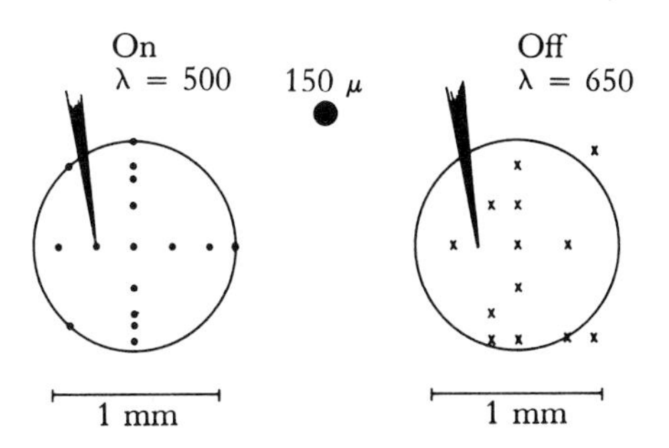

Figure 4.33. Receptive field plots of the separate component responses of the same ganglion cell taken with stimuli of different wavelengths, as indicated above each plot. The position of the microelectrode is symbolized in the upper left quadrant but should be interpreted as actually placed so that the axis is normal to the plane of the plot, intersecting with the tip of this illustration. Note that the tip is not located at the center of the response area. The stimulating spot was 150 μ in diameter, with an intensity of 1.5 μW/cm² when set at 650 mμ, and 0.5 second duration. From Wagner, MacNichol, and Wolbarsht (1963).

citatory). But accentuating one influence or the other (by use of longer or shorter wavelengths) shows that both the excitatory and inhibitory influences acting on the same ganglion cell are widely distributed over the receptive field (Fig. 4.33). Evidently the opposed influences not only overlap in the intermediate "on-off" zones, but they are also superimposed over the entire receptive field.

The apparent purity of the influences in the central and peripheral zones seems to result from the relative sensitivity and efficacy of the two opposing processes in these zones. For example, Figure 4.34 shows that there can be sizeable inhibitory influences in the center of an "on" type receptive field and sizeable excitatory influences in the center of an "off" type receptive field. It is the *imbalance* of the two influences in one way or the other, rather than a total absence of one or the other, that gives rise to the apparently pure excitatory or inhibitory zones.* Thus, even though both influences may extend over the whole of the receptive field, their summation could easily yield the familiar distributions of concentric zones of "on," "on-off," and "off" responses, or the reverse. (Note the formal similarity between this interpretation and the convolution of excitatory and inhibitory influences illustrated in Figure 3.36.)

The above experiments, in which the excitatory and inhibitory influences could be manipulated independently of one another, provide very convincing evidence that the "on," "on-off," and "off" responses result from the balance of these influences. But to account fully for the observed transient bursts of activity the temporal properties of the opposed influences—as well as their relative strengths—must be taken into account. To elicit an "on" burst, for example, the excitatory effect would have to be active for at least a brief period before the onset of the inhibitory influences. Similarly, an "off" burst would be produced only if the excitatory influences persisted longer than the inhibitory influences. The well-known "post-inhibitory rebound" (see Fig. 4.39 below) might also facilitate the generation of an "off" discharge. In any event, pure "on," pure "off," and mixed "on-off" responses must depend critically on the timing of the opposed influences. (This problem will be treated in more detail in a later section of this chapter.)

In summary, it appears that all of the above investigations on the patterns of the responses of optic nerves and central ganglia in vertebrates, molluscs, and arthropods—the three major phyla having well-developed eyes—are compatible with the notion that the highly specialized transient "on," "on-off," and "off" responses are not the direct

* The earlier observations by Granit (1948) that the ratio of "on" to "off" responses in some "on-off" ganglion cells of the cat changes with the wavelength of illumination are also consistent with this interpretation.

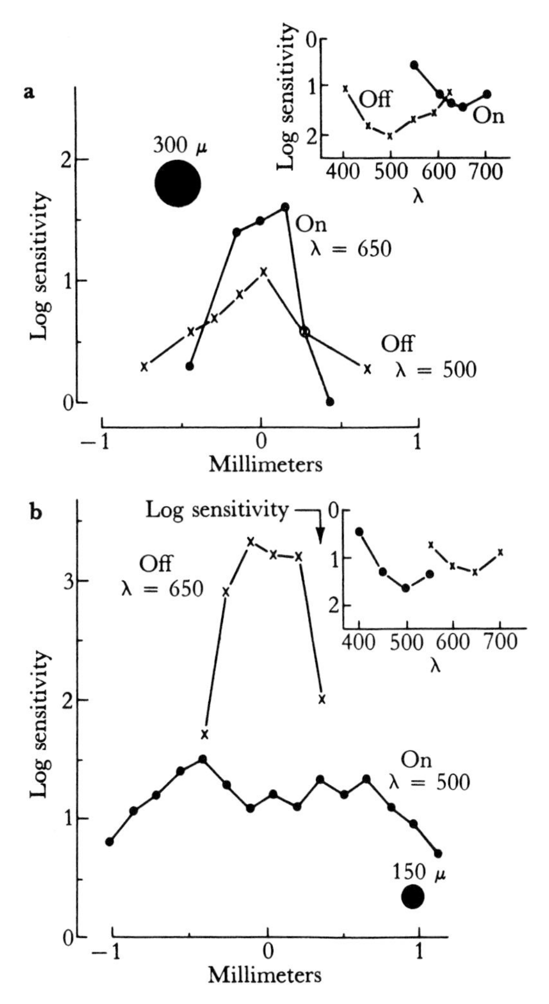

Figure 4.34. *Sensitivity profiles of the "on"- and "off"-component responses taken across the receptive fields of an "on"-center* (a) *and an "off"-center* (b) *color-coded ganglion cell. The ordinate shows the reciprocal of the intensity necessary to evoke a constant response. For* (a), *0 log units = 23 μW/cm², for* (b), *0 log units = 12 μW/cm². The large spots are the stimulus size with wavelengths in mμ as indicated. The abscissa shows the position of stimulus spot on the retina. The spectral sensitivity functions of the response components to diffuse retinal illumination are indicated in the upper right insets of* (a) *and* (b). *For these plots 0 log units in* (a) *= 0.12 μW/cm², in* (b) *= 0.2 μW/cm². The duration for all stimuli is 0.5 second. From Wagner, MacNichol, and Wolbarsht (1963).*

product of receptor activity. They seem to be the product of integrative activity, that is, the interplay of excitatory and inhibitory influences somewhere between the receptors and some second- or third-order level of neurons in the visual system.*

Intra-retinal mechanisms A great deal is known about the photochemistry of the receptors and the responses of retinal ganglion cells, but the nature of the processes that intervene between the photochemical events in the receptors and the discharge of impulses in the ganglion cells is still poorly understood. Until recent times, knowledge of these intervening processes was based almost entirely on indirect evidence obtained either from psychophysical experiments or from analyses of the composite electroretinogram, which is obtained by amplifying and recording the light-responsive changes of the potential difference between an electrode on the cornea of the eye and an indifferent electrode placed elsewhere on the body.

The composite electroretinogram is extremely complex and difficult to interpret, but even so the many analyses based on the modifications of it that result from interference of retinal function by anoxia, blocking or destructive drugs, and disease have been very informative (for surveys see Granit, 1947, 1955; and Brindley, 1960). With improved techniques, however, it has become possible to record electroretinograms from localized regions of the retina by means of electrodes placed directly on the surface of the retina and to record localized intra-retinal activity by means of very fine microelectrodes which actually penetrate to cells lying deep within the retina. (See Tomita, 1963 for review.) Because these more direct observations on localized electroretinograms and on intra-retinal and intracellular responses are more pertinent to the subject of

* There is at least one possible exception: the eye of the scallop *Pecten*. This scallop has approximately 100 eyes, each with a lens, a double retina, both of which are inverted, and a reflecting tapetum. Each retina has its own optic nerve, with fibers that apparently arise directly from the receptor cells. The nerve from the proximal retina gives a maintained "on" discharge in response to steady illumination, but the nerve from the distal retina responds only with an "off" discharge (Hartline, 1938a). (Incidentally, Aristotle noted over 2000 years ago that the scallop must have a visual sense, because it closes its shell abruptly in response to a moving shadow.)

If these two retinas in the scallop eye are functionally independent then considerable doubt would be cast on the view that the "off" response always results from neural interaction. Unfortunately, the histological evidence on this point is ambiguous. Some early histologists reported evidence of interconnections, others saw no such evidence. Modern studies with the electron microscope have been concerned mainly with the microstructure of the receptors themselves (Miller, 1958) and it is still uncertain whether or not the two retinas are interconnected. In any event, whether there are neural interactions between the two must be determined by physiological rather than histological methods.

this chapter than are the studies on the composite electroretinogram, the following discussion will be confined to a few of them.

Motokawa, Oikawa, Tasaki, and Ogawa (1959) reported that the carp retina, when detached from the pigment epithelium, mounted receptor side up on a flat indifferent electrode, and touched on the receptor surface with a micropipette recording electrode gives a characteristic slow reponse when a spot of light is scanned across the retina near the site of the recording electrode (Fig. 4.35). When the spot is almost directly on the recording site, a positive response is obtained, but as the spot is moved away from the recording site the response becomes negative. Motokawa, Yamashita, and Ogawa (1961) have since noticed that the spatial distribution of this slow localized response is closely related to the discharge pattern of retinal ganglion cells.

Murakami and Sasaki (unpublished results referred to by Tomita, 1963) have compared the effects of the action of chemicals on these slow local responses and on components of the more widespread composite electroretinograms. They found that ethyl alcohol (which is known to suppress a supposedly inhibitory component of the composite electroretinogram) turns the normally positive central response into a negative one, and that sodium azide (which ordinarily suppresses a supposedly excitatory component of the composite electroretinogram) turns the normally negative peripheral response into a positive one. These findings suggest that the over-all response shown in Figure 4.35 is the result of competition between central inhibitory influences and peripheral excitatory influences. This discovery agrees with the finding that in the carp retina the ratio of "off" center "on" surround to "on" center "off" surround types of retinal ganglion cells is approximately ten to one. In other words, an over-

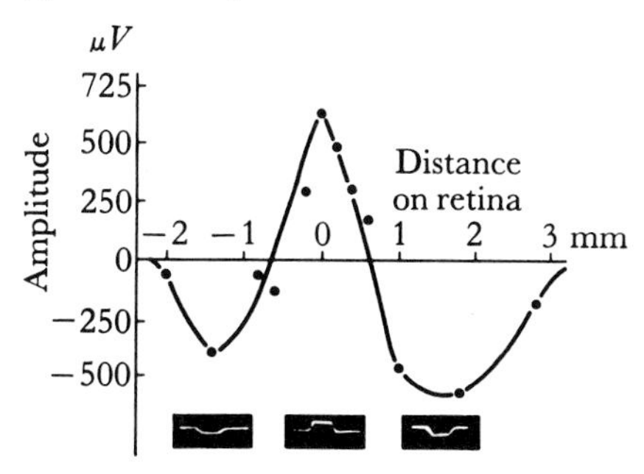

Figure 4.35. *Spatial distribution of the "slow" response recorded from the retina of the carp. Sample records at bottom of figure show (from left to right) the change in polarity of responses to short flashes of light located at the left of the recording electrode, centered on the electrode, and at the right of the electrode, respectively. From Motokawa, Oikawa, Tasaki, and Ogawa (1959).*

whelming dominance of inhibition generally appears at the central point of stimulation, while excitation predominates in the surrounding region.

A causal link has not yet been established between these signs of excitation and inhibition appearing in the localized slow potentials recorded from the receptor surface of the retina and the signs of excitation and inhibition seen in the discharge of the retinal ganglion cells on the other side of the retina. There is some evidence, however, on what the intra-retinal precursors of the events recorded at the level of the ganglion cell may be. Recording from electrodes inserted into the retina, Svaetichin (1953) found sustained intra-retinal potential changes in the fish retina which he at first attributed to the receptors, calling them "cone action potentials." (See also Svaetichin, 1956.) Following Svaetichin's report, Tomita (1957) found similar sustained potentials in the fish retina, but on the basis of records obtained simultaneously from two electrodes inserted to different depths in the retina, he concluded that they originated in post-receptor layers.

Tomita's conclusions proved to be essentially correct. Experiments ingeniously designed by MacNichol, Macpherson, and Svaetichin (1957), to determine the location of the electrode tip by means of a stain electrophoretically forced from the electrode itself into the tissue show that the source of these sustained potentials must be proximal to the receptors. (See also MacNichol and Svaetichin, 1958; Mitarai, 1958, 1960; Oikawa, Ogawa, and Motokawa, 1959; Gouras, 1960; and Brown and Tasaki, 1961.) These responses are evidently not "cone potentials," and therefore they have been renamed. They are now known as "S potentials," following a suggestion by Motokawa that they be named after Svaetichin, who first observed them (see Tomita, Murikami, Sato, and Hashimoto, 1959).

Of particular interest here are three fundamentally different types of spectral response curves that the S potentials exhibit (Fig. 4.36). One type (*L*) has a single maximum at about 575 millimicrons, another type (*R-G*) has a maximum in the red part of the spectrum and a maximum of opposite polarity in the green part, and a third type (*Y-B*) has its two maxima of opposite polarity in the yellow and blue regions of the spectrum. (Some species of fish have both of these latter types and some have one or the other.) The similarity between these opposed spectral responses in the retina and Hering's opponent-colors theory is evident, and has been greatly emphasized in articles by Svaetichin (1956) and by Hurvich and Jameson (1960). For similar views based on other evidence see Willmer (1950 and 1955).

MacNichol, Macpherson, and Svaetichin (1957) found that the simple *L* type of response curve was recorded from the region of the large

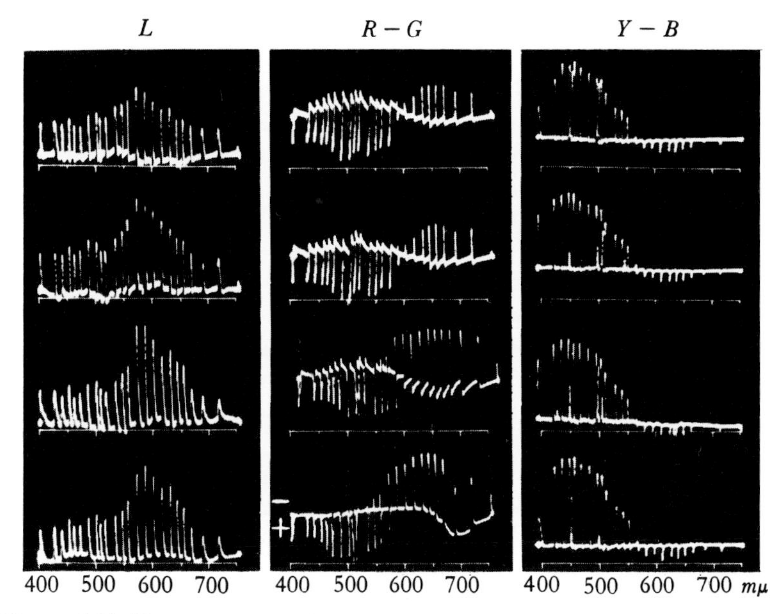

Figure 4.36. *Types of spectral response curves revealed by "S potentials" recorded from the fish retina. From Svaetichin (1956).*

synaptic endings of the cones and the horizontal cells. The more complex *R-G* and *Y-B* responses were recorded 20 to 30μ deeper, probably in the bipolar layer of the retina. The *R-G* and *Y-B* responses fractionate into two components by selective adaptation with monochromatic light; the *L* response, however, does not fractionate (MacNichol and Svaetichin, 1958). Thus it appears that the more complex responses result from the activity of at least two different types of receptors. The different latencies of the two components in both the *R-G* and *Y-B* potentials also lend support to this conclusion. Furthermore, the two components in each of the complex types mutually interfere with one another, and—due to their different latencies—give only "on" and "off" responses when activated equally and simultaneously. This fact indicates that the complex potentials are not responses of single receptors, and also is compatible with the observation that they are recorded at a level where neural interaction could take place. The fact that the simpler *L* type of response is recorded at a level nearer the photoreceptor layer also agrees with the assumption that the more complex responses result from integrative processes in the retina.

Although there is general agreement on the approximate depth in the retina at which the luminosity and chromatic responses may be recorded, the results of attempts to determine the exact cell type in which these S potentials originate are not in full agreement. The several candidates are (a) the horizontal cells for luminosity and the bipolar cells for the chromatic response (MacNichol, Macpherson, and Svaetichin, 1957); (b) the horizontal and amacrine cells (Mitarai, 1958); (c) the bipolar cell layer and inner plexiform layer (Tomita, Murakami, Sato, and Hashimoto, 1959); (d) the horizontal cells (Oikawa, Ogawa, and Motokawa, 1959); and (e) the bipolar cells (Mitarai, 1960). Recently, Fatehchand, Svaetichin, Mitarai, and Villegas (1961) have concluded, on the basis of some unpublished work by Svaetichin, that the luminosity response originates in the large horizontal cells of the bipolar layer which are thought to be neuroglia (interstitial tissue supporting the essential elements of nervous tissue). To further complicate matters, it is not yet definitely established whether the responses are recorded from intracellular or extracellular locations.

It is evident that the problems of the nature and the exact site of origin of the S potentials have not yet been solved. Not only is the site of origin of both the localized surface potentials and the sustained intraretinal potentials poorly understood, but the physiological role they may play is also obscure. While it is tempting to assume that the activity in optic nerve fibers may be generated by these graded retinal potentials, the fact remains that there is no direct evidence that they are, in fact, causal links in the chain of retinal events leading up to the discharge of impulses. Only in cells which give rise directly to optic nerve fibers does good evidence exist that graded sustained potentials are directly related to the discharge of impulses.

Intracellular records obtained by Wiesel (1959) from retinal ganglion cells in the eye of the cat show changes in the membrane potential of the kind that one would expect to accompany the changes in the frequency of discharge of the cell (Fig. 4.37). Similar intracellular records from ganglion cells have been obtained from the frog retina by Naka, Inoma, Kosugi, and Tong (1960) and Tomita, Murakami, Hashimoto, and Sasaki (1961). These effects closely resemble the changes in membrane potential produced by excitation and inhibition in the eye of *Limulus* described above (Fig. 3.31). But it is not yet clear, however, whether the inhibition in the vertebrate retina is exerted directly on the cell giving rise to the optic nerve fiber (as it is in *Limulus*), or whether it occurs earlier in the system and the ganglion cell merely passively reflects some change in the level of excitation that has taken place elsewhere in neurons intermediate between it and the receptors. In either event, the evidence is good that the "off" response is concomitant with a release from inhibition that is produced at some level or another during the period of illumination.

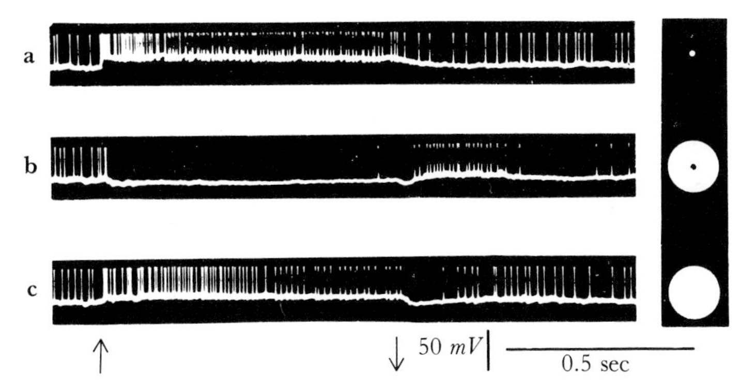

Figure 4.37. Intracellular record from retinal ganglion cell of cat. Membrane potential about 65 mV. Onset and cessation of illumination marked by arrows. The area illuminated to obtain each record is shown in white at the right of the figure. (a) *Small spot of light of 1° (0.25 mm) diameter;* (b) *annular stimulus outer diameter 12°, central area of 1° is not illuminated;* (c) *entire receptive field illuminated. All stimuli were superimposed on a dim background of illumination. From Wiesel (1959).*

Transient responses in the lateral eye of Limulus Experiments on the simpler eye of *Limulus* lend further support to the general view that inhibitory influences play a major role in the generation of transient responses. In fact, both the excitatory and the inhibitory components of the activity in the optic nerve from the lateral eye exhibit marked transient responses to stimulus changes. MacNichol and Hartline (1948) found that the steady discharge of a single receptor unit in response to constant illumination is modulated in the following characteristic way to step increments or decrements in the intensity of illumination. A relatively small increase in intensity produces a large transient increase in the frequency of response which gradually subsides to a steady level only slightly greater than that preceding the change in illumination. Similarly, a small decrease in intensity produces a large momentary decrease in the frequency of discharge, which then returns to a level slightly below that preceding the change in illumination. For moderate changes in illumination, as in the experiment illustrated in Figure 4.38, the transient responses to an increment (*a*) and an equal decrement (*b*) are almost exactly equal but are, of course, opposite in sign.

Because of the inhibition, excitatory transients in one receptor unit produce similar but opposite effects in the frequency of response of *steadily* illuminated neighboring receptor units. In the experiment illustrated in Figure 4.39, the frequency of response was recorded simultaneously from two units near one another. One (solid circles) was illuminated steadily with a small spot focussed on it alone throughout the

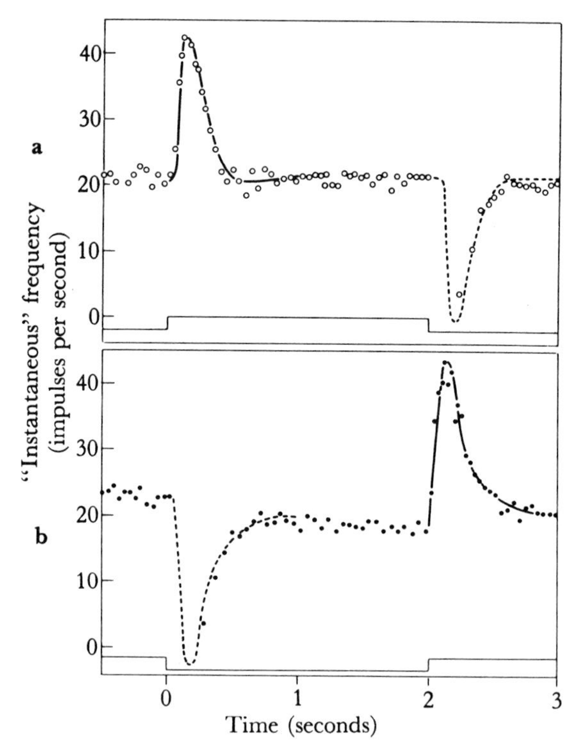

Figure 4.38. *Changes in optic-nerve discharge frequency for incremental and decremental stimuli. Light-adapted steadily discharging* Limulus *single optic-nerve preparation stimulated by an incremental 2-second flash* (a) *or 2-second decrement* (b). *Open and closed circles represent experimental determinations of "instantaneous" frequency of response (reciprocal of time between successive impulses). The bottom lines in each half of the figure indicate onset and termination of the stimulus. Solid lines fitted by inspection to changes in frequency of response during upward-step stimuli; broken lines are mirror images of the solid lines (for each half of the figure, respectively). Log adapting $I = -0.26$; log I during increment $= 0.0$; log I during decrement $= -0.50$. From Ratliff, Hartline, and Miller (1963).*

period shown; the other (open circles) along with several of its immediate neighbors, was illuminated with a larger spot, until the time $t = 0.0$, when a step increment was added to the illumination.* The illumination then remained steady at this higher level until $t = 2.0$, when it was re-

* The fact that the large inhibitory effect resulted from the combined inhibitory influences from a group of *several* receptors (about half a dozen) was not made clear in the description of this figure in the review article (Ratliff, 1961) in which it originally appeared. Only the response of one member in the center of this group, however, was recorded.

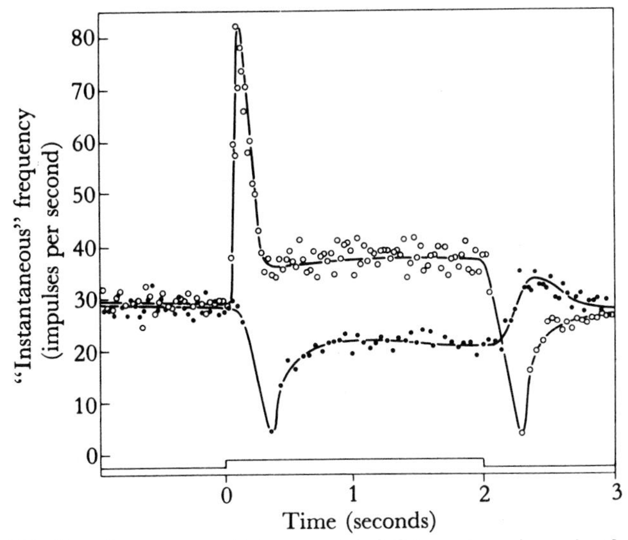

Figure 4.39. *Simultaneous excitatory and inhibitory transients in the responses of neighboring ommatidia in the lateral eye of* Limulus. *From Ratliff (1961).*

duced to the former lower level, as indicated at the bottom of the graph. Accompanying the marked excitatory changes in this element, which presumably also occur in the others illuminated along with it, are slightly delayed and opposite effects in the other elements—first an inhibitory transient, then a lesser steady inhibition, and finally a release from inhibition. *Movement* of step or gradient patterns of illumination, of course, produces similar effects. Thus the transient responses are far more effective in signalling an edge or contour in a pattern than are the comparable steady-state effects. As in the vertebrate eye, a change in the level of illumination is a most effective stimulus. The effectiveness arises not only from the marked excitatory transients themselves, but also from the concomitant and opposite inhibitory transients that they produce in neighboring elements.

Using the Mach pattern in a "cup," illustrated in Figure 4.40, the reader may easily demonstrate the effectiveness of temporal changes in the intensity of illumination. Fixate steadily on the dark point in the middle of the gradient of the Mach pattern. Then, with this point as a center, slowly oscillate the pattern back and forth (about 30° or so) in its own plane. The marked alternating lightening and darkening of the gradient gives it a wavy appearance. Presumably this effect results from transient excitation and inhibition similar to that described above.

Latent periods and "backward inhibition" An appreciable time elapses between the onset of a stimulus (or a change in a stimulus) to a

Figure 4.40. Mach pattern in a "cup" to illustrate effects of transients in illumination.

photoreceptor before the discharge of impulses in the optic nerve is affected. In particular, the initial latent periods may vary tremendously (see Fig. 3.25 above) depending upon the intensity of illumination, state of adaptation, inhibitory influences exerted by neighbors, and so forth. These effects add even more complexity to the already complex patterns of response. In one extreme and rather bizarre case, for example, they seem to cause inhibitory influences to flow backwards in time.

An example of this "backward" influence in human vision (Crawford, 1947) is illustrated in Figure 4.41. A "conditioning" stimulus 12° in

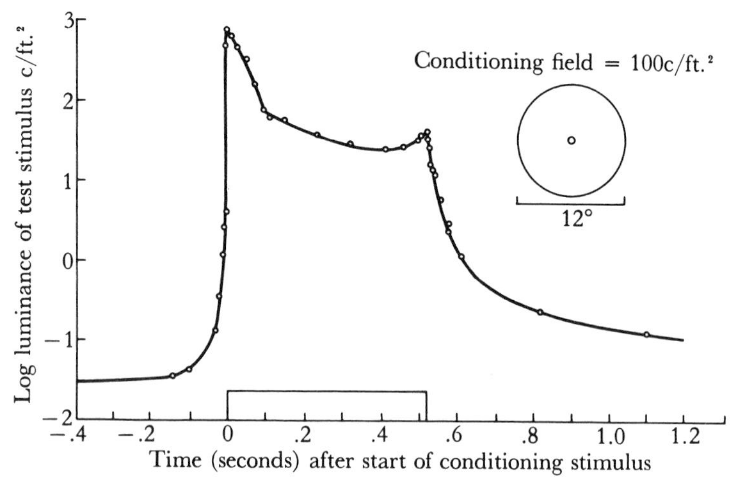

Figure 4.41. "Backward" influences on the threshold in human vision. Redrawn after Crawford (1947).

diameter and of fixed intensity, viewed foveally, was exposed for 0.525 second. In the center of this field (inset) a test stimulus 0.5° in diameter was exposed for 0.01 second, and by repeated exposures at various intensities, the intensity required for it to be just visible was determined. The test stimulus was then exposed at various other times before, during, and after the conditioning stimulus. It was found that the threshold of the test stimulus began to rise about 0.15 second *before* the conditioning stimulus was turned on. Similar effects are also observed if the conditioning flash is placed to one side of the test stimulus. (Note the significant peaks that probably result from effects of the "on" and "off" transients in the retinal responses to the conditioning flash.)

"Backward" inhibition may be a little disturbing at first, for it seems to contradict the generally accepted principle that the order of the temporal succession of events is irreversible. But the theoretical explanation usually offered for "backward" effects of this sort is quite straightforward and does not require any reversal of time's arrow. One need only assume that somewhere along the neural pathway the inhibitory influence overtakes the excitatory influence that was generated earlier. (For a review of these and related phenomena in the auditory, cutaneous, and visual senses, see Raab, 1963.)

These same effects can be observed directly in the neural network in the lateral eye of *Limulus*. It has been shown that the inhibitory influences do not appear until a considerable time (about 100 milliseconds or so) after the impulses that produce them. In addition, the time from the onset of a stimulus to the production of nerve impulses can range from 40 to 100 milliseconds or more, depending upon the various conditions mentioned above. With these variables under experimental control, it is an easy matter to shift the excitatory and inhibitory influences back and forth in time with respect to one another.

Consider, for example, the experiment illustrated in Figure 4.42. One

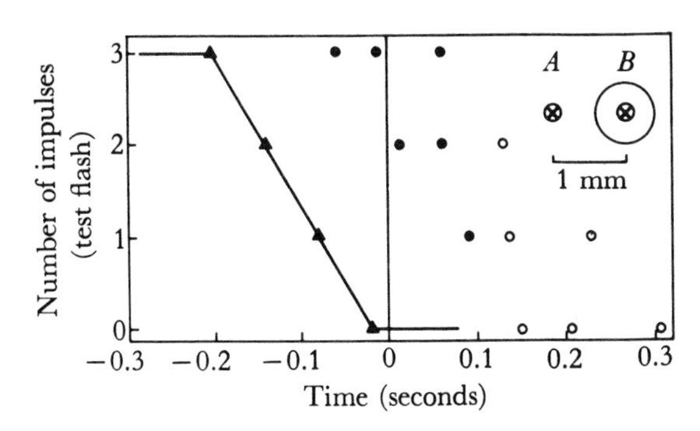

Figure 4.42. *"Backward" inhibition in the lateral eye of* Limulus. *From Ratliff, Hartline, and Miller (1963).*

test receptor *A* and a neighboring group of five receptors *B* were illuminated with short (0.05 sec) flashes to produce short compact bursts of impulses in their axons. The response of one receptor in the center of the group *B* was taken as a measure of the activity of the group as a whole. The test receptor *A* was weakly illuminated with a near threshold flash just sufficient to produce 3 impulses when *A* was illuminated alone, and the neighboring group *B* was illuminated with a high intensity flash. Consequently, impulses in *A* were discharged after an extremely long latent period and in *B* after an extremely short latent period. When the stimuli were presented asynchronously and with the proper time relations, the inhibitory influence appeared to be exerted backwards in time. That is, if the numbers of impulses discharged in *A* are plotted in terms of stimulus onsets (solid triangles) then the effect of *B* on *A* seemed to appear *before* *B* was illuminated, as in Crawford's experiment on human vision.

The inhibition is actually forward in ordinary time, as can be seen if the graph is plotted in terms of times of occurrence of the *responses,* rather than the times of the stimuli that produce them. (Solid circles represent the impulses which actually occurred; open circles represent the impulses which, according to control experiments, would have occurred had there been no inhibition.) In the "backward" inhibition the stimulus to *A* actually did come some time ahead of the stimulus to the neighboring group of receptors *B*, but since the latent period of the discharge in *A* was very long, the response of the rapidly acting group *B* had time to appear and exert its inhibitory influence before the appearance of the response of *A*, which was illuminated first. Seen from this point of view, then, "backward" inhibition is simply a special case of ordinary "forward" inhibition.

Synthetic "on-off" responses It is evident that with the proper adjustment of variables that determine latencies of response, as in the "backward" inhibition experiment, it is possible to obtain the response of some elements far in advance of others even though all are illuminated simultaneously. Under proper conditions, those that respond first can completely inhibit the response of others. That is, the inhibitory influences from one group of receptors can reach another receptor before it has time to respond at all, and if the influences are strong enough, can completely suppress its response throughout an entire period of maintained illumination. Alternatively, conditions may be arranged so that the inhibitory influences are exerted later in order to allow a few impulses to escape from this unit and thus generate a simple "on" burst of activity before it is completely inhibited. In much the same way various other factors that determine the time of cessation of the inhibitory influences and the strengths of the after discharge and the post-inhibitory rebound may be manipulated to generate "off" discharges.

This situation is more than mere speculation. By suitable combination and balance of the several factors just described, it has been possible, partly by accident and partly by design, to generate "on-off" and "off" responses (a and b respectively in Fig. 4.43) in some members of an interacting group of receptors in the eye of *Limulus* (Ratliff and Mueller, 1957). When illuminated singly, each of these receptors would ordinarily yield a simple maintained discharge of impulses. These "synthesized" transient responses resemble qualitatively those that occur normally in the vertebrate retina. Thus these experiments lend further support to the view that "on-off" and "off" responses result from the complex interplay of excitatory and inhibitory influences by showing that the experimental

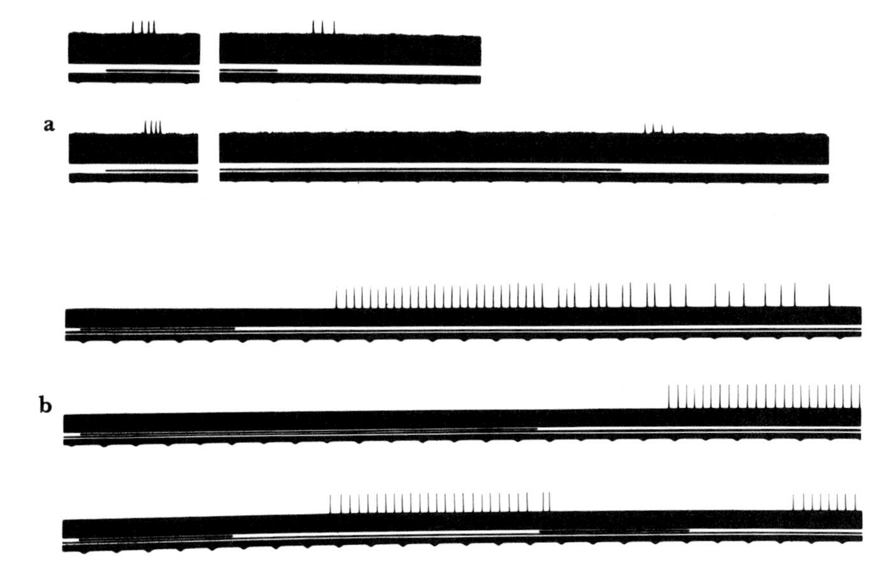

Figure 4.43. *Oscillograms of diverse "types" of impulse discharge pattern in single fibers of* Limulus *optic nerve. The typical response to steady illumination of a single ommatidium is a sustained discharge. In the records shown the ommatidium was illuminated simultaneously with other nearby ommatidia, which exerted inhibition upon it. Depending on the conditions of illumination, various kinds of responses can be "synthesized."* (a) *Record of synthetic "on-off" responses produced by two different durations of illumination in which approximately one second was cut from the middle of each record.* (b) *Records of synthetic "off" responses for various durations of illumination. In the lower record of* (b) *the "off" response, comparable to that in the upper record, was inhibited by reillumination. Time is marked in fifths of a second. Signal of exposure to light blackens the white line above the time marks. From Ratliff, Miller, and Hartline (1958).*

manipulation of these influences can, in fact, yield such transient responses.

The organization of more complex receptive fields The responses of practically all retinal ganglion cells are strongly dependent upon the spatial and temporal pattern of illumination on their receptive fields. Some are more highly specialized than others, and respond selectively to a rather restricted set of conditions, such as a particular configuration of the pattern of light and shade, or a particular direction of its movement on the retina.* But this specialization is generally somewhat less clear-cut than the names and classifications of the cells might suggest. Seldom, if ever, does a retinal ganglion cell respond *only* to a single unique set of conditions; generally, the most one can say is that certain conditions are somewhat more effective than others. Furthermore, the symmetry of the receptive fields of most retinal ganglion cells leads necessarily to some ambiguity in the significance of their responses—even in the case of the most highly specialized types. To what extent inhibitory interaction may play a role in shaping these more highly specialized responses to particular spatial and temporal configurations remains to be shown. This field of study is relatively new and the investigations carried out thus far have been largely qualitative and descriptive. Until more analytic studies are completed, one can only speculate about the physiological mechanisms.

Further experiments by Barlow and Levick (1965) on the directionally sensitive ganglion cells found in the rabbit retina (see Fig. 4.28 above) strongly suggest that lateral inhibition may be an important factor in determining the character of this type of response. Figure 4.44 illustrates schematically one hypothetical mechanism that these investigators have proposed as a possible explanation of the directionally sensitive ganglion cells.

Localized regions of the receptor mosaic are represented by the groups of photoreceptors R. Light falling on them gives rise to neural activity which is transmitted both downward and laterally. The influence transmitted directly down to the bipolar cells B is assumed to be excitatory; the lateral influence transmitted over the horizontal cells H is assumed to be inhibitory. A further assumption is that the lateral transmission of the inhibitory influence requires a considerably greater time Td than does the straight-through transmission of the excitatory influence. Such an assumption is physiologically realistic. (See Figs. 3.25 and 3.32.)

* Mach even suggested that a single ganglion cell might be able to transmit information about depth as a result of the shading on three-dimensional objects, but because a particular pattern of light and shade is not uniquely related to a particular form, this information alone could be ambiguous.

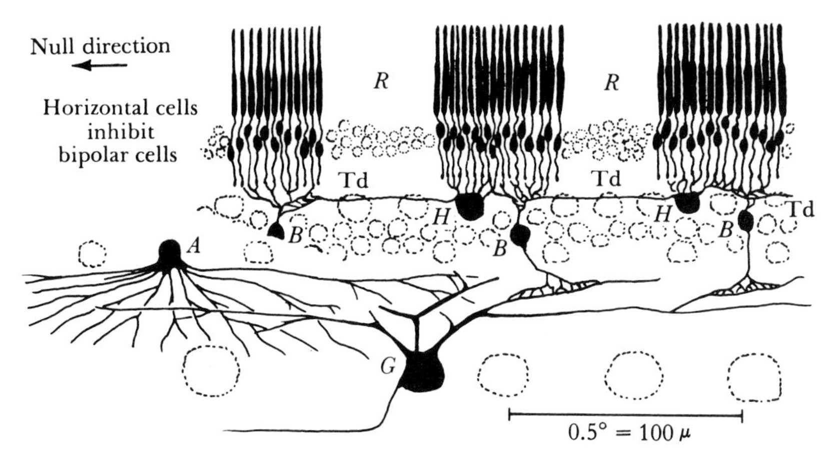

Figure 4.44. Schema of a directionally sensitive inhibitory network. After Barlow and Levick (1965).

At the level of the bipolar cells *B* in the network the inhibitory influences and the excitatory influences are integrated and the net effect is then transmitted to the ganglion cell *G* at the next level. (The function of the amacrine cell *A* need not be considered in this schema.) With movement of a stimulus in the null direction there is a good chance that the opposed influences, which are advancing in the same direction across the retina, would reach their common pathways in the bipolar cells *B* at about the same time (depending on the velocity of the movement of the stimulus) so that the responses transmitted to the ganglion cells *G* would be diminished. With movement in the preferred direction, however, excitatory influences almost certainly would reach and pass through the bipolar cells without obstruction because the delayed lateral inhibitory influences are being transmitted, in a direction opposite to the stimulus motion, to bipolar cells that have already responded. In short, such a network would respond maximally to motion in the preferred direction and minimally to motion in the null direction.*

Inhibition may also be of significance in networks that respond maximally to particular configurations of illumination. For example, Taylor

* If the time delay *Td* is assumed to be constant, the response of the network would probably depend critically on the velocity of the stimulus. If, however, the time delay were assumed to be variable—as might be the case if it depended partly on the summation of inhibitory potentials at synapses between the horizontal and bipolar cells, which summation in turn depended on the vigor of the response generated by the photoreceptors—then the response of the system might be expected to be independent of the velocity of the stimulus over a considerable range. The assumption of such a variable time delay in an inhibitory network is not unphysiological; it has been observed in the lateral eye of *Limulus*. (See Lange, 1965.)

noted in his model of an inhibitory network that, in general, the transformation from stimulus to response produces high frequency responses in regions where the contours of a pattern of illumination change direction and remain close together, and lower frequencies where the contours are widely spaced and there are no abrupt changes in their direction. Thus the corners of a square (Fig. 4.45) produce large signals (high frequencies), the sides produce intermediate signals, and the signal strength is approximately constant at a lower level over the central part of the square. (Taylor made some use of this principle in an automatic pattern recognition device.) Assuming a threshold at some point in the system, it would be easy to duplicate in such a network the behavior of a ganglion cell that responds vigorously to a corner of an object and not at all to a straight side of the same. (It is interesting to note that under certain conditions photographic film also responds maximally to small objects and for essentially the same reasons as those just described. See Chapter 5.)

Reichardt and MacGinitie (1962) have investigated the possible application of the Hartline-Ratliff model of reciprocal inhibition in a system for automatic pattern recognition. Assume a network as shown in Figure 4.46 in which lines from all elements eventually converge on a common point. Only one dimension is shown here, but the system is to be thought of as a two-dimensional array of receptors and interconnections. Each receptor is interconnected with all others in the array, but the inhibitory influences diminish with distance. Assume that all parts of the pattern projected on the receptor mosaic produce the same excita-

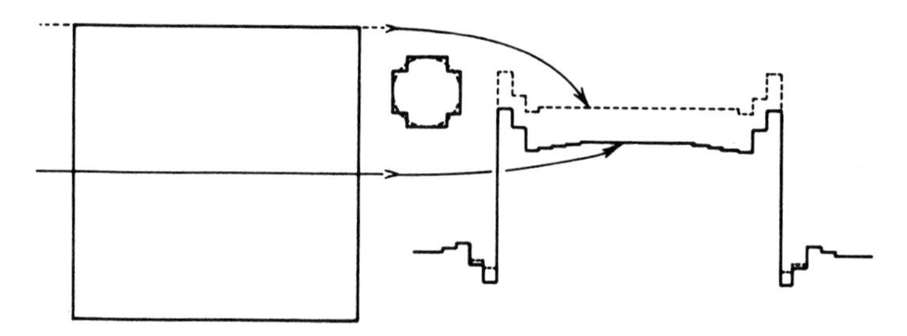

Figure 4.45. *The output of a two-dimensional inhibitory network in response to a stimulus in the form of a large square of uniform intensity. Two cross sections of the output are shown: the solid line and the dashed line are the response distributions across the center of the square and along one edge, respectively. The circle indicates the size of the inhibitory field. Superimposed on it is the rectilinear approximation to the circular field that was used to compute the two response curves. The small steps in the response curves correspond to the dimensions assumed for the units in the network. Redrawn after Taylor (1956).*

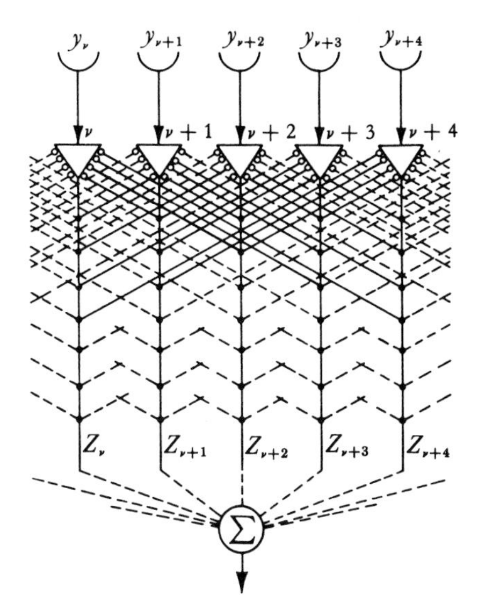

Figure 4.46. *Section of an analog computer model to simulate the inhibitory network found in the lateral eye of Limulus.* Y_ν *represents the amplitude of the generator potential in each unit and* Z_ν *the frequency of discharge in the optic nerve fiber which arises from that unit. The diagonal lines represent the plexus of interconnections over which each unit exerts inhibitory influences back onto its neighbors. The triangles are operational amplifiers, the outputs of which are connected by return lines to the inputs of neighboring units, and which thus diminish (or inhibit) their outputs. Diodes connected with each amplifier prevent changes in polarity of the output (that is, outputs equivalent to negative frequencies are not allowed). The summation of all the outputs indicated at the bottom of the figure is not intended to represent a physiological process but is for computation of the summated response of the whole network to patterns such as those shown in Figure 4.47. From Reichardt and MacGinitie (1962). A similar analog computer was designed by C. C. Yang; see Hartline, Ratliff, and Miller (1961).*

tory effect in each receptor. Since the system is entirely uniform, a particular pattern of fixed area may be moved about and oriented in any direction without changing the output. Changing the shape of a pattern of fixed area, however, will generally change the output of the system. The more compact the figure, the greater is the mutual inhibition and the less the total response. Conversely, the more spread out the figure, the less the inhibition among the elements and the greater the total response. Examples of the effect on the response of changing an elongated triangle to a right triangle and an elongated rectangle to a square are shown in Figure 4.47.

There is practically no end to the variety and complexity of retinal networks that nature could construct using only simple excitatory and

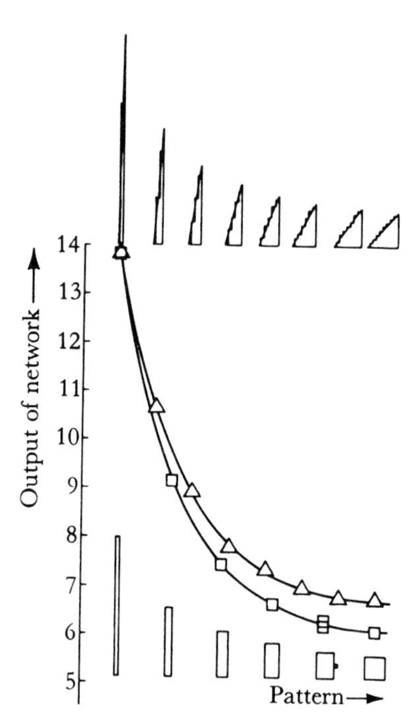

Figure 4.47. *The summated output of a two-dimensional inhibitory network in response to various rectangular and triangular input patterns (data points represented by rectangles and triangles, respectively). The network, similar to that illustrated in Figure 4.46, consisted of 36 units. Because of the finite dimensions of the units, the triangles (straight lines) could only be approximated (zig-zag lines). Also, one rectangular patterns (second from right) could be formed with only 35 units. The sum was calculated for this pattern and for the same pattern with an extra unit alongside it. Both data points are shown on the curve. From Reichardt and MacGinitie (1962).*

inhibitory elements arranged in various spatial configurations. When the the outputs of several of these more or less independent retinal networks converge on some common point, as in the higher centers of the visual system, the possible degree of complexity and specialization is increased even further. In conclusion, let us briefly consider some of the observations and speculations on the functions of neural networks in these higher centers.

The lateral geniculate body (the next higher level above the retina) seems to be more of a "way station" than an integrative center because the receptive fields of cells in it are generally similar to those of the ganglion cells in the retina; that is, they are of the familiar concentric "on" center, "off" surround type (or the reverse). This at least seems to be the case in the cat (Hubel and Wiesel, 1962). In fact, even the properties of some cortical neurons seem to differ little from those of the retinal ganglion cells; Figure 4.48 shows one such example. In this experiment (Baumgartner, 1965) responses were recorded from a predominantly "on" type of neuron in area 17 of the visual cortex of the cat. A band of light 2°48′ wide and 32° long (visual angle) was focussed on the retina. The light was turned on for 900 milliseconds, then turned off and moved to a new position, as in the experiment illustrated above in Figure 4.27. The diagram shows the frequency of discharge of impulses from the neuron with the band stepped across the retina in a horizontal position and in a vertical position. "On" and "off" responses to a uniform illumination of a 32° field are shown by the lighter curves (low in the center of the graph).

There are many cell types in the visual cortex (Fig. 4.49), however, that are clearly different from and more complex than the retinal and lateral geniculate cells (Hubel and Wiesel, 1962). Two of the more common types, those labeled *C* and *D* in Figure 4.49, have elongated rather narrow medial areas, either excitatory *C* or inhibitory *D*, flanked on either side by areas of the opposite type. In general, a moving edge or slit of light is most effective when it is oriented parallel to the elongated

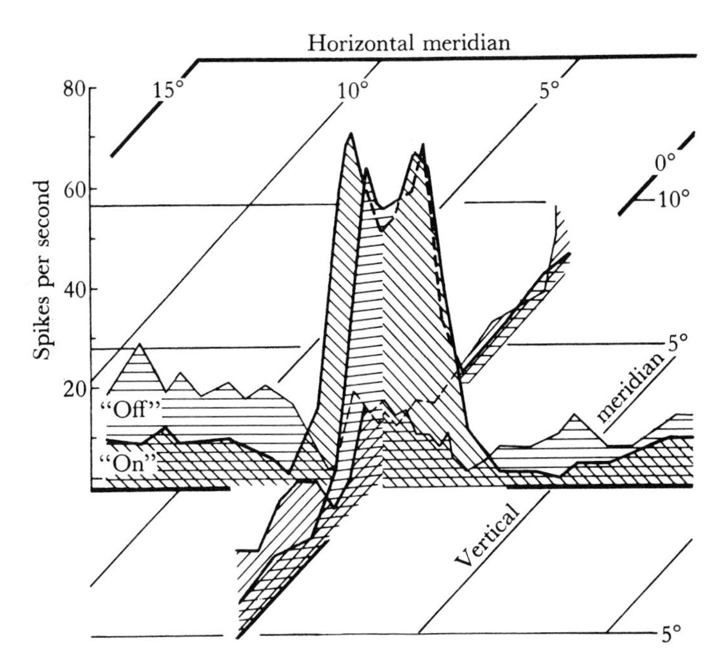

Figure 4.48. Response of a neuron in the visual cortex of the cat. From Baumgartner (1965).

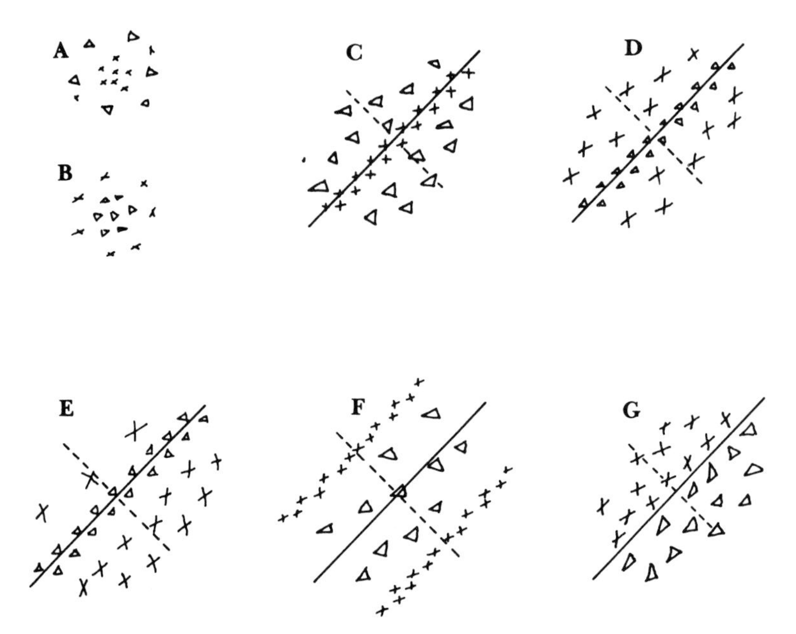

Figure 4.49. *Common arrangements of lateral geniculate and cortical receptive fields.* (A) *"On"-center geniculate receptive field.* (B) *"Off"-center geniculate receptive field.* (C-G) *Various arrangements of simple cortical receptive fields.* x, *areas giving excitatory responses ("on" responses);* Δ, *areas giving inhibitory responses ("off" responses). The receptive-field axes are shown by continuous lines through field centers. In the figure these are all oblique, but each arrangement occurs in all orientations. From Hubel and Wiesel (1962).*

area of the field. Hubel and Wiesel suggest that these fields in the visual cortex may simply be an elaboration of the simpler receptive fields seen at the level of the retina and lateral geniculate body, as illustrated in Figure 4.50. That is, a cortical cell of the type C (Figure 4.49 above) might receive projections from several lateral geniculate cells, each having "on" center receptive fields, which are arranged in a row and overlap one another. These several separate fields would then form the substructure of the more elaborate cortical field.

One can easily imagine how, with even more elaborate and perhaps asymmetrical projections from one level to another, and with the integration of a variety of retinal receptive fields, extremely complex and highly specialized cortical receptive fields could be produced. Just as the integration of the activity of many receptors by means of the retinal network leads to more specialized functions of the receptive fields of retinal ganglion cells, so can the integration of the activity of many receptive fields lead to more complex and highly specialized functions at higher levels.

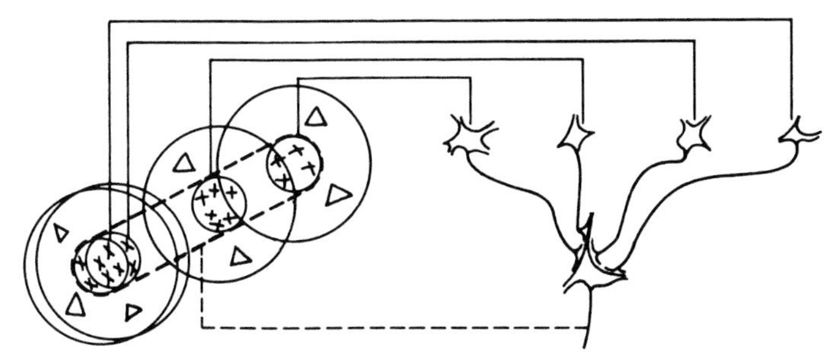

Figure 4.50. *Possible scheme for explaining the organization of a cortical receptive field. A large number of lateral geniculate cells, of which four are illustrated in the upper right in the figure, have receptive fields with "on" centers arranged along a straight line on the retina. All of these project upon a single cortical cell, and the synapses are supposed to be excitatory. The receptive field of the cortical cell will then have an elongated "on" center indicated by the interrupted lines in the receptive-field diagram to the left of the figure. From Hubel and Wiesel (1962).*

Since these functions represent the integration of information obtained from several different "points of view" the ambiguities and uncertainties inherent in the narrower "views" of a particular receptor, or of a particular receptive field, are thus diminished.

Man is the measure of all things. Protagoras

CHAPTER FIVE *Appearance and reality*

The relation between appearance and reality is now and always has been a crucial issue for the theory of knowledge. It was crucial when Plato wrote his allegory of the cave in *The Republic* over two thousand years ago; it was crucial when Berkeley wrote *An Essay Toward a New Theory of Vision* some two hundred years ago; it was crucial when Russell wrote *Our Knowledge of the External World* a few decades ago, and it still is.

The issue is crucial because two of the most widely accepted interpretations of the relation between the sensory appearance of an object and its "true" reality are diametrically opposed. One of the two—that appearance *is* reality—leads to idealism and, carried to an extreme, to solipsism, while the other—that reality transcends appearance—leads to realism and, pursued to an extreme, to metaphysics (in its narrow meaning of the science of the supersensible). Although these two interpretations are contradictory, both are based on the same factual evidence. Furthermore, everyone makes essentially the same distinction between appearance and reality, irrespective of his philosophical position. Rather than enter directly into this age-old philosophical dispute, an investigation will be made first to show, by specific factual examples, *what* the issue is and then *how* it is resolved in actual practice.

In brief, the practical problem is how to determine—in the sense of Sir W. Hamilton's definition of things objective—"that which belongs to or proceeds from the object known, and not from the subject knowing." There *is* a problem, for the distinction between "object known" and "subject knowing" is not always clear-cut; one has often been mistaken for the other, both in science and in everyday life. For example, in such diverse instances as the first several attempts to determine the wavelength of X rays, the numerous early measurements of the size of the earth's shadow on the moon, and the search for the cause of complaints about the quality of pigments used in the famous Gobelin tapestry works, properties of the observer were mistaken for properties of the thing observed. These particular mistakes are of special interest here because all were caused by Mach bands or similar contrast phenomena and because they provide a most instructive lesson on the meaning of objectivity—the further elucidation of which is the aim of this chapter.

THE WAVELENGTH OF X RAYS

Roentgen's discovery of X rays in 1896 aroused considerable interest throughout the world. The possible practical uses of X rays in medicine, surgery, and industry were quite apparent, and many studies were undertaken at once. For example, Mach (1896b) immediately investigated the stereoscopic application of X rays. Laymen, as well as scientists, were naturally intrigued by the fact that it was now possible to "see" into or through opaque objects. Women were not only intrigued by this possibility; they were also concerned about the transparency of their clothing. But they did not have long to worry, for charlatans were quick to offer expensive "X-ray proof underclothing."

The fundamental scientific problem, however, was concerned with the physical nature of X rays. Maxwell had just proposed his electromagnetic theory of radiation, and the obvious scientific question was whether X rays were a part of the electromagnetic spectrum described by Maxwell's equations, or were a unique form of radiation with their own special properties. Some evidence pointed to the first of these two possibilities. For one thing, the photographic effect of X rays did not appear to differ significantly from the effects of visible and near visible light rays. Furthermore, Roentgen found in his early investigations that X rays—like other forms of radiation—were transmitted more effectively through some materials than through others. But the index of refraction for all substances seemed to be very nearly equal to 1.0; that is, no appreciable reflection or refraction of the X rays could be observed.

The production of interference phenomena by diffraction therefore seemed to be the only way in which it might be possible to demonstrate that X rays were wavelike. But such a demonstration proved to be very difficult so that success was not achieved until 1912, when von Laue used crystals in place of the usual diffraction slits and gratings. In the meantime, however, many attempts were made to diffract X rays and to produce interference effects by means of ordinary diffraction slits. It is now known that such experiments could only fail, yet at the time when they were carried out many of them appeared to succeed.

Fomm's striae Very soon after Roentgen reported his discovery, L. Fomm (1896) published an account of some experiments on the diffraction of X rays. In this research Fomm used a large pear-shaped "Hittorf tube" which emitted X rays from a small area (about the size of a silver dollar) of the flat glass wall opposite the cathode. A brass plate with a slit cut in it was placed against the face of the tube to restrict the effective source of X rays to a narrow line. Some of the rays from this slit passed through a second narrow slit (the diffraction slit) and then fell on a photographic plate, as shown schematically in Figure 5.1. Because of the small apertures formed by the slits and the low efficiency of the source, the plate had to be exposed for nearly an hour in order to obtain a satisfactory photograph. The resulting image on the photograph did not appear to differ very significantly from the calculated geometrical image of the source; that is, there was no appreciable widening or dispersion of the image. Furthermore, there were no perceptible interference bands at the edges of the image. Within the slit image, however, there were light and dark striae, later known as *Fomm's striae.*

The striae were too indistinct to permit an exact measurement of their amplitude, number, and location. But with properly chosen distances from source to diffraction slit to photographic plate, and with a particular width of diffraction slit (all indicated in Fig. 5.1), Fomm found a fairly clear-cut central minimum in the photograph of the slit image. This minimum was quite similar to the first central minimum that one observes in Fresnel diffraction of visible light as the slit width is gradually increased. With the help of the available formulae and tables on diffraction that Lommel had published, Fomm calculated the wavelength of X rays to be 0.000014 mm, or about 1/15 the wavelength of the smallest wavelengths previously found in the ultraviolet. Fomm regarded this number as only a probable upper limit, however, because he was not able to determine with any great precision either the location or the

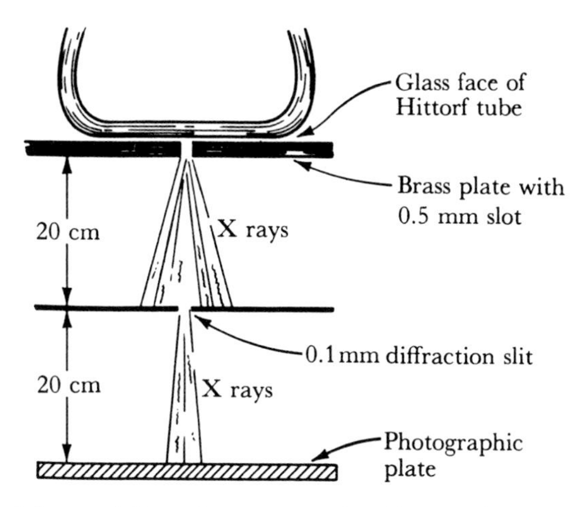

Figure 5.1. *Schema of Fomm's apparatus for his experiment on the diffraction of X rays (not drawn to scale).*

amplitude of the first central minimum and the two adjacent maxima in his photographs.*

The explanation of Fomm's striae Stimulated by the apparent success of the diffraction experiments carried out by Fomm and others, H. Haga and C. H. Wind (1899) undertook a series of similar experiments hoping that they might be able to determine the wavelength of X rays more exactly. The apparatus they used was almost identical to that used by Fomm: a slit 0.5 mm wide placed over the face of the tube providing the X rays, a diffracting slit 0.14 mm wide placed 20 cm from the source, and a photographic plate 20 cm beyond this diffracting slit. The experiment itself, however, was slightly different from the one reported by Fomm. First the lower half of the photographic plate was covered with a lead sheet and the upper half was exposed to the X rays that passed through the 0.14 mm diffraction slit. Next the upper half of the plate was covered with the lead, the diffraction slit was widened to 9 mm (keeping one edge of the slit fixed in its original position), and the lower half of the plate was exposed to the X rays.

* At about the same time several other investigators reported the results of similar experiments on X rays. Using a screen grating, G. Sagnac concluded that X rays did not have wavelengths greater than 0.0004 mm. L. Calmette and G. T. Lhuillier, who used double slits and metallic pins in rectangular windows for their diffraction apparatus, also observed light and dark zones, but were unable to determine the wavelength of the X rays with any precision. However, Perrin, who used a single very broad slit in his apparatus, did not detect any fringes or striae in the photographic image and he concluded that if X rays were periodic, their period must be shorter than that of visible light.

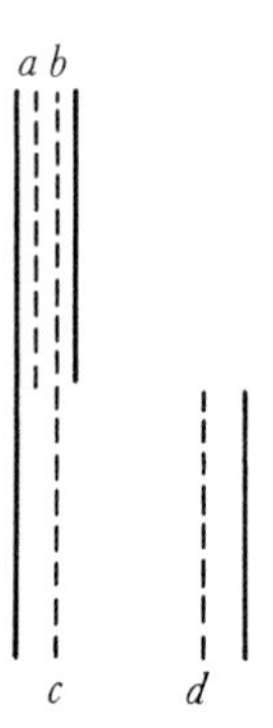

Figure 5.2. *Position of Fomm's striae (broken lines) in two images formed by a rectangular diffraction slit. From Haga and Wind (1899).*

As expected, Fomm's striae were clearly evident in the images of the narrow and wide slits, which appeared one above the other on the developed plate (Fig. 5.2). The spatial arrangement of the striae, however, was not as expected. One stria (*b*) in the upper half of the image appeared to be a continuation of a stria (*c*) in the lower half of the image. That is, both were located at the same distance from the left margin of the image, the margin that corresponded to the fixed edge of the slit. The other two striae (*a* and *d*) were not in line with one another, but both were at the same distance from the right-hand margin of the image, which corresponded to the variable edge of the slit. Thus the striae all seemed to be at some constant distance from one or the other of the two edges of the image of the diffraction slit. To test this phenomenon, a wedge-shaped diffraction slit was substituted for the variable slit, and a single photograph was taken of the image thus formed. Again the two striae seemed to be parallel to the two edges of the image of the slit. They even approached and crossed over one another at the narrow end of the slit, as shown in Figure 5.3.

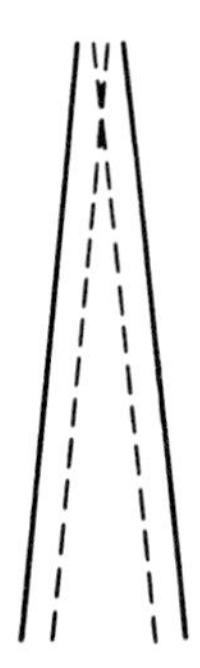

Figure 5.3. *Position of Fomm's striae (broken lines) in the image formed by a wedge-shaped diffraction slit. From Haga and Wind (1899).*

A further consideration of diffraction theory led Haga and Wind to the hypothesis that Fomm's striae might be produced by radiation of *any* wavelength, provided that proper slit widths and proper distances from source to slit and from slit to photographic plate were used. They proved this theory by using a 4.0 mm wide slit source of visible light, a 1.5 to 7.0 mm variable diffraction slit at a distance of 70 cm from the slit source, and a screen 300 cm beyond the diffraction slit. The two maxima they saw corresponded closely to the Fomm's striae obtained with X rays. Furthermore, with a wedge-shaped slit, the visible light produced a pattern like the one that they had obtained with X rays.

The similarity of the phenomena obtained with X rays and with visible light, which was known to have wavelike properties, was so striking that Haga and Wind hoped to find in this correspondence some firm ground on which to establish that X rays themselves were wavelike. But the peculiar manner in which the striae crossed over one another in the images formed by the wedge-shaped slit could not be reconciled with the existing theory of diffraction. Indeed, further measurements of the positions of the striae showed, as Figure 5.4 illustrates, that they were always located at sharp flections in the intensity distribution given by the simple *geometrical* image of the source of radiation, whether the radiation was X rays or visible light.

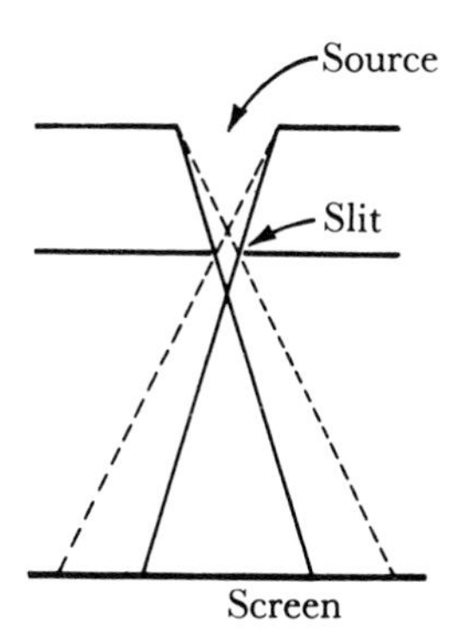

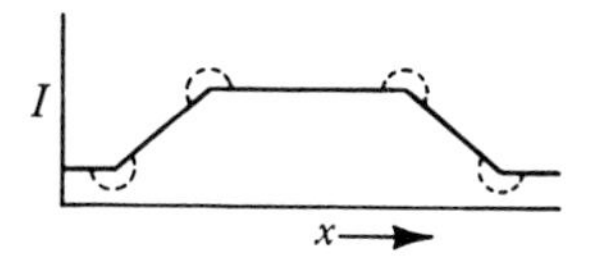

Figure 5.4. *Location of Fomm's striae in the geometrical image of source of X rays formed by a diffraction slit. Above: schema of apparatus. Below: distribution of intensity in the image (solid line) and Fomm's striae (broken lines). From Haga and Wind (1899). (Compare with Figs. 2.3 and 2.4).*

In short, as Wind (1899) later discovered, Fomm's striae are nothing more than Mach bands. They are no doubt caused by the superposition of opposed excitatory and inhibitory influences in the observer's visual system, rather than by the superposition of transverse waves of radiant energy.*

THE SIZE OF THE EARTH'S SHADOW ON THE MOON

For many years astronomers were puzzled by the apparent enlargement of the earth's shadow on the moon during lunar eclipses. Calculated on the basis of direct telescopic observations, the radius of the shadow was always slightly larger than the radius calculated by geometrical optics from the known dimensions of the earth, sun, and moon, and from the known distances between them. Estimates of the magnitude of the enlargement, expressed as a fraction of the expected radius, were quite variable but were nevertheless quite significant. For example, the mean value of a large number of calculations of this fraction, based on observations of lunar eclipses that occurred between the years 1776 and 1888, was about 1/55. (For a survey of the early literature on this subject see Hartmann, 1891.)

Many and diverse explanations for this phenomenon were proposed from time to time. One of the most common was that rays of the sun tangent to the surface of the earth might be absorbed sufficiently by the relatively dense lower portions of the earth's atmosphere to produce a noticeable enlargement of the shadow cast on the moon. Certainly the sun does appear less bright when on the horizon than when at the zenith. But H. Seeliger (1899) pointed out that, even if the lower atmosphere were completely opaque up to a height of some 36 kilometers, the refraction of light passing through the upper atmosphere would counterbalance the effect and the shadow cast at the distance of the moon would not be significantly larger than that calculated by simple geometrical methods.

Following Lambert's suggestion that the apparent enlargement of the shadow might be accounted for in terms of *physiological* optics rather than physical optics, Seeliger undertook a number of experiments to

* The periodic nature of visible light was first suspected from the work of Grimaldi, published in 1665, on the shadows cast by small opaque objects in bright light admitted through small apertures. In this work Grimaldi made a remark which indicated that superposition of rays of light could produce darkness, or what would now be called interference. As Mach points out in his *Principles of Physical Optics* (see the 1953 English edition, pp. 134-135), this would have been an important anticipation of later knowledge, had it not been a physiological rather than physical phenomenon; it was, in fact, nothing more than a special case of the Mach bands.

determine what point in an artificially graded distribution of illumination—one similar to that occurring naturally at the edge of the earth's shadow on the moon—would appear to skilled astronomical observers to be the boundary between lighter and darker areas. After some trial and error with more cumbersome methods, Seeliger finally turned to the use of rotating discs. These discs have the advantage, mentioned earlier, that any chosen distribution of illumination can be obtained easily by painting black and white sectors on the discs, each with one radial boundary having approximately the same curvature as the desired distribution.

For example, assume that the area Oba of the disc shown in Figure 5.5 is painted white and the remainder painted a dull black. According to the Talbot-Plateau law, when the disc is rapidly rotated the brightness at the distance $r = Om$ from the center is proportional to the angle $\alpha = mOa$, assuming the brightness of the black part to be negligible. The curve of "brightness" $h = f(r)$ thus can be calculated easily, and discs constructed for any desired light distribution.

As expected, Seeliger found that a dividing line appears along the circle with radius $r = Om$ if the calculated brightness curve shows a discontinuity at m. Because such a discontinuity was generally considered necessary for the appearance of a dividing line, he was therefore surprised to find that a sharp dividing line was also seen when the curve itself was generally steady and only the differential quotient dh/dr showed a discontinuity at m (for example, when the curve Omb was formed by two straight lines meeting at an angle $Omb = \mu$). Even if the curve at m shows only a strong curvature, rather than a real break, the dividing line is still quite noticeable, although it is no longer as sharp and distinct. This finding indicated to Seeliger that a change in the second differential quotient d^2h/dr^2 alone (or perhaps more correctly $(d^2 \log h)/dr^2$) may be sufficient to produce a noticeable transition from light to dark. But the edge itself often seemed to appear in nearby regions where the differential quotients showed no striking properties.

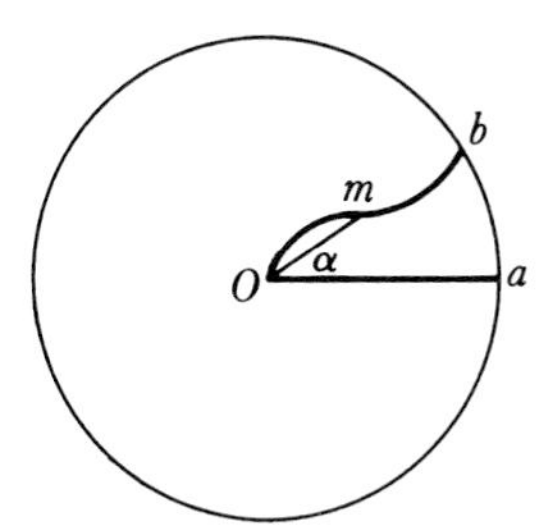

Figure 5.5. *Schema of disc used to produce smoothly graded artificial penumbra. From Seeliger (1899).*

Not knowing of Mach's prior work, Seeliger concluded that brighter portions in the environs of less bright ones appear still brighter, and vice versa, because of contrast effects in the visual system. In particular, he noticed that a dark band appears near the outer edge of an umbra and a light band at the outer edge of a penumbra. This dark band, he reasoned, must influence visual estimates of the exact location of the transition from umbra to penumbra, and might well be the cause of the overestimates of the size of the earth's shadow on the moon.

To test this hypothesis, Seeliger constructed a rotating disc (Fig. 5.6) based on a consideration of the effects of the earth's atmosphere, the shape of the solar disc, and the distribution of the intensity across the solar disc. The boundary of the geometric umbra of the earth on the moon is at an angle $\gamma = 2471.2''$, where γ is the angular distance from the center of the umbra as seen from the earth. The average estimate of the apparent increase in the size of the earth's shadow is 50.6″, and thus a more or less distinct dividing line is generally seen at about $\gamma = 2521.8''$. The disc used in the experiments was constructed so that the brightness at its center corresponded to that part of the earth's shadow on the moon at $\gamma = 2460''$. The outer edge of the disc, 15 cm from the midpoint, corresponded to that part of the shadow at $\gamma = 2560''$. If the construction accurately represented the brightness distribution across that part of the earth's shadow on the moon, then the dividing line should appear at about 9.3 cm from the midpoint of the disc (corresponding to the edge of the apparently enlarged umbra at about $\gamma = 2520''$), rather than at

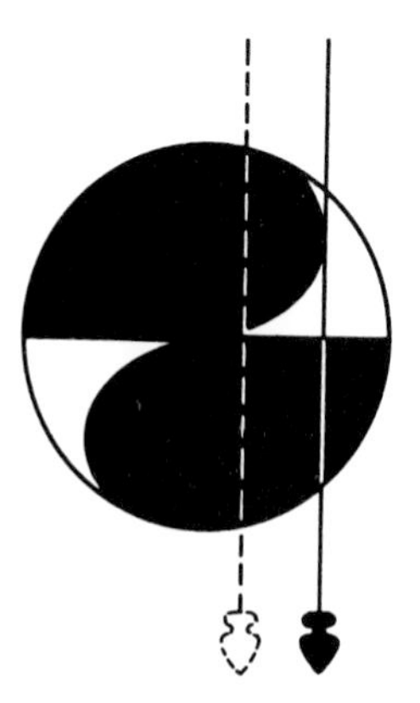

Figure 5.6. *Disc used to produce intensity distribution comparable to the intensity across the edge of the earth's shadow on the moon during a lunar eclipse. Broken vertical line: calculated location of line tangent to the edge of the artificial umbra. Solid vertical line: location of plumb bob set tangent to the apparent edge of the umbra. Redrawn after Seeliger (1899).*

1.5 cm from the center of the disc (corresponding to the geometric edge of the umbra at about $\gamma = 2470''$).

A millimeter rule was placed horizontally in front of and slightly below the rotating disc and a thin thread was fastened to a plumb bob hung in front of the disc. This thread could be moved sideways by the observer (seated 5 meters in front of the disc) in order to set it tangent to the apparent dividing line, first to the right and then to the left of the center of rotation. The two positions of the thread were read from the millimeter rule and the average taken as the distance of the apparent dividing line from the center. (The intensity of the illumination, provided by a kerosene lamp set at the proper distance from the rotating disc, was comparable to the intensity of the illumination of the moon during an eclipse.)

The settings of the plumb thread by the seven skilled observers who served as subjects in the experiments were variable, but the average setting turned out to be very close to 9.3 cm, rather than the 1.5 cm that corresponded to the geometric edge of the umbra of the artificial shadow. As Seeliger remarked, the close correlation between the observations of the artificial shadow in the laboratory and the observations of the real shadow of the earth during lunar eclipses was probably fortuitous, but the results left little doubt that there was no mysterious enlargement of the earth's shadow on the surface of the moon. The apparent enlargement was taking place in the observer's visual system.

COMPLAINTS INVOLVING THE QUALITY OF PIGMENTS USED IN THE GOBELIN TAPESTRIES

In the early 1800's M. E. Chevreul was called upon to superintend the dyeing department of the Gobelin tapestry works in Paris. This famous establishment was founded as a dyehouse by the Gobelin family in the sixteenth century and was later made a royal manufactory under Louis XIV in 1662. At the time of Chevreul's appointment a great many complaints were being made about the quality of certain pigments prepared in the dyeing laboratory, and to preserve the good name of the Gobelin works it was necessary for him to discover and to eliminate the cause of these complaints.

Chevreul found at once that complaints about the gradual fading of some light blues, violets, grays, and browns were well founded, and he immediately began chemical research to determine the cause of the impermanences. But there seemed to be no foundation at all for the persistent complaints that the weavers made about the lack of vigor in some other colors, particularly the blacks that were employed in making shades in blue and violet draperies. Indeed, no perceptible difference could be observed between the black-dyed wools produced at Gobelin's and the finest of black wools that Chevreul could obtain from other famous workshops in France and elsewhere. He therefore theorized—and soon demonstrated by experiment—that the lack of vigor complained of in the blacks and in certain other colors was caused not in the dyeing, but in the weaving: the appearance of a particular yarn in the finished product was determined not only by the color and tone of that yarn itself, but also by the color and tone of the other yarns woven together with it.

Color and brightness contrast had been known and studied since ancient times and their effects had been usefully employed by artists and artisans for centuries. But Chevreul's rediscovery and analysis of these phenomena were of great significance because the practical problems he faced led him to formulate a general law of simultaneous contrast soundly based on experimental observations. In his now-famous book "De la loi du contraste simultané des couleurs" (first published in 1839) he gives the following account of some of his experimental methods of demonstrating and observing the phenomena. The quotations which follow are from the third edition of the English translation of Chevreul's book by Martel (1890). (Figures 1, 2, 3, and 3(bis), referred to in the quotations, are all reproduced here in Figure 5.7).

> ***Definition of simultaneous contrast*** If we look simultaneously upon two stripes of different tones of the same colour, or upon two stripes of the same tone of different colours placed side by side, if the stripes are not too wide, the eye perceives certain modifications which in the first place influence the intensity of colour, and in the second, the optical composition of the two juxtaposed colours respectively.
>
> Now as these modifications make the stripes appear different from what they really are, I give to them the name of *simultaneous contrast of colours;* and I call *contrast of tone* the modification in intensity of colour, and *contrast of colour* that which affects the optical composition of each juxtaposed colour. The following is a very simple method of convincing ourselves of the twofold phenomena of simultaneous contrast of colours.
>
> ***Experimental demonstration of contrast of tone*** Take two portions, *O, O′*, fig. 1, of a sheet of unglazed paper of about twenty inches square, coloured light grey by means of a mixture of whiting and lamp-black; fix them in any manner upon a piece of brown-holland, placed opposite to a window, *O* being distant from *O′* about twelve inches. Then take two portions *P* and *P′* of another sheet of unglazed paper which differs from the first by being deeper, but still a grey composed of the same black and white. Fix *P* next to *O*, and *P′* at about twelve inches from *P*.

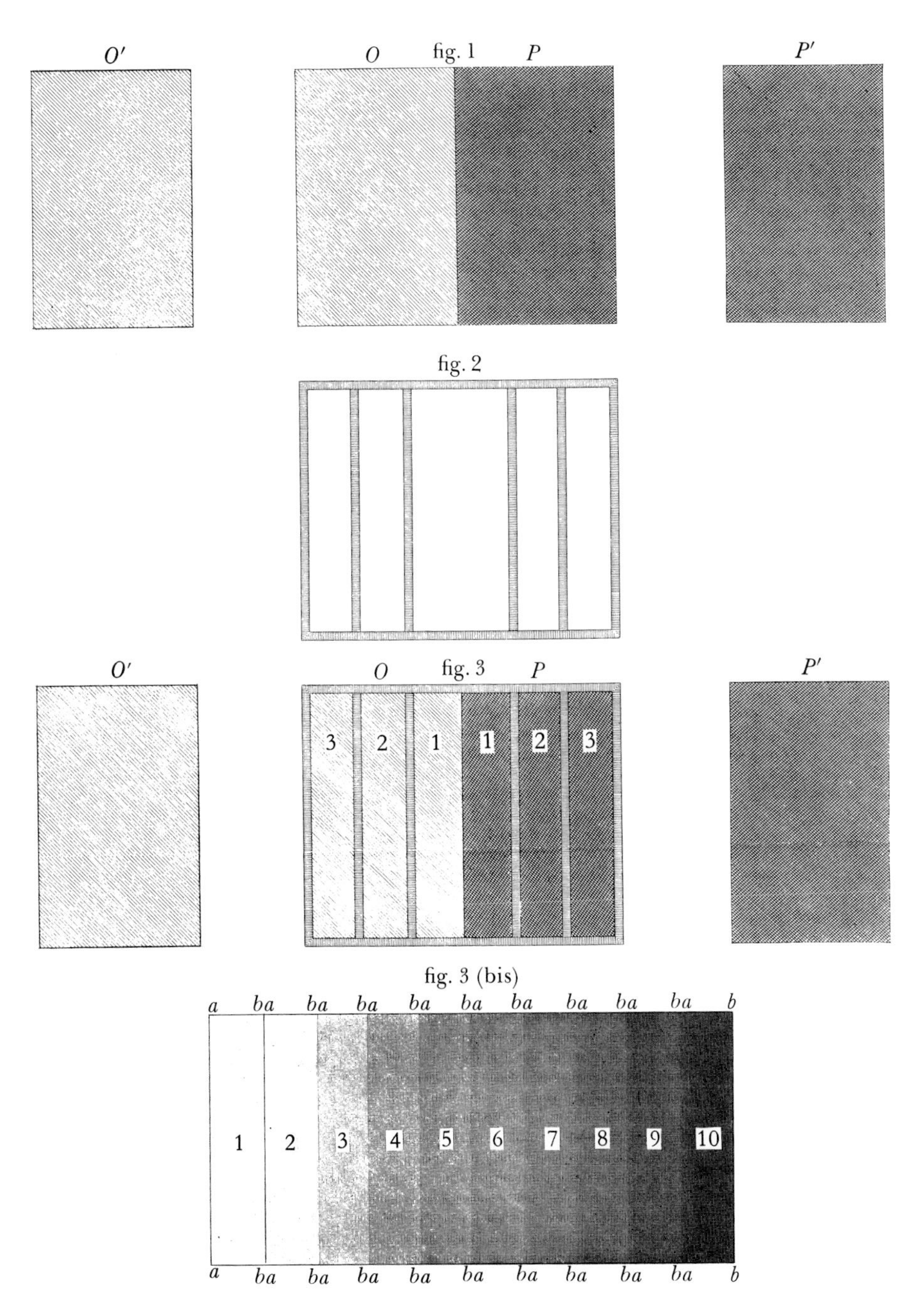

Figure 5.7. *Chevreul's patterns for the demonstration of simultaneous contrast. From Chevreul (1890).*

If we now look at these four half-sheets, *O*, *O′*, *P*, *P′*, for some seconds, we shall see that the piece *O* contiguous to *P* will be lighter than *O′*, while *P* will, on the contrary, be deeper than *P′*.

It is easy to prove that the modification is not equally intense over the whole extent of the surfaces of *O* and *P*, but that it becomes gradually weaker from the line of contact. It is sufficient to place a piece of card, fig. 2, cut out in the center, upon *O P*, in such manner that *O* and *P* each present three grey stripes; as is shown in fig. 3, the stripes 1, 1, are more modified than the stripes 2, 2; and these latter are more modified than the stripes 3, 3.

For this modification to take place, it is not absolutely necessary for *O* and *P* to be contiguous; for if we cover the stripes 1, 1, we shall see the stripes 2, 2, 3, 3 modified.

The following experiment, the natural sequence of the two preceding, is very suitable for demonstrating the full extent of contrast of tone.

Divide a piece of cardboard into ten stripes, each of about a quarter of an inch in width, 1, 2, 3, 4, 5, 6, 7, 8, 9, 10, and cover it with a uniform wash of Indian ink, fig. 3. (bis.). When it is dry, spread a second wash over all the stripes except the first. When this second wash is dry, spread a third over all the stripes except 1 and 2; and proceed thus to cover all the stripes with a flat tint, each one becoming darker and darker, as it recedes from the first.

If we take ten stripes of paper of the same grey, but each of a different tone, and glue them upon a card so as to observe the preceding gradation, it will serve the same purpose.

On now looking at the card, we shall perceive that instead of exhibiting flat tints, each stripe appears of a tone gradually shaded from the edge *a a* to the edge *b b*. In the band 1, the contrast is produced simply by the contiguity of the edge *b b* with the edge *a a* of the stripe 2; in the stripe 10 it is simply by the contact of the edge *a a* with the edge *b b* of the stripe 9. But in each of the intermediate stripes 2, 3, 4, 5, 6, 7, 8, and 9, the contrast is produced by a double cause: one, the contiguity of the edge *a a* with the edge *b b* of the stripe which precedes it; the other by the contiguity of the edge *b b* with the edge *a a* of the darker stripe which follows it. The first cause tends to raise the tone of the half of the intermediate stripe, while the second cause tends to lower the tone of the other half of this same stripe.

The result of this contrast is, that the stripes, seen from a suitable distance, resemble channeled grooves (*glyphs*) more than plane surfaces. For in the stripes 2 and 3, for instance, the grey being insensibly shaded from the edge *a a* to the edge *b b*, they present to the eye the same effect as if the light fell upon a channeled surface, so as to light the part near to *b b*, while the part *a a* will appear to be in the shade; but with this difference, that in a real channel the lighted part would throw a reflection on the dark part.

Contrast of tone occurs with colours, properly so called, as well as with grey; thus, to repeat our experiment (fig. 1.) with the two portions O', O of a sheet of paper of a light tone of a certain colour, and the two portions P', P of a sheet of paper of a deeper tone of this same colour, we shall perceive that O contiguous to P will be lighter than O', and P will be deeper than P'. We can demonstrate, as we have done before, that in starting from the point of contact the modification is gradually weakened.

Experimental demonstration of contrast of colour If we arrange as before two portions O, O' of a sheet of unglazed coloured paper, and two portions, P, P' of a sheet of unglazed paper of a different colour from the first, but resembling it as nearly as possible in intensity, or rather in *tone*, in looking at these four half-sheets O', O, P, P' for a few seconds, we shall see that O differs from O', and P from P'; consequently the two half-sheets O, P appear to undergo reciprocally a modification of tint which is rendered apparent by the comparison we have made of their colours with those of O' and of P.

It is easy to demonstrate that the modification which colours undergo by juxtaposition, is a tendency to weakening starting from the line of juxtaposition; and that it may be perceived between two surfaces without their being in contact, it is sufficient to experiment as above. (Chevreul, 1890, pp. 7-9.)

The evident simultaneity and reciprocity of the contrast of contiguous colors and contiguous tones led Chevreul to attempt to represent the phenomena in quasi-mathematical formulae which would express these facts succinctly. As may be seen in the quotation which follows, the attempt was not very successful, largely because at that time there were no suitable psychophysical methods for measuring quantities of either color or tone. Nevertheless, these crude formulae are worthy of notice because they represent one of the first attempts to express the simultaneous and mutual interaction among neighboring areas of the retina in a quantitative mathematical form.

The law of simultaneous contrast of colours, and the formula which represents it After satisfying myself that the preceding phenomena constantly recurred when my sight was not fatigued, and that many persons accustomed to judge of colours saw them as I did, I endeavoured to reduce them to some general expression that would suffice to enable us to predict the effect that would be produced upon the organ of sight by the juxtaposition of two given colours. All the phenomena I have observed seem to me to depend upon a very simple law, which, taken in its most general signification, may be expressed in these terms: *In the case where the eye sees at the same time two contiguous colours, they will appear as dissimilar as possible, both in their optical composition and in the height of their tone.*

We have then, *at the same time,* simultaneous contrast of colour properly so called, and contrast of tone.

For two contiguous colours, O and P, will differ as much as possible from each other when the complementary of O is added to P, and the complementary of P is added to O: consequently, by the juxtaposition of O and P, the rays of the colour P, which O reflects when it is seen separately, like the rays of the colour O which P reflects when viewed separately, rays which are active under these circumstances cease to be so when O and P are placed in contact; for in this case, each of the two colours losing what is analogous, must differ the more.

The following formulae will make this perfectly intelligible. Let us represent:

The colour of the stripe O by the colour a whiter by B;
The colour of the stripe P by the colour a' whiter by B';
The complementary colour of a by c;
The complementary colour of a' by c'.

The colours of the two stripes viewed separately are

The colour of $O = a + B$,
The colour of $P = a' + B'$.

By juxtaposition, they become

The colour of $O = a + B + c'$,
The colour of $P = a' + B' + c$.

Let us now show that what this expression amounts to is, that the taking away from the colour a of O the rays of the colour a', and taking away from the colour a' of P the rays of the colour a, we must suppose

$$B \text{ reduced to two portions } \begin{cases} \text{white} = b, \\ + \text{ white} = (a' + c'). \end{cases}$$

$$B' \text{ reduced to two portions } \begin{cases} \text{white} = b', \\ + \text{ white} = (a + c). \end{cases}$$

The colours of the two stripes viewed separately are

The colour of $O = a + b + a' + c'$,
The colour of $P = a' + b' + a + c$.

By juxtaposition, they become

The colour of $O = a + b + c'$,
The colour of $P = a' + b' + c$,

an expression which is evidently the same as the first, excepting the values of B and B'.

I have stated that simultaneous contrast may influence both the optical composition of the colours, and the height of their tone;

consequently, when the colours are not of the same degree of intensity, that which is deep appears deeper, and that which is light, lighter; that is to say, the first appears to lose as much of white light as the second seems to reflect more of it.

Therefore, in looking at two contiguous colours, we have Simultaneous Contrast of Colours, and Simultaneous Contrast of Tone. (Chevreul, 1890, pp. 11-12).

Earlier investigators had generally ascribed these and similar effects to "successive contrast." That is, they assumed that by looking at one color the eye became fatigued with respect to the major spectral components of that color, and when the eye then fixated on another color it received a relatively weak impression from those components which were common to the two colors. The appearance of the second color would therefore be determined mainly by the relatively strong impression received from the complements of the components in the first color. But Chevreul showed that this reaction was apparently not the case in his experiments. The gaze is not shifted from one color to another; instead, the interacting colors are viewed all at once and the modification in the appearance of all is simultaneous, even though it may take some time to develop. He therefore concluded that: "Whenever the eye sees two differently colored objects simultaneously, the analogous character of the sensation of the colors undergoes such a diminution that the difference existing between them is rendered proportionately more sensible in the simultaneous impression of these two colors on the retina." Furthermore, his experiments seemed to show: (1) that the contrast effect radiates out from the line of juxtaposition of the two colored surfaces; (2) that it is reciprocal between two equal surfaces juxtaposed; and (3) that the effect still exists when these two surfaces are at a distance from each other, only it is less evident than when they are contiguous.

Chevreul's "law of simultaneous contrast" solved at once a great number of the most perplexing problems which the director of the Gobelin works had assigned to him and, at the same time, proved to be of inestimable value to others in the textile industry who had been led into error on the same account. Consider, for example, the following instances of "false judgment of recipes" and "true tints misunderstood" which he cites.

False judgment of the value of recipes for colouring compositions

At a calico-printer's they possessed a recipe for printing green, which up to a certain period had always succeeded, when they fancied it began to give bad results. They were lost in conjecture upon the cause, when a person, who at the Gobelins had followed my researches on contrast, recognized that the green of which they complained, being printed upon a ground of blue, tended to become yellow, through the influence of orange, the complementary of the ground. Consequently, he advised that the proportion of blue in the colouring composition should be increased, in order to correct the effect of contrast. The recipe modified after this suggestion gave the beautiful green which they had before obtained.

This example demonstrates that every recipe for colouring compositions intended to be applied upon a ground of another colour must be modified conformably to the effect which the ground will produce upon the colour of the composition. It proves also that it is much easier for a painter to correct an effect of contrast than it is for a calico-printer, supposing that both are ignorant of the law of contrast: for if the first perceives in painting a green pattern on a blue drapery that the green comes too yellow, it is sufficient for him to add a little blue to the green, to correct the defect which strikes him. It is this great facility in correcting the ill effect of certain contrasts which explains why they so often succeed in so doing without being able to account for it.

True tints of designs printed upon coloured grounds misunderstood In treating of the modifications perceptible in bodies through the medium of light, I have instanced cottons of a coloured ground printed with patterns which the calico-printer intended making colourless; but, owing to the imperfection of the process, were really of the colour of the ground, but of an exceedingly light tint; we may be satisfied of this by looking at them after they are isolated from the ground by means of a white paper cut out like the pattern. I have remarked that, notwithstanding their colour, the eye judges them to be colourless, or of the tint complementary to that of the ground.

I will now explain the cause of these appearances, because they have been the subject of questions frequently addressed to me by manufacturers of printed stuffs and by drapers; it is due to the law of simultaneous contrast of colours. In fact, when the patterns appear white, the ground acts by contrast of tone; if they appear coloured (and this appearance generally succeeds to that where they appear white), the ground then acts by contrast of colour; the manufacturer of printed stuffs, therefore, will not seek to attribute the cause of these phenomena to the chemical actions manifested in his operations.

Ignorance of the law of contrast has among drapers and manufacturers been the subject of many disputes, which I have been happy to settle amicably, by demonstrating to the parties that they had no possible cause for litigation in the cases they submitted to me. I will relate some of these, to prevent, if possible, similar disputes.

Certain drapers having given to a calico-printer some cloths of a single colour,—red, violet, and blue,—upon which they wished black figures to be printed, complained that upon the *red* cloths he had put *green* patterns, upon the *violet* the figures appeared *greenish-yellow*,—upon the *blue*—they were *orange-brown* or *copper-coloured*, instead of the *black*, which they had ordered. To convince them that they had no ground for complaint, it sufficed to have recourse to the following proofs:

1°. I surrounded the patterns with white paper, so as to conceal the ground; the designs then appeared black.

2°. I placed some cuttings of black cloth upon stuffs coloured red, violet, and blue; the cuttings appeared like the printed designs, —*i.e.*, of the colour complementary to the ground, although the same cuttings, when placed upon a white ground, were of a beautiful black. (Chevreul, 1890, pp. 182-184.)

Throughout his book Chevreul strongly emphasizes the view that these contrast effects are perceptual phenomena. Indeed, in his preface he reminds the reader "never to forget when it is asserted of the phenomena of simultaneous contrast, *that one color placed beside another receives . . . a modification from it* that this manner of speaking does not mean that the two colors, or rather the two material objects that present them to us, have a mutual action, either physical or chemical; it is really only applied *to the modification that takes place before us* when we perceive the simultaneous impression of these two colors." In short, he finally concluded—as Haga and Wind were later to conclude in their study of X rays, and as Seeliger was to conclude in his study of lunar eclipses—that the critical effects observed were to be attributed to the "subject knowing" rather than to the "object known."

ON THE MEANING OF OBJECTIVITY

That which is called "subjective" is frequently mistaken for that which is called "objective" simply because in one important respect they *are* one and the same: both are based on phenomena that are seen, heard, felt, or otherwise experienced. On what grounds, therefore, can the one be called objective, or real, and the other only subjective, or apparent? Ultimately, there is only one criterion for objective truth: *collective agreement*. And, in general, agreement exists that whatever there is about knowledge that transcends the peculiarities of particular points of view and the peculiarities of particular individuals is objective. As Arthur O. Lovejoy (1930) expressed it in his book, *The Revolt Against Dualism*:

The business of knowing, then—if by the word we mean anything more than bare sensation or pure revery—is the business of tran-

> scending standpoints; it is the quest of content which can be believed to have some character identical in nature (if not in existence) with a character which belongs to (or is present in) the specified object or locus of reference independently of the knowing and within its own limits. . . . What we call, in the practical or moral sense, "seeing things in perspective" is in fact seeing them out of perspective—correcting the foreshortenings and distortions which arise from their temporal proximity to us, or from their differing relations to our transient moods or preoccupations or passions. It is equally evident that the transcendence of standpoints is the essential of that kind of reasonableness which makes man (to some small extent) a social being.

But it must be borne in mind that although the aim of objectivity is to transcend the peculiarities of particular standpoints taken to achieve experience, it cannot transcend experience itself. One cannot experience anything that he does not experience; he cannot know anything that he does not know. And here lies the source of much of the confusion and error that arise when one attempts to distinguish between the "object known" and "subject knowing." For no matter what one may *believe* about things existing independently of the knowing, it is contradictory to assert that one *knows* that something exists independently of knowing.

The "object known" The sense experiences are the given subject matter of science and the source of our commonsense knowledge about the external world, but for one reason or another they may not be given equally to all of us. Therefore any time that there is more than one observer there is some chance that they may not agree on what they see, hear, and feel. An extreme case in fiction (but of a kind not uncommon in real life) occurred when Shakespeare's Macbeth "saw" Banquo's ghost and asked:

> Can such things be,
> And overcome us like a summer's cloud,
> Without our special wonder? You make me strange
> Even to the disposition that I owe,
> When now I think you can behold such sights,
> And keep the natural ruby of your cheeks,
> When mine is blanch'd with fear.

And Ross, who saw nothing, replied:

> What sights, my lord?
>
> (*Macbeth,* III, iv).

It seems obvious that collective agreement by a number of supposedly rational and unbiased observers with normal sensory capacities is a necessary criterion for assuring that the character of a particular phenomenon does not depend upon a particular observer. But this requirement that several observers, given the same conditions, be able to experience and report essentially the same phenomena is not easy to meet if it is very strictly observed, for some quite substantial differences exist between the sensory capacities of even apparently normal observers. And if we press too hard for perfect agreement we are certain to end up asking one another "What sights, my lord?" (or the equivalent) about every fine detail.

Recognition of these normal individual differences led to the so-called personal equation, which was of great importance in astronomical observations during the last century. But before it was recognized and taken into account, there was a great deal of confusion about which one of the various discrepant observations of a stellar transit time was correct and should be regarded as the real transit time. The following is a brief account of this problem; for more details see Boring (1929).

In the late eighteenth and early nineteenth centuries astronomers observed stellar transit times directly. The observer viewed the star through a fixed telescope with cross hairs perpendicular to the direction of motion of the star. He listened to one-second beats of a clock, watched the moving star, and estimated to the nearest tenth of a second the time at which the star crossed the critical cross hair in the reticle. This was a difficult observation—the observer had to remember the location of the star at the time of the beat just before it reached the cross hair and its position at the time of the next beat, and then estimate the location of the cross hair along this interval. Although the observation was very difficult to make, it was generally accepted as being accurate to one- or two-tenths of a second, that is, to one- or two-tenths of the angular distance between the two critical positions of the star.

A most serious defect in this method came to light at the Greenwich Observatory in 1776. Kinnebrook, an assistant to the royal astronomer Maskelyne, consistently observed stellar transit times almost a second later than his superior did. It was assumed, of course, that the royal astronomer's observations were correct and that the assistant's were incorrect. The assistant was dismissed, but the matter did not end there. The whole affair came to the attention of Bessel, at Königsberg, a few years later. Concerned about the accuracy of the method in view of the magnitude of this supposed error, Bessel undertook to compare his own observations with those of several other experienced and reputable observers—all famous astronomers. He found differences as large as one second among them. It was now evident that the discrepancies among various observations could not be attributed to the incompetence of one particular assistant because in *every* case the observed transit time of a star depended upon who the observer was. In order to bring the discrepant data into agreement so-called personal equations had to be determined for each of the several astronomers whose observations were to be pooled and compared. To make matters worse, it was also found that observations by any one individual were much more variable than had been supposed. All this, of course, was no trivial problem for astronomy; these were fundamental observations upon which many important calculations were based.

These errors were discovered because the observations did not meet one important criterion of objectivity—that the character of the phenomenon observed not be critically dependent upon any *particular* observer. Ultimately, the problem was resolved by the development of sensitive instruments. The observer was still essential, however; but now he was simply assigned to the less critical task of observing the instrument. It was still required that this latter observation be inter-subjective, that is, that all observers agree within some acceptable small limits on their readings of the instrument.

This criterion of invariance of all observers within tolerable limits is necessary to distinguish between object and subject, but in itself it is not sufficient. This fact is well illustrated by the Mach bands. All normal observers agree that they see the bright and dark bands; there is no question or disagreement about whether one region is "really" brighter and the other "really" darker than the surroundings. Thus, since the general appearance of these phenomena does not depend upon a particular observer they are sometimes mistakenly assumed to represent directly and faithfully the distribution of illumination on the object, a property that supposedly exists independently of the observer. But observation of the phenomena requires a particular sense organ—the eye —and the eye has its own peculiarities and special properties so that what is seen is determined by these properties as well as by the properties of the object itself.

Nevertheless, commonsense objectivity generally accepts specific sense experiences as indicative of or identical with the properties of real objects, provided there is collective agreement. For example, it is generally believed that leaves *are* green, that snow *is* white, and that ice *is* cold— for that is the way that they usually appear to all normal observers under ordinary conditions. Only when there is something incongruous or unusual about the objects perceived, or about the conditions under which they are perceived do we say that one appearance of an object is illusory, and that another that is more in accord with usual experiences is real. For example, snow in the shade appears bluish, but we are likely to say that it is *really* white because that is the way that is usually appears. But when more credence is placed in one appearance of an object than in all the others, we are narrowing our point of view and adopting a single standpoint rather than transcending standpoints.

To transcend the purely visual and sometimes doubtful appearances of an object (without resorting to the use of instrumental aids) one must make use of another sense as did Macbeth when he asked,

> Is this a dagger which I see before me,
> The handle toward my hand? Come, let me clutch thee.
> I have thee not, and yet I see thee still.
> Art thou not, fatal vision, sensible
> To feeling as to sight? Or art thou but
> A dagger of the mind, a false creation,
> Proceeding from the heat-oppressed brain?
> (*Macbeth,* II, i).

It is very common for us to turn to the sense of touch when in doubt about the reality of an object. For example, William Harnett's *trompe l'oeil* painting *Music and Good Luck,* which hangs in the Metropolitan Museum of Art in New York, may soon have to be covered with glass to protect it from inquisitive fingers. Many persons who view the painting (Fig. 5.8) cannot resist the temptation to touch it in order to determine whether or not some of the objects represented in it really stand out from the surface of the canvas as they appear to do. In fact, whenever the several appearances of an object are incongruous, as in this painting, reliance on that which is tangible generally takes precedence over all else.

It is not at all surprising, however, that a higher reality is ascribed to the tangible characteristics of an object than to the intangible. As Mach pointed out, the relatively greater permanence of the tangible seems to form a sort of a constant nucleus with a more or less definite location in space which appears to be the vehicle of the ephemeral colors, sounds, odors, etc. which are associated with it. Indeed, the word *tangible* not only means perceptible to the touch, it also means externally real, substantial, and objective. And whenever the need arises to be more objective, as in the construction of things, in the exchange of goods, in the laying out of boundaries of property, in the measurement of time, and so forth, we turn to tangible standards of weights and measures. The most primitive of these standards—apart from our own bodies—were rigid tangible objects such as measuring rods, the vertical post or *gnomon*

Figure 5.8. Music and Good Luck *by William Harnett. Courtesy of the Metropolitan Museum of Art, Wolfe Fund, 1963, New York.*

of a sundial, simple equal arm balances and standard weights, measuring cups, and similar items.

The extent to which everyday technology, the adoption and use of standard weights and measures, and the mechanical conception of nature associated with them have influenced and continue to influence the development of the exact sciences is generally not appreciated. Indeed, until relatively recent times there was some hope among scientists that all physical phenomena—and perhaps all of nature—could be completely reduced to the purely mechanical movements of elementary particles of mass. Apparently this hope has now been abandoned, but the various tangible accoutrements of the mechanical conception have not. For example, a standard unit of length, a bar of platinum iridium with some parallel lines engraved in it, is so important both for technology and for the mechanical conception of physics that it is still literally enshrined at the *Bureau International des Poids et Mesures* at Sèvres, France, even though it has been replaced by a new standard. It is no wonder that science has preserved and protected this bar of platinum iridium with as much zeal as a church preserves its relics, for, as Mach remarked, "The numerical measurement of mass is given by a ratio of accelerations, and measurement of time can be reduced to measurement of angles or lengths of arcs. Consequently measurement of lengths is the foundation of all [physical] measurements."

There was always the danger, of course, that the original platinum bar might be injured, or damaged, or even lost. Therefore, several copies were made and enshrined elsewhere, but more important, new indestructible standards have since been developed. The first of these was developed by Michelson and Wadsworth using the Michelson interferometer. They found that 1,553,163.5 wavelengths of a bright red line emitted by the metal cadmium (Cd 6438 Å) is equal to the standard meter. The present standard, adopted in 1960, utilizes the isotope krypton 86. Since it is thus possible to construct a substitute standard of length based on the periodicity of light emitted from an object, rather than on the spatial extent of a particular object, it is at least conceivable that the original standard could have been constructed in this way. In any event, physical science may one day be able to discard all of the tangible remnants of its lowly origins in the use of simple mechanical implements and contrivances of antiquity.* (See Mach, 1915, on the prehistoric origins of mechanics.)

Even now none of the fundamental physical units of measure (length, mass, and time) depends critically on any particular sense organ or on any particular observer although the measurements must, of course, be made by some observer using some sense organ. And here is where commonsense objectivity and the objectivity of physical science have come to the parting of their ways. In everyday life specific sense experiences are still accepted as being more or less directly indicative of the properties of objects. But even though most fundamental physical concepts have

* A new standard of time, based on properties of the cesium atom, was adopted in the fall of 1964.

had their origins in similar specific sense experiences, scientists have attempted to make all physical concepts and theories independent of specific sense experiences. For example, in his *Principien der Wärmelehre* (1896a) Mach gives the following historical account of how objective thermometery grew out of and yet became independent of thermal sensations.

> Among the sensations that we consider to be stimulated by the bodies that surround us, thermal sensations constitute a specific series (cold, cool, lukewarm, warm, hot) or a specific class of interrelated elements. The bodies which act as the stimulators of such sensations demonstrate a particular physical reaction in association with these sensation characteristics, as far as they themselves are concerned, as well as towards other bodies. A very hot body glows, shines, melts, evaporates, or burns in the air; a cold one stiffens. A drop of water evaporates with a sizzling sound on a hot iron plate, while it freezes on a cold one, and so on. The essence of this physical behavior of the body in association with the characteristics of the thermal sensation (that is, the entirety of these reactions) we call the *thermal state* (Wärmezustand).
>
> We could pursue the physical phenomena which belong here only with difficulty and incompletely if we were limited to the thermal sensation as the characteristic of the thermal state. If in a container B we mix cold water from a container A with hot water from a container C (Fig. 5.9), dip our left hand into container A for several seconds, similarly our right hand into container C, and thereafter both hands into B, then *the same* water seems warm to the left hand, but cold to the right one. The air in a deep cellar seems cold in the summer, but warm in the winter, although one can actually convince oneself that its physical thermal reaction is almost the same in both cases. That is, the sensation is influenced not only by the body which stimulates it, but also by the state of the organ on which the preceding conditions have had an influence. In this way the same lamplight seems bright if we come from a dark room, but it seems dull if we come from a sunlit room. It is just that the sense organs are adapted not for the furthering of physical knowledge but for the preservation of favorable living conditions.
>
> As long as we deal with our sensation, it *alone* has to make the final decision. It is without doubt, then, that a body which reacts

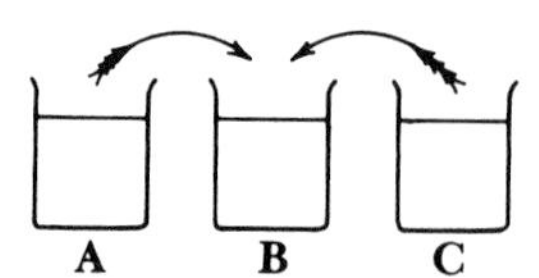

Figure 5.9. Ambiguous thermal sensations. *From Mach (1896a).*

> physically in the same way, seems to be *warm* one time and *cold* another. There would be no sense in saying that the body, which we sense to be *warm,* is actually *cold.* However, if we are concerned with the *physical* reaction of a body towards another body, then we must look for a *characteristic* of this reaction which is *independent* of our sense organs, which are difficult and cumbersome to control. Such a characteristic has been found.
>
> It has long been known that the same body, depending upon whether it seems colder or warmer under otherwise equal conditions, also acquires a smaller or larger *volume.* This change in volume is particularly apparent in the case of air. Even Heron of Alexandria was familiar with it. However, it seems that Galilei, the founder of dynamics, was the first to have the fortunate idea of using the volume of the air as a *characteristic* of its *thermal state,* and to construct a *thermoscope* and a *thermometer,* respectively, by that method. For, on the basis of the apparent observation that unequally warm bodies which touch each other soon appear to be equally warm, it was considered obvious that such an apparatus also shows the thermal state of the body it touches. (Mach, 1896a, pp. 3-4.)

Similarly, in all other physical measurements either one object is compared with another or the effect of one object on another is observed, rather than relying on an unaided direct observation of the particular object itself. The object compared, or the effect of one object on another, must of course be observed in some way or another, but this can be done in such a way that the sense organ involved plays a less critical role. For example, the accuracy of the visual observation of the location of the end of a column of mercury in a thermometer is limited by the observer's visual capacities, but the scale can be greatly expanded so that his errors are minimal, and in any event, they are not ordinarily affected by the thermal state of the substance being measured. In this way an attempt is made to reduce all physical concepts to a set of basic dimensions, mass, length, and time, each of which—at least in principle—does not require the use of any particular sensory system for its measurement. These measurements thus transcend the peculiarities of *particular* senses and *particular* individuals, but they do not transcend all sensory observations or all observers. And neither do they transcend the physical point of view.

Physical optics was slow to achieve even this degree of objectivity, however. Until relatively recent times the eye was indispensable for the measurement of light; the essential observations which led to the classical wave theory of light were all *visual* observations. The critical measures were generally measures of the location of some feature of the brightness and color of illumination seen directly by the observer, such as the locations of maxima and minima in the brightness of a diffraction pattern, or the locus of the transition from one level of brightness to another. The measurement of such loci, of course, involves the measurement of distance from some fixed point, and sometimes, as in the determination of the velocity of light, the measurement of time is also significant. Thus prior to the development of instrumental methods for the measurement of radiant energy, the ultimate dimensions of light were a curious mixture of two "objective" quantitative dimensions, length and time, and a "subjective" qualitative dimension, brightness. The manner in which concepts of physical optics, originally based entirely on visual experience, gradually became independent of visual experience has been described elsewhere (Ratliff, 1962). It is sufficient to point out here that the visible spectrum can now be studied in the same way that the much broader invisible portions of the electromagnetic spectrum are. We rely on physical instruments; the eye is no longer essential.

Nevertheless, the fact that practically all of the major concepts in the theory of light had their origin in visual phenomena and the fact that for such a long time there was no way to measure light except by visual photometry has left an indelible mark on the whole science of physical optics. Even today many of the fundamental principles of physical optics are taught by demonstrations of the *visual* effects of interference, diffraction, and the like, rather than by means of actual physical measurements. This special and continuing role of one particular sense organ in the study and teaching of physical optics has no parallel in other branches of physics.

The various errors described in the first part of this chapter all resulted because this one particular sense organ—the eye—played such a critical role in each of the observations and because the observations in a given experiment were all made, as it were, from a single standpoint. At first it was taken for granted in each case that the visual appearance of a supposed X-ray diffraction pattern, the visual appearance of the edge of a shadow, and the visual appearance of a dyed strand of yarn should correspond more or less directly to the pattern, intensity, and spectral composition of the light that stimulated the eye observing these phenomena. But none of these supposedly real physical properties of light was measured independently of the *visual* appearance. It is evident, therefore, that there was ample opportunity to confound properties of the observer and properties of the thing observed.

Despite this interdependence, there are many degrees of objectivity, and it was possible to discover that something was wrong even while continuing to use the eye to make the critical observations. Haga and Wind did this by showing—among other things—that the Fomm's striae that were seen in the photographs obtained using both visible light and the invisible X rays were essentially identical. In neither case were the locations of the light and dark bands consistent with predictions based on the already well-established diffraction theory. Similarly, Seeliger showed that the apparent edge of a gradient of illumination observed on a rotating disc in the laboratory did not correspond to the location of the edge calculated on the basis of the simple and straightforward principles involved in the construction of the disc, and therefore there was no reason to expect the apparent edge of the earth's shadow on the moon to have the same location as the calculated edge. Chevreul showed that when viewed alone the color of a dyed strand of yarn differed greatly from its color when seen next to other differently dyed strands. The apparent color of that one strand of yarn, therefore, was evidently not determined solely by light reflected from it. Thus by simply adopting different standpoints with respect to the phenomena observed—even though the same sense organ was used to make all the critical observations—all of these investigators were able to achieve a considerable degree of objectivity.

With the diverse instrumental methods that are now available for the measurement of radiant energy independently of the eye, it would be very easy to show that these various errors result from peculiar properties of the observers' visual systems. But although the use of such instruments may eliminate the eye as a source of error, it does not eliminate all sources of error. Now, instead of properties of the observer's eye being confounded with properties of the object, properties of the observing instrument may be confounded with properties of the object. Sometimes an instrument also sees "daggers of the mind."

Instrumental errors Any instrument which transduces energy from one form to another or which transmits information from one point to another will almost certainly either degrade or accentuate some feature of the spatial and temporal configuration of the energy transduced or of the information transmitted. For example, an ordinary black and white photograph is never an exact replica of the pattern of light on the object photographed. The lens and aperture stop introduce some distortion at the very outset. The scattering of light within the emulsion on the film and reflections from the support backing the emulsion introduce additional distortions. Finally, the development and fixation of the latent image on the film lead to still further distortions. Most of these undesirable effects can be greatly reduced if proper care is taken, but they cannot be eliminated altogether.

One effect in the development process is of special interest here because it is somewhat analogous to the Mach bands, both in the way in which it occurs and in the result that is produced. In the process of development the sodium salt of the developer reduces the silver bromide which was exposed to light with the result that metallic silver is deposited in that part of the film, and other end products of the development process remain in solution. The whole process may be represented crudely as follows:

$$\mathrm{Na(D)} + \mathrm{AgBr} \rightarrow \mathrm{Ag} + \underline{\mathrm{NaBr}} + \mathrm{(D)}$$

inhibition

where (D) represents the components of the developer other than the sodium. In accordance with the law of mass action, a high concentration of end products may stop or even reverse a chemical reaction. In this particular case, the soluble bromide has such a retarding or inhibiting effect on the development process as is indicated—in a highly schematic way—by the arrow labeled "inhibition" (see Baines, 1958; and Mees, 1954).

Heavily exposed areas of the photographic film produce high concen-

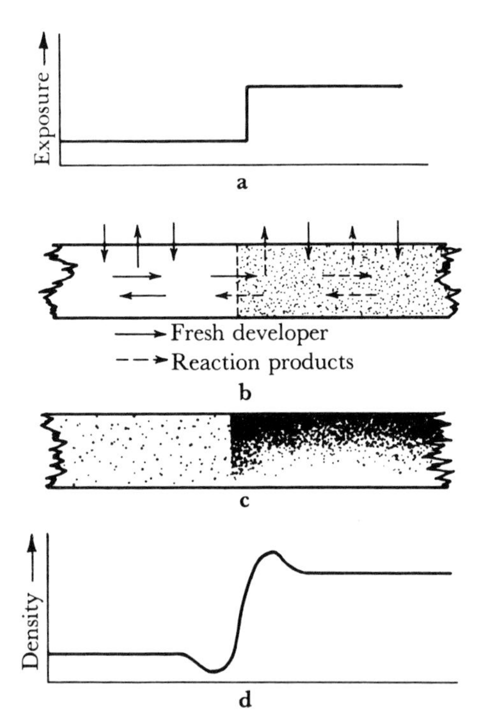

Figure 5.10. *Schematic diagrams showing the nature of border and fringe effects in the photographic process. From Mees (1954).*

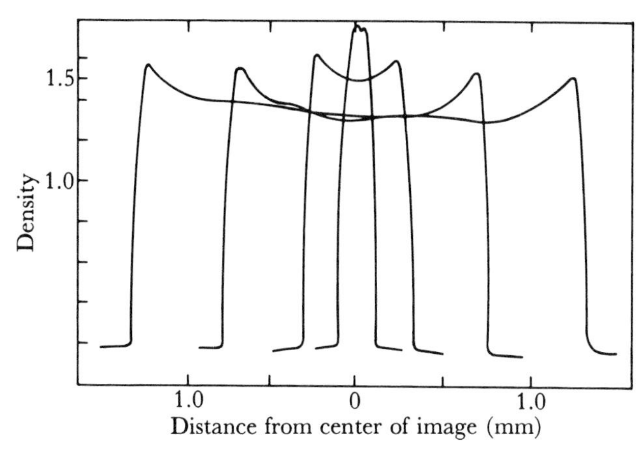

Figure 5.11. *Microdensitometer traces across images of various sizes, exposure constant. From Mees (1954).*

trations of the end products of development which tend to inhibit subsequent development, not only locally, but also in more distant areas as the inhibitor diffuses. The amount of inhibition is graded with distance because more of the inhibitor diffuses to nearby, rather than to distant areas. Less of the inhibitor is produced in the inhibited regions, so they exert less effect back on the regions where strong development has already taken place. This process is shown schematically in Figure 5.10 in which the actual exposure is represented in a, the diffusion of the fresh developer and the reaction products in b, a cross section of the developed emulsion in c, and the density of the developed film in d.

As one would expect, these mutual inhibitory effects taking place within the film produce maxima and minima in the density of the developed image that are not present in the optical image itself. Furthermore, the magnitudes of the effects are strongly dependent on the intensity of exposure and the area of film exposed. Figure 5.11, which illustrates the latter effect, shows microdensitometer traces across images of various sizes with a constant exposure. (Note the similarity between these curves and those calculated for an inhibitory network in Figure 4.45 above.)

Generally, agitation of the film during development is sufficient to spread the inhibitor more or less evenly over the whole film so that only slight edge effects are observed. (Since these tend to sharpen contrast, photographers sometimes make no special effort to eliminate them.) Very marked and undesirable effects occur, however, if the film or plate is developed in a vertical position without any agitation because the inhibitor, which has a higher specific gravity than the rest of the solution, gradually sinks to lower parts of the film. Thus graded streaks of poor development occur below the regions of high exposure (Fig. 5.12). Similarly, uniform movement in one direction, as in some commonly used spiral film holders, may leave streaks of poor development behind regions of high exposure.

These inhibitory effects in the development process are remarkably similar to the inhibitory effects in the retina. In some particular cases, illustrated in Figures 5.10 and 5.11, the edge effects produced in the development of the film closely resemble Mach bands, and could easily be mistaken for them. To make matters even worse, the names of the

Figure 5.12. *Streak of poor development in lightly exposed area below a heavily exposed spot on lantern slide plate. The plate was developed in a vertical position with no agitation. Note sharpness of lower edge of spot.*

effects, as well as the effects themselves, are similar. These purely photographic effects are known as *Mackie* lines.*

A televised image may suffer from a number of distortions introduced at various points along the way from the television camera to the viewing screen. Some of these can be tolerated by the viewer and no effort is made to correct them. Indeed, in some cases, the distortions may be of some practical use in emphasizing certain features of an image and may deliberately be accentuated for special purposes. One effect which occurs in the television camera itself is of interest here because it is somewhat analogous to the physiological and photographic effects described above. A particular part of the electronic image formed on the mosaic of photosensitive elements in the camera may exert an opposing "inhibitory" influence on neighboring parts.

The iconoscope, a television camera invented by V. K. Zworykin, is shown schematically in Figure 5.13. The optical image of the scene to be televised is formed on a photosensitive surface which is not a continuous conductor but rather a mosaic of separate photosensitive elements on a sheet of mica. These photosensitive elements (commonly silver sensitized with cesium) are quite small compared with the details of the optical image. The mosaic may thus be regarded as a continuous photosensitive insulating surface. The other side of the photosensitive sheet, the signal plate, is coated with a thin conducting layer of platinum.

Electrons are emitted from each illuminated element of the photosensitive mosaic in numbers proportional to the amount of light falling on it, and are attracted to the anode. The result is that the brightly illuminated portions of the mosaic are more positively charged than the dimly illuminated portions. A sharply focussed 1000 volt electron beam periodically scans the mosaic in a standard pattern, serving as a commutator which sweeps across each element of the mosaic and restores its potential to an equilibrium value. This dissipation of the charge on each element that has been stored by the photoemission of electrons since the preceding scan causes the release of a charge of opposite sign from the signal plate. The released charge generates the picture signal voltage as it passes through the input resistor of the preamplifier. Thus each element of the photosensitive mosaic may be regarded as an inde-

* Several different names have been given to variants of these retardation effects. The increase in density at a dark edge is sometimes called the *border effect;* the decrease in density at the light edge is called the *fringe effect;* both together are called *edge effects* or *Mackie lines;* the area effect illustrated above is called the *Eberhard effect;* and the retardation of development between two small images is called the *Kostinsky effect.* All of these terms, of course, basically apply to one and the same effect. See Mees (1954) for a detailed account.

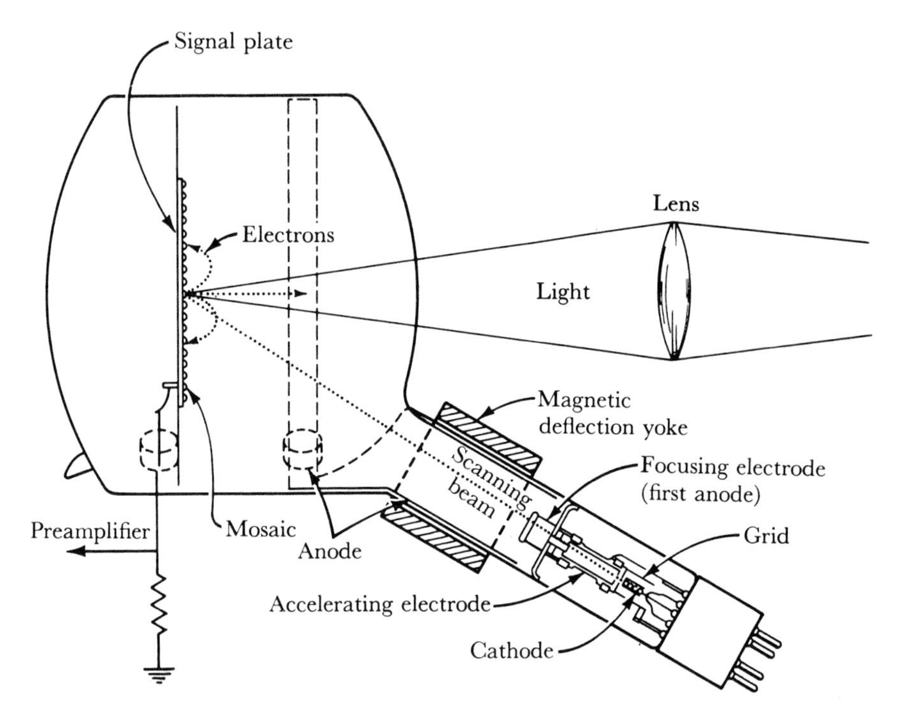

Figure 5.13. *Schematic diagram of the iconoscope type of television camera tube. Redrawn after Zworykin and Ramberg (1949).*

pendent photocell, the illumination on which is "measured" by the number of electrons required from the scanning beam to restore those lost by photoemission since the preceding scan. Because the signal voltage is continuously modulated as variously charged portions of the mosaic are scanned, the optical image incident upon the photosensitive mosaic is transduced into a temporally varying electrical signal which can be transmitted over long distances by various means.

A detailed examination of the iconoscope in operation (Zworykin, Morton, and Flory, 1937) shows that the above ideal conditions are not realized in actual practice. In addition to the photoemission of electrons from the elements of the mosaic, there is also a substantial secondary emission resulting from the impact of the electrons in the scanning beam. Not all of the photo- and secondary-electrons which leave the mosaic reach the anode where they are supposed to be collected. Instead, some fall back in a shower both on the element from which they were emitted and upon neighboring parts of the mosaic. These redistributed electrons reduce the charge on the photoelements and thus reduce the strength of the picture signal that they generate when the scanning beam reaches them. Therefore, secondary emission of electrons from areas of the mosaic corresponding to bright parts of the optical image "inhibits" the signal from neighboring regions (as well as producing "self inhibition" on the element from which they are emitted) and results in a spurious darkening of those regions in the televised image. In the iconoscope these spurious effects have to be compensated by combining special "counter-shading" signals with the picture signal. In the image orthicon, a later version of the television camera, a mesh-like screen very close to the point of emission of secondary electrons serves as a more efficient collector and thus reduces the spurious shading effects, but does not eliminate them altogether (see Rose, Weimer, and Law, 1946). As in the photographic effect described above, the cause of the spurious shading is in the instrument and not in the eye of the viewer.

Some widely used xerographic processes (such as the one used in the electrostatic copier manufactured by the Xerox Corporation) show very marked edge or fringe effects similar to border contrast effects in human vision and steps have to be taken to overcome them if one wishes to reproduce a photograph in continuous tone. In xerography, a uniform electrostatic charge is first imparted to the surface of a grounded selenium plate. The image of the document or photograph to be copied is then projected onto the charged plate. The charge is lost where the light parts of the image fall on the plate, but the charge is retained where the dark parts fall. A black powder, which is then spread evenly over the plate, clings by electrostatic attraction to the charged areas. Finally, the powder is transferred by another electrostatic process to a sheet of paper pressed against the plate and is then permanently fused to it by heat to form the final copy. In general, the strength of an electrostatic field at any point is given by adding vectorially the fields produced at that point by each positive charge. Thus the amount of black powder attracted to any point on the charged plate is determined not by the charge at that point alone, but by the integrated effects of all charges whose fields act at that point. The resulting effect is quite similar to those described above—more powder is attracted wherever there is an abrupt change from a light (uncharged) area to a dark (charged) area than in the uniformly dark and uniformly light areas. As Figure 5.14 shows, only the boundaries of the dark areas in the original (a) are reproduced in the final copy (b). To obtain a copy with a continuous tone (c), one merely breaks up the image with a halftone screen so that there are changes from light to dark everywhere.

Figure 5.15 shows graphically the physical basis for the edge effects in xerography and, at the same time, how breaking the image into small components with a halftone screen enables one to reproduce the full

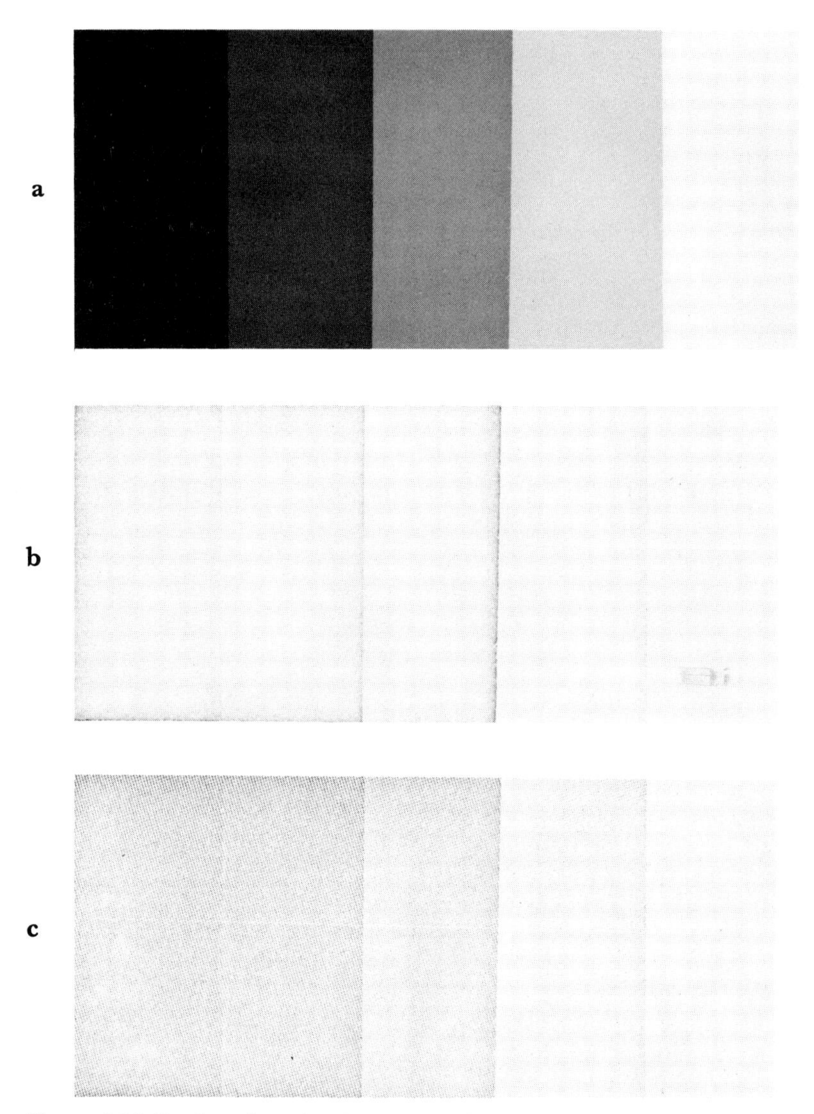

Figure 5.14. Border effects in the xerographic process.

range of tones in the original with considerable fidelity. The top graph shows the optical density D across an extended black area A of the test object to be reproduced and several narrow areas B (of the same density) such as those that might be produced by covering the extended area with a halftone screen. The exposure of a charged xerographic plate to these two density distributions will then result in the charge distributions or images shown in the middle graph in which charge density Q is plotted as a function of distance across the plate. The lower graph is a plot of the normal component of the electric field as a function of position across the charge images of the test object. Note that the field above the center of the extended area is nearly zero and that there are large positive components only near the points corresponding to the boundaries of the test object. Note also that the field passes sharply through zero at these boundaries, and then remains negative for some distance as it gradually returns to zero. (It is interesting to find that long ago Mach, 1882, remarked on the similarity of equipotential curves and the curves representing visual contrast phenomena.)

The field above a large extended charged area of a xerographic plate is essentially the field which would exist on the *outside* of a parallel plate condenser of comparable extent with a material of high dielectric constant between the two plates. That is, at the center of the charged area on the xerographic plate the field is very weak as it is at the center of the plates on the outside of a condenser. (Most of the strength of field is to be found *within* a condenser, between the two plates.) Near the edge of a charged area of the xerographic plate, however, the field is strong—just as it is near the edge of the outside of a parallel plate condenser, because of the so-called fringing effect. For a narrow test object, the electric field is made up almost entirely of the strong fringing fields. Thus the xerographic process reproduces edges and narrow lines about equally well. Because the strength of the field above a charged area is approximately proportional to the density of the corresponding test object which produced it, breaking up extended dark areas into many narrow lines or dots yields many narrow fields of full strength

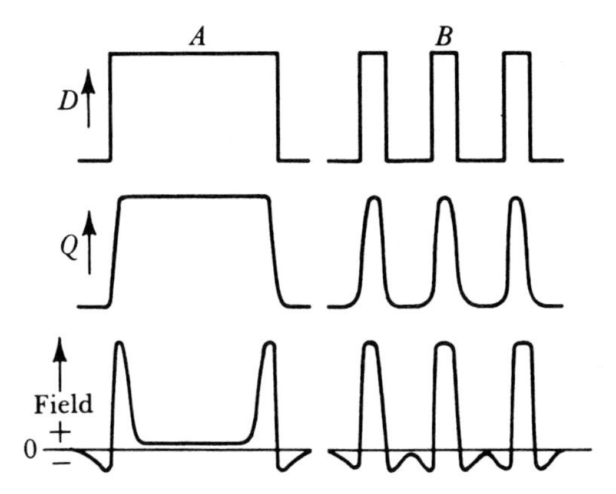

Figure 5.15. *Optical density, charge density, and electric field relationships for a test object with an extended dark area* A *and for the same object broken up into several narrow areas* B. *Redrawn after Dessauer, Mott and Bogdonoff (1955).*

throughout the center of the area where the field would otherwise be zero.

The retardation of development of one part of a photographic film by the by-product of the development of an adjacent part, the neutralization of charge on one part of the photosensitive mosaic of a television camera by electron showers from another part, and the fringe effects in the electrostatic field at the edges of uniformly charged areas on xerographic plates all produce distortions of the final image that are similar to the distortions produced by inhibitory interaction in the visual system. The distortions are similar because the causes are similar: in each case neighboring points in the system are interdependent.

These few examples of instrumental error were chosen because of their obvious similarity to the Mach bands. They are by no means exhaustive, nor are all instrumental errors as obvious as these. *Every* physical instrument used as an extension of or as a substitute for one of the sense organs, however, must have some defects or limitations. Indeed, the perfect transducer and transmitter probably do not exist, although the imperfections may be difficult to recognize. When the shortcomings of the instrument are known, spurious or distorted signals can either be tolerated if they cause no serious difficulties or enhanced if they are found to produce some desirable effect. But if all the properties of the instrument are not known—as must always be the case—and if the instrument is the only measure of the properties of the object under observation, then there is always the possibility that properties of the instrument and properties of the object may be confounded. Thus even though a physical instrument may help to ensure that properties of the observer's sense organs are not confounded with those of the object observed, the possibility remains that the same kind of error may be made with the instrument itself. And this possibility increases with the increasing complexity of the instruments that are used and with the resulting increasing remoteness of the observer from the object observed.

The "subject knowing" It is essential to view the "subject knowing" with the same detachment as one views the "object known," if any communicable scientific knowledge about the subject and about so-called subjective phenomena is to be achieved. This must be done to some extent in everyday life for human beings do communicate effectively with one another about such things in ordinary language—in fact, it has been most convenient throughout this book to use such terms as sensation, experience, appearance, see, hear, and others, without having to define them. The superb utility of ordinary language as a social instrument is beyond question. Practically everyone immediately understands words such as "darker," "brighter," and so forth, so that it is very easy to ask someone whether one part of a pattern he is looking at is brighter or darker than another part and to get a meaningful reply. Indeed, it is so easy to give instructions to a subject about where to sit, what to look at, what to say, when and how much he will be paid, and other matters, that one tends to forget what a long and tedious process the acquisition of a common language by the experimenter and his subject actually was and what an important role it plays in experiments on sensory processes. But even worse, one tends to forget what the actual data in such experiments comprise; they are observable *responses* by the subject in the presence of observable *stimuli,* rather than the phenomena that we ourselves might experience if we took the subject's place.

All this is brought forcibly to our attention whenever we undertake similar experiments on lower animals, for one of the main problems is the lack of a common language for communicating with the subject. As has been shown before, the precise measurement of subjective contrast effects is a difficult task even when using a sophisticated human subject. Comparable psychophysical experiments on lower animals pose even more problems because the animal must somehow be given "instructions" about what to do in the experiment and must then make a "report" to the experimenter about what it sees—all without recourse to an already existing common language. All we have to begin with is the natural empathy we feel toward any living being, and we are inclined to hold this in check lest we be accused of anthropomorphism.

One way to give the animal instructions and to get his report is by means of the so-called operant conditioning techniques developed by B. F. Skinner and his associates. First the animal is motivated to perform by depriving him of food. He is then "instructed" on how to perform by giving him food "reinforcements" when he makes the appropriate responses. Under certain stimulus conditions one response is reinforced; under other stimulus conditions a different response is reinforced. Obtaining the food is thus contingent upon making a particular response in the presence of a particular stimulus. If the animal is hungry, he soon learns to "pay attention" to the stimulus and to make the appropriate response.

In a method developed by Ratliff and Blough (1954) for the study of contrast effects in the visual system of the pigeon (Fig. 5.16), the stimulus itself was placed under the animal's control. The method was based on a method of human audiometry developed by Békésy (1947) and a method of measuring human visual thresholds developed by Craik and Vernon (1941).

The pigeon faces two spots of light—one of fixed intensity, the other variable. If the intensity of the left-hand spot is higher than the in-

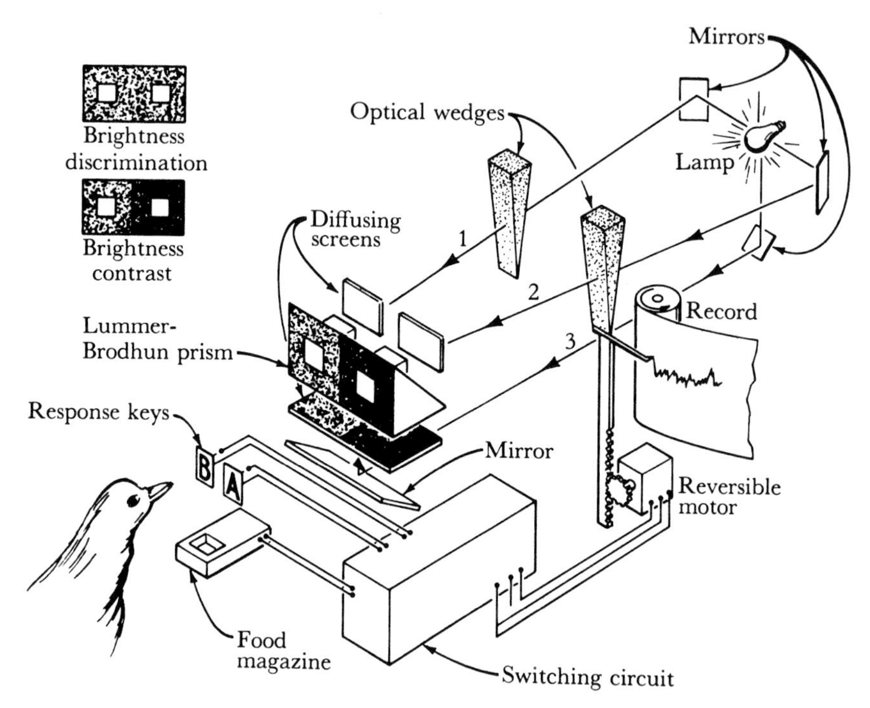

Figure 5.16. *Schema of apparatus for measuring brightness discrimination and brightness contrast in the pigeon. By means of a double Lummer-Brodhun prism light from three transilluminated screens is combined to form patterns of illumination such as those shown in the upper left. Channel 1 provides a spot of some fixed intensity. Channel 2 produces a similar spot, the intensity of which can be adjusted by the pigeon by pecking on the two keys* A *and* B. *Channel 3, entering the prism from below, provides a surround of any desired pattern and intensity. To simplify the sketch a number of optical components have been omitted. From Ratliff (1962).*

tensity of the right-hand spot, the pigeon must peck on the left-hand key to obtain food; if the intensity of the right-hand spot is higher, he must peck on the right-hand key. Pecking on the right-hand key, however, decreases the intensity of the right-hand spot; pecking on the left-hand key increases the intensity of the right-hand spot. Thus, to make a high proportion of correct responses, the animal must shift his responses from one key to the other as first one spot of light and then the other becomes relatively more intense.

The system is self-regulating: the animal's responses control the stimulus, which in turn controls the animal's responses. The result is that a well-trained animal shifts his responses from one key to the other in such a way that the intensity of the variable stimulus oscillates within a narrow range about the point of equality with the fixed stimulus (as shown in the first segment of the record in Figure 5.17). All of the foregoing occurs under the conditions labeled "brightness discrimination" in the inset. If, while the stimuli are thus closely matched, a dark field is placed around one of the two stimuli (the conditions labeled "brightness contrast") the animal now drives the variable stimulus to a new lower level (second segment of the record) and maintains it there until the uniform field is restored, whereupon he once again keeps the two stimuli physically matched (third segment of the record). Using the same apparatus, a human observer makes essentially the same adjustments (see Fig. 2.23 above). For further details on this method see Blough (1961) and Ratliff (1962).

On the basis of this experiment one might be tempted to say that the stimulus with the darker field around it "appears" brighter to the pigeon than does the one with the lighter field around it. But any such anthropomorphic statement about how the stimulus appears to the pigeon (or about the pigeon's visual experience in general) would be superfluous because all that is actually known is that the animal responded in certain ways under certain conditions. In somewhat the same way our statements in our ordinary language about sense experiences, consciousness, and other mental processes that take place in other persons are statements about what they *say* or *do* in various situations.

Nevertheless, the statements "he sees," or "he experiences" seem to be more than succinct descriptions of a person's behavior, and, in fact, they are. They have an excess meaning; that is, they carry with them much of what the statements "I see" or "I experience" bring to mind. In short, we

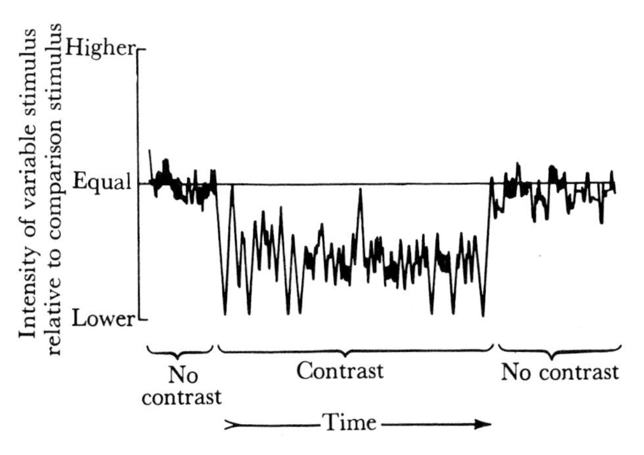

Figure 5.17. Records indicative of simultaneous contrast effects in the pigeon. From Ratliff (1962).

attribute to other persons experiences similar to our own, which seems to be a reasonable thing to do. And for this very reason what a person says can be far more informative than what he does (or rather, what he does other than saying, since saying is a form of doing). In a few well-chosen words he can tell us whether or not the two spots of light (in the experiment above) appear uniform over their whole extent, whether there are any color changes, whether the surround is visibly affected by changing the intensity of the variable spot, whether he hears the sound of a microswitch in the apparatus, and so on. All of these responses, which are accomplished in a few seconds, would probably take months or years if we could not use language, and it might never be accomplished if the subject were a lower animal. But it is most important to remember that if we rely on language we literally have to take the subject's word for all the things that he claims to see or otherwise experience. In any event, all we can know about the subject's experience is what we ourselves experience, and—in the final analysis—that is limited to observations of what he says and does.

In short, the "subject knowing" that I observe is an "object known" to me (albeit a very special kind of object because I attribute experiences like my own to him), and this leads to a very peculiar situation. I can perceive any number of things that seem to me to exist independently of any other person; he and they do not have to co-exist in my experience, and for practical purposes I can *conceive* of other persons and objects existing independently of myself. But I cannot experience anything about them that I do not experience, I cannot know anything about them that I do not know; and therefore it would be a contradiction for me to say that I *know* that they exist independently of my experience and knowing. Even the practical conception that they do so exist is a part of my experience. But who and where is *the* prime subject, this *I* about whom we all speak?

According to Wittgenstein (1922, pp. 151-153):

> I am my world. (The microcosm.)
>
> The thinking, presenting subject; there is no such thing.
>
> If I wrote a book "The world as I found it" I should also have therein to report on my body and say which members obey my will and which do not, etc. This then would be a method of isolating the subject or rather of showing that in an important sense there is no subject: that is to say, of it alone in this book mention could *not* be made.
>
> The subject does not belong to the world but it is a limit of the world.
>
> *Where in* the world is a metaphysical subject to be noted?

You can say that this case is altogether like that of the eye and the field of sight. But you do *not* really see the eye.

And from nothing *in the field of sight* can it be concluded that it is seen from an eye.

For the field of sight has not a form like this:

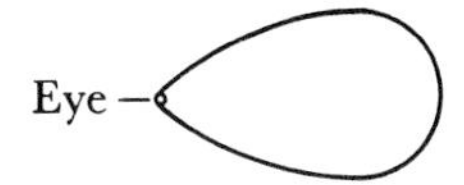

This is connected with the fact that no part of our experience is also a priori.

Everything we see could also be otherwise.

Everything we can describe at all could also be otherwise.

There is no order of things a priori.

Here we see that solipsism strictly carried out coincides with pure realism. The I in solipsism shrinks to an extensionless point and there remains the reality co-ordinated with it.

There is therefore really a sense in which in philosophy we can talk of a non-psychological I.

The I occurs in philosophy through the fact that the "world is my world."

The philosophical I is not the man, not the human body or the human soul of which psychology treats, but the metaphysical subject, the limit—not a part of the world.

Perhaps the dilemma that we thought we faced at the beginning of this chapter—the choice between solipsism and pure realism—does not exist. And perhaps the furtherance of objective knowledge of what we call the real physical world is not the most pressing problem of our times. Rather, it may be that what we require most of all—to sustain mankind and civilization—is further knowledge of man himself.

PART TWO

Mach's papers on the interdependence of retinal points

TRANSLATOR'S NOTE

Acknowledgments are due the following who assisted me in translating several difficult passages and who read the translation through and compared it with the original: Miss Christine Rosner, Mrs. Maria Lipski, and Dr. Eric G. Heinemann.

The six translated papers are numbered and presented here in the order of their original dates of publication. Throughout the translation, Mach's references to other works are cited in footnotes rather than in the general bibliography at the end of this book. References which he made to his own papers included in this translation have been changed to refer to the number of the paper as presented here. A few English translations of old books now available, and some other relevant works, are cited by name of author and date of recent publication in translator's notes; the complete references for these are given in the general bibliography. F.R.

ERNST MACH

1. *On the effect of the spatial distribution of the light stimulus on the retina**

By chance, I have noticed a phenomenon involving rotating discs with black and white sectors, the further investigation of which has led me to a more general law of physiological optics.

I will first of all describe this phenomenon. When one rapidly rotates the discs in Plate I-1a or 1b, the image 1c results. It appears gray, increasing in darkness toward the rim, but is interrupted by narrow, brighter, somewhat washed-out rings in regions where the black sectors end in points or inflect. The phenomenon of the bright rings will astonish anyone who seeks its theoretical explanation, because it is apparent that when both discs 1a and 1b are rotated they should show the same brightness relation, according to the Talbot–Plateau law.† From

* Translated from: E. Mach, "Über die Wirkung der räumlichen Vertheilung des Lichtreizes auf die Netzhaut," Sitzungsberichte der mathematisch-naturwissenschaftlichen Classe der kaiserlichen Akademic der Wissenschaften, 1865, Wien, 52/2, 303-322.

† Talbot, *Philosophical Magazine*, Ser. III, Vol. V, p. 321. Plateau, *Bulletin de l'acad. roy. des sciences de Bruxelles*, 1835, No. 2, p. 52. No. 3, p. 89. [Translator's note: For a modern account of the Talbot-Plateau law, see Le Grand (1957).]

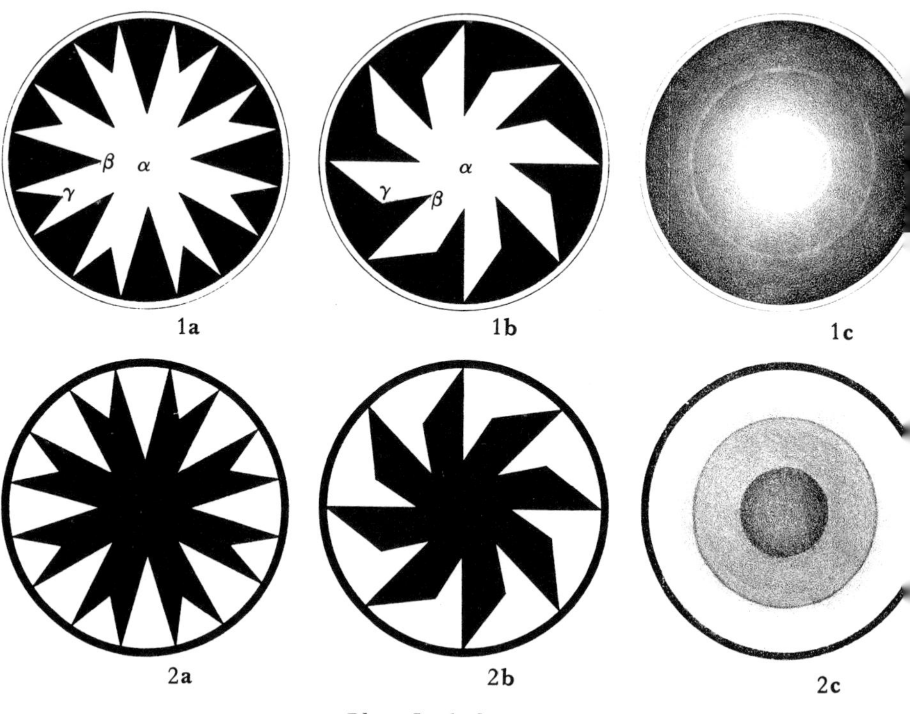

Plate I—1, 2

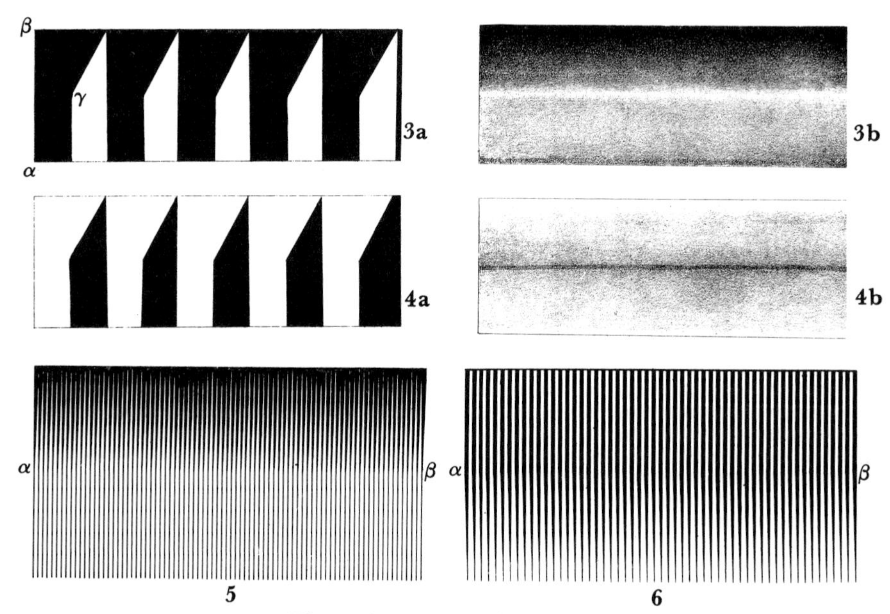

Plate II—3, 4, 5, 6

the center α to the ring going through β they should appear uniformly white. At β the black sectors begin and should cause a gray increasing uniformly in darkness toward γ. From γ on, where the sector is inflected, or respectively, a new sector begins, the darkness should increase more rapidly. A priori, one would not expect that the rings β and γ would be brighter than their surroundings, but that their brightness would lie between that of the next outer and next inner rings. Accordingly, they would not interrupt the continuity of the illumination.

The actual appearance of the rotating disc is, as mentioned, a different one. Figure 1(a) gives the brightness of the rotating disc according to the Talbot–Plateau law, in which the radius is plotted as abscissa (x), and the light intensity as ordinate (y). In the same way, Figure 1(b) shows the actual appearance of the rotating disc. Moreover, it should be noted that with rotation the inner zone does not appear white, but grayish, and the part between the two bright rings appears almost uniformly gray except for a slight darkening toward the outer border.

The discs in Plate I-2a and 2b are the negative images of I-1a, 1b and accordingly appear during rotation as I-2c, which is the negative image of I-1c. The discs in I-2a and 2b show dark rings at each place where bright rings appeared in I-1a and 1b. If, as before, one constructs the curve for the light intensity, one finds that the rings which now appear dark also correspond to flections of the light curve, which are, however, convex with respect to the axis of the abscissa.

By means of various forms of light and dark sectors on rotating discs and on the surface of a rotating cylinder, one can vary the light in-

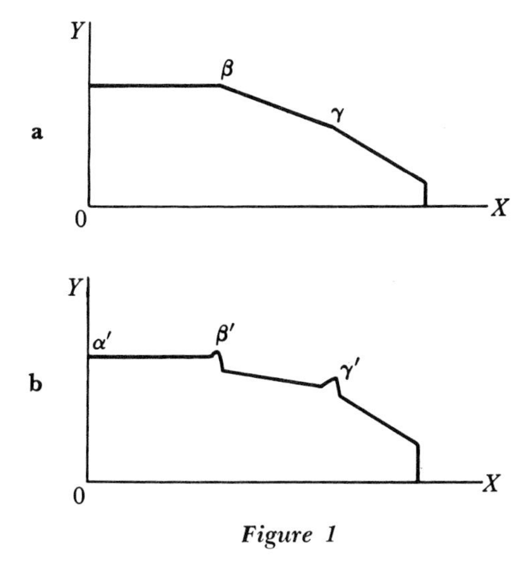

Figure 1

tensity from place to place according to any chosen rule and thus demonstrate the generality of the phenomenon mentioned. Every point where the light intensity curve has a flection will appear brighter or darker than its surroundings. The point where the flection is concave toward the axis of the abscissa is brighter; where the flection is convex toward the axis of the abscissa, it is darker.

Plate II-3a represents the surface unrolled from around a cylinder with axis of rotation parallel to $\alpha\beta$. Plate II-3b shows the appearance of the rotating surface, with a bright stripe corresponding to the flection γ.

Plate II-4a is transformed by rotation into 4b. One can now guess at once how Plate III-7, 8, and 9 would appear as surfaces of rotating cylinders. All confirm the rule formulated above.

One can now easily show that the phenomenon is not peculiar either to rotating discs or intermittent light; rather, it appears wherever the corresponding brightness relations exist.

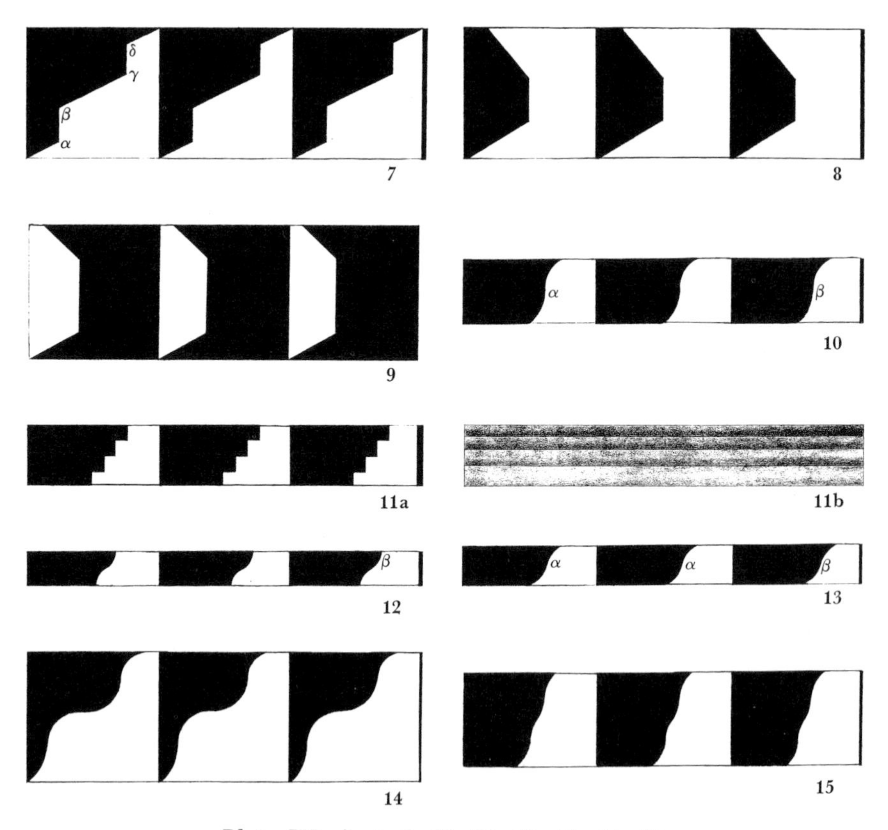

Plate III—7, 8, 9, 10, 11, 12, 13, 14, 15

I wanted to obtain the same light gradation with stationary and continuously illuminated surfaces as with the rotating discs. To this end, I proceeded first of all to photograph the discs during rotation, assuming that the photographic paper, like the retina, would react according to the Talbot–Plateau law. This assumption being supported by the complete resemblance of the photographs to the rotating discs, I then succeeded, through several experiments, to obtain even stronger confirmation. In so doing I kept in mind the fact that a negative is first obtained and then from this the positive picture is made.

First, let us ask to what extent the photograph and the original generally present the same brightness relations. Let the original be a rectangular strip whose brightness varies along its length. If we call the light intensity of one point y and its distance from one end of the strip x, we have $y = f(x)$. If the blackening of every part of the photographic paper up to its total capacity is proportional to the exposure time and proportional to the intensity of the irradiation, we thus have for the image $y_1 = p + qf(x)$. The constant q depends upon the exposure time, and the constant p must be added, since the brightness of unexposed paper can vary considerably. Furthermore, since some light passes through the darkest parts of the negative, even those parts of the positive image which actually should have remained completely white become darkened. According to these assumptions, the light curve of the image would be derived from the original by multiplying all the ordinates of the latter by the same factor, and then displacing the whole curve parallel to the ordinate. The new curve is affinitive to the old one. Since now

$$\frac{dy_1}{dx} = q\left(\frac{dy}{dx}\right), \qquad \frac{d^2y_1}{dx^2} = q\left(\frac{d^2y}{dx^2}\right), \qquad \text{etc.,}$$

one can see that the light curve of the image has the same gradation and curvature relationships as those of the original. The flections must, therefore, also remain fixed, since they are only special cases of curvatures.

Now let us turn to the photography of the rotating discs. I first photographed a disc such as utilized by Helmholtz* and Brücke† in their studies of intermittent light stimuli. It was divided into six concentric rings, with each ring half black and half white. The innermost ring had one black sector, the next 2, the next 4, and so on up to 32. I exposed this disc from one to 15 seconds, varying the speed of rotation from one to 30 revolutions per second. In all of these cases the picture of the disc

* Helmholtz, *Physiol. Optik*. [Translator's note: The English translation of Helmholtz's treatise, first published by the Optical Society of America in 1925, has recently been republished. See Helmholtz (1962).]

† Brücke, "Über den Nutzeffect intermittirender Netzhautreizungen." *Sitzb. Wiener Akad.*, **49.**

became uniformly gray so that one could not distinguish the concentric rings one from the other. If the effect of illumination on the photographic paper builds up gradually at the onset and diminishes gradually at the cessation as for the retina, which appears certain from Bequerel's experiments on fluorescence, this must occur in an extraordinarily short time. Thus the photographic effect resulting from equal light intensity depends only on the irradiation time, irrespective of any interruptions of the irradiation.

We will next consider the influence of brightness. A white disc (Fig. 2) was provided with three concentric rings a, b, c. The outermost, a, was half black; the second, b, was one-fourth black; and the third, c, was one-eighth black. The central part of the disc remained white. When the disc was photographed during rotation, three unequally bright rings resulted. Rings were cut from these parts of the photograph and pasted on the central white portion. The ring a', cut from a, covered one-eighth of the periphery; the ring b', cut from b, one-fourth; and the ring c', cut from c, one-half. When the photograph was rotated, a', b', and c' appeared equally bright.

This experiment leads to the following conclusions. When a rotating disc shows, according to the Talbot–Plateau law, the brightness curve $y = f(x)$, there results in its photograph the brightness curve $y = p + qf(x)$. This curve therefore shows the same gradation, curvature, and flection relations as those of the original.

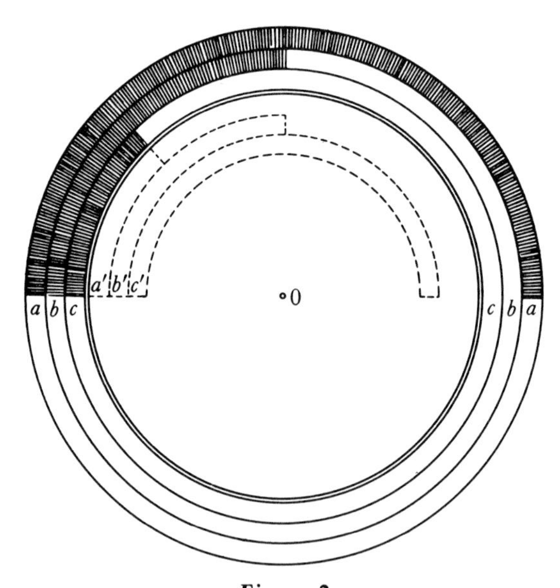

Figure 2

For our purposes the exact realization of all of these conditions is not necessary. We need merely accept the notion that the light intensity in the photograph is some continuous function of the irradiation intensity and the exposure time, and also that the differential quotient of this function is continuous. If $y = f(x)$ for the light curve of the original, then $y_1 = F(y)$ for that of the photograph, and it follows that

$$\frac{dy_1}{dx} = \left(\frac{dF(y)}{dy}\right)\frac{dy}{dx}.$$

If $(dy)/(dx)$ is discontinuous for any x, then $(dy_1)/(dx)$ must also be discontinuous; that is to say, the flections in the light curve of the photograph must correspond to the flections in the light curve of the original.

The photographs of my rotating discs appear exactly like the rotating discs themselves. If I photograph the disc Plate I-1a, then the negative itself is the picture in I-2c, and the positive picture made from it is I-1c. Naturally, since I-2c is a negative picture, it is like the rotating disc I-2a. It must not be concluded that the bright and dark rings are objective phenomena because they appear in the photograph. On the contrary, I have shown that objective photography follows the Talbot-Plateau law and since the rings are not explainable in terms of this law, their subjective nature is demonstrated. Only when the objective photograph gives the same brightness relations as the rotating disc must they appear subjectively equal. Both must, of course, be viewed by eye. I would not emphasize this fact if I had not often heard this objection.

The photographs show the bright and dark rings very beautifully and strikingly. They appear even sharper when one rotates the photographs in exactly the same way as the originals because this movement eliminates the disturbing small irregularities. I have never seen such beautifully uniform surfaces as those obtained with rotating discs. On the other hand, one can make the rings appear less distinct on the original rotating discs, by shading them with an irregular window glass.

In addition to the photographs, one can produce still other stationary and continuously illuminated surfaces which show analogous phenomena under analogous brightness conditions. Plate II-5 is a system of fine vertical parallel black lines lying near one another. From $\alpha\beta$ downward, these remain equally thick, but from $\alpha\beta$ upward they thicken gradually. If one now observes this array through a cylindrical lens with a vertical cylinder axis which disperses only in the horizontal direction, then a brighter horizontal line appears at $\alpha\beta$. The same phenomenon is also seen if one merely moves the sketch to a somewhat greater distance from the eye so that the lines become indistinct and the sheet appears gray. The conditions on which this phenomenon depends are evidently the

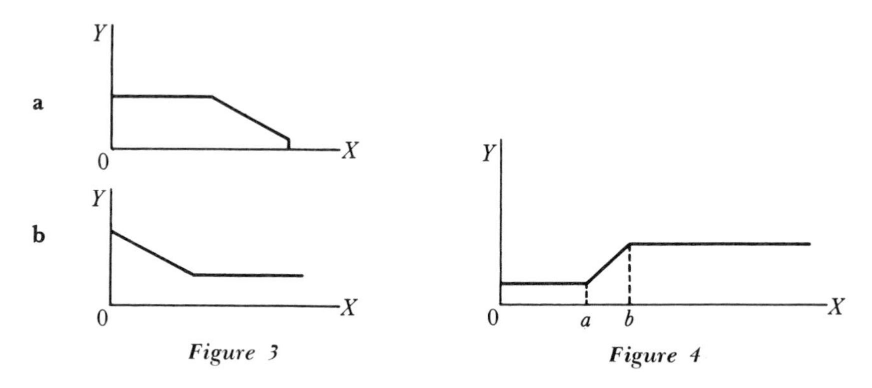

Figure 3

Figure 4

same as with the rotating discs and with the photographs. If we construct the light curve of the stripe in Plate II-5 as it is under the influence of the horizontally dispersing lens, representing the distance from the lower end as abscissa (x), and the corresponding light intensity as ordinates (y), we then obtain Figure 3(a). The bright line appears at the point of flection. The stripe of Plate II-6 shows a dark line at $\alpha\beta$, and, from there downward the black lines thin gradually. The light curve of this stripe is shown in Figure 3(b).

Once the phenomenon of the bright and dark lines is known, they are easily found under the most common conditions. For example, one can observe them in almost every shadow which is cast in the light from a bright extended light source. Let us construct the light curve of a shadow. The full-shadow extends from 0 to a in Figure 4, and is represented with a small constant value on the ordinate. From a to b we find the half-shadow whose light intensity increases toward b, where the fully illuminated space begins. At the border of the full-shadow and half-shadow there should appear a line which is darker than the full-shadow itself. The outer border of the half-shadow, however, is a bright line which exceeds the light intensity of the fully illuminated space. The phenomenon as I have constructed it theoretically is actually found if, when the sky is unclouded, one intercepts the shadow of the edge of a house with a piece of smooth white paper. The ground on which the shadow falls by chance is usually too nonuniform to show the lines distinctly, but they appear sharper if the shadow is intercepted on a rotating white disc.

With the help of shadows, one can easily produce an illumination which appears quite similar to Plate I-1c and 2c. If one uses a small lamp* which throws the shadow of a little circular pasteboard disc on a sheet of smooth paper, a circular full-shadow is obtained which is bounded by a dark line enclosed in a gray ring ending in a bright circular line. Instead of using a small lamp with a globe, one can place a

* Translator's note: "Moderateurlampe" in the original text.

pasteboard screen, with a circular opening on which has been pasted some oil paper, in front of a candle flame.

Having shown the phenomenon under these various circumstances, we can, without hesitation, establish the following principles. Wherever the light-intensity curve of an illuminated surface (the light intensity of which varies in only one direction) has a concave or convex flection with respect to the axis of the abscissa, that particular place appears brighter or darker, respectively, than its surroundings.

An already long-known phenomenon may be regarded as a special case of this principle. Namely, Plate III-11a, which is on the surface of a rotating cylinder, appears as 11b, where each stripe appears brighter where it borders on the darker one. This results simply because the light curve always has a simultaneously convex and concave flection at the same place. Here, we find that the dark lines appear one after the other, which, in Plate III-7 appear alternately but separated. This picture is also reproduced by photography.

Flections are nothing but very sharp curves. I can, therefore, ask whether or not the phenomenon could be caused, to a lesser degree, by less sharp curvatures of the light curve. The experimental answer is "yes." Sectors which have mere curves in the corresponding places instead of knees show the phenomena on rotating discs; only, in this case, the bright and dark lines are weak, washed-out shadowy forms. Concavity with respect to the abscissa results in an increase in brightness, while convexity results in a decrease. What will we now see at the point of inflection? On one side there is a concavity, on the other a convexity; at the point of inflection itself, there is no curvature at all. The point of inflection thus must give a sharp border between light and shadow, which, in fact, it does, when it lies between two fairly strong curves which suddenly turn one into the other.

If we rotate the cylinder shown in Plate III-10, we see a border between dark and light at $\alpha\beta$. The upper part appears very slightly brighter than the lower, although objectively it is even darker. Only near the edge does the objective brightness show its effect. One sees the phenomenon more distinctly in Plate III-13, where the curvature is stronger, and yet more distinctly in Plate III-12, where the objective brightness has an effect in the same direction. Plate III-14 and Plate III-15 are so constructed that the objective brightness increases continuously from above to below. They nevertheless show stripes which are horizontal and shadow-like, alternating brighter and darker, and which border fairly sharply on one another. At the point of inflection the convex arc suddenly turns over to a concave one.*

* Of course, with curves of different strength of curvature, the point of transition from one to another acts like a point of inflection.

In the lecture room, the collection of phenomena in Plate III-7, -11, and -15 can be demonstrated on the rotating cylinders very easily. The sector curves here are, at the same time, the light curves, and present all types of bends, curvatures, and points of inflection.

Our principle shall take this form at present: Curvatures of the light curve which are concave toward the abscissa result, for that place, in an increase in the sensation of light proportional to the curvature, and convex curvatures result in a decrease.

It would now be desirable if we could also determine these facts quantitatively. This is difficult, however. Measurement on merely curved sectors on rotating discs has proved to be impossible because the brightening and darkening is too insignificant to permit exact measurement and the disturbance due to surrounding conditions is too great. Further, quantitative generalizations from bends to curvatures become uncertain.

I must therefore restrict myself to the consideration of three easily verifiable facts, which, so long as proper measurements are not available, do provide a sufficient basis for quantitative conclusions:

(1) First of all, I noticed that both the bright and dark rings and the shaded stripes on my rotating discs were equally distinct in all intensities of irradiation in which they could be seen at all. I have experimented in bright sunshine, in twilight, and by candle light and the rings always contrast equally well with any surrounding background of the same objective intensity as the rings themselves. Let us call the intensity of the ground i and introduce an increment of objective brightness Δ, so that i and $(i + \Delta)$ are as distinctly different as the ring and its ground. If we now increase the illumination q-fold, the imaginary objective brightness difference of the ring, according to psychophysical laws,* must also increase q-fold. Now, qi and $(qi + q\Delta)$ would be as distinctly discriminable as the previous i and $(i + \Delta)$. Nothing can be said against the mere mathematical fiction of an objective brightness difference of the ring and ground, which, according to psychophysical laws, would correspond to the subjective. In no way does it affect the actual facts.

(2) Let us consider the arrangement shown in Figure 5. A series of black sectors with slight bends are placed on the surface of a cylinder. These sectors are covered with the paper ring as indicated in the figure by dotted lines. The ring can be shifted so that the cut out parts corresponding to each sector expose either more or less of the black and white areas. If the paper ring is black one can cause the white parts to vanish almost

* G. T. Fechner, *Elemente der Psychophysik,* 1860. Translator's note: An English translation is to be published in 1965. See Fechner (1965). For general surveys of psychophysical methods, see Guilford (1936) and Boring (1942).

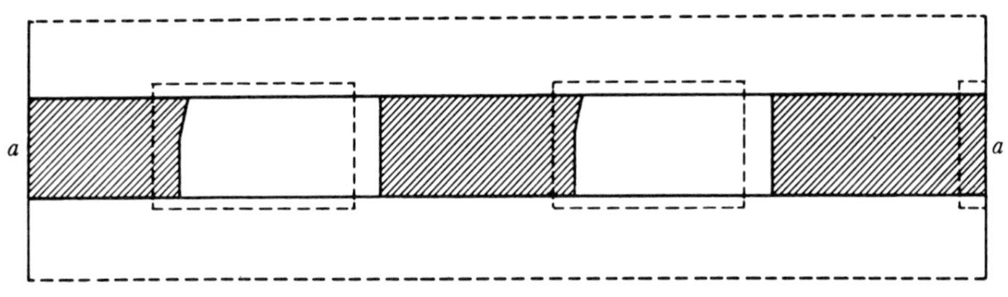

Figure 5

entirely. If it is white, the black parts can be made to vanish almost completely. It is found that the hardly noticeable stripe visible at the bend becomes more distinct when the black is increased; it disappears, however, with an increase in white. One should not be deceived by the appearance of Plate III-7. At γ there appears a darker stripe than at α; at β a brighter stripe than at δ. It is to be noted, however, that the brightness or darkness of the ground are added at γ or β, and that, therefore, the stripe δ is more sharply defined than is β. The most pronounced is γ, because here all the favorable conditions act together.

(3) Finally, with the increasing sharpness of the curvatures, their effect, as previously mentioned, increases correspondingly.

Let us now consider these three facts. From (1), it follows that the rings remain unaltered when the light curve $i = f(x)$ is translated to $i = qf(x)$.

From (2), it follows that the rings can be made to vanish when the light curve $i = f(x)$ is transformed to $i = p + f(x)$ where p is positive and large.

The third fact, mathematically expressed, says that the distinctness of the rings is a direct function of $(d^2i)/(dx^2)$.

Now let us set the previously mentioned

$$\Delta = k \frac{\left(\frac{d^2i}{dx^2}\right)^2}{i}$$

where k is a constant. We thus have given it all its essential properties. Let $i = f(x)$ be transformed to $i = qf(x)$. Thus

$$\Delta = k \frac{\left(q \frac{d^2i}{dx^2}\right)^2}{qi} = qk \frac{\left(\frac{d^2i}{dx^2}\right)^2}{i}.$$

That is to say, Δ is transformed to $q\Delta$, which means the noticeable difference between the ground and ring remains the same. If we change $i = f(x)$

to $i = p + f(x)$, then, by increasing i, Δ becomes smaller. Thus, the noticeable difference between the ring and ground diminishes. Finally, our Δ has the property to increase when $(d^2i)/(dx^2)$ (the curvature) increases. Now we need only establish that Δ shall have the opposite sign of $(d^2i)/(dx^2)$, which we can express as follows:

$$\Delta = -k \frac{\left(\sqrt{\rho}\, \frac{d^2 i}{dx^2}\right)^2}{i},$$

where ρ would signify the coefficient of direction of $(d^2i)/(dx^2)$.

If we accept Fechner's formula* for the intensity of light sensation as correct, and think of a surface whose intensity of irradiation varies only in the direction x, we thus have for each point the corresponding sensation e in the expression

$$e = a \log \left\{ \frac{i}{b} \pm k \frac{\left(\frac{d^2 i}{dx^2}\right)^2}{i} \right\}.$$

In this formula a and b are the familiar Fechner constants, the plus or minus sign is chosen depending on whether or not $(d^2i)/(dx^2)$ is positive or negative. The formula completely represents our data. It is useless only in the case where $(d^2i)/(dx^2)$ is infinite when we are dealing with a true vertex. Even though a true vertex does not actually occur in any light curve, should it occur, it would be blurred due to the dioptric imperfections of the eye. Furthermore, this case of our formula can no more be expected to be strictly correct than can Fechner's formula in the case of an infinite stimulus. In addition, it is certainly only an approximate formula, since the retina, according to the general opinion, consists of a finite number of sensory elements of finite extent. Therefore, when we are dealing with the actual properties of the retina, one can no longer speak of di, dx, but only of Δi, Δx.

One should note that the law set forth for vision is of no slight teleological significance. According to this law, the strong curves and bends in the light curve mainly attract attention through prominent brightening or darkening. The gradient is of lesser effect. Surfaces of uniform and not-too-rapid increase of illumination are often even taken to be uniformly bright. Their brightness, as a preliminary experiment seems to indicate to me, appears equal to the average brightness. On my rotating disc in Plate I-1(c), as well as on the photograph of the same, the space between the two bright rings rr, r_1r_1 appears almost uniformly gray,

* *Op. cit.*

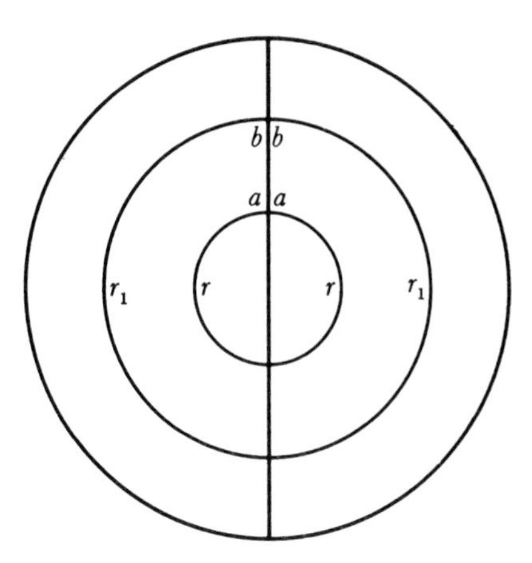

Figure 6

although it is significantly darker toward the outer rim (see Fig. 6). One hardly notices a difference between the positions *aa* and *bb*. This, however, is significant when one cuts the photograph diametrically and slides the two halves along one another so that the cut portions at *a* and *b* lie immediately next to one another. The bends and curves are thus much more striking than are the gradients. I would say that the gradients make themselves felt only through their end result, while the curves and bends act directly. The latter evidently appear mainly in the contours of the retinal image, and it is these which are of the most significance for the perception of external objects.

Helmholtz* has called attention to the fact that, due to a peculiar distribution of light, the circles of dispersion resulting from chromatic aberration of the eye cause only a slight distortion. For example, if, as in Figure 7, *abc* is the light curve for a sharp retinal image, then, according to Helmholtz, as a result of the chromatic aberration it would be something like *adef*. Helmholtz attributes the distinctness of the image to the sharp decline of the curve at the border *e*. According to my experience I must also hold as very essential the transition from concave to convex and the point of inflection at *e*. These relationships may be very easily demonstrated in the lecture room on the rotating cylinder surfaces in Plate III-13, 14, and 15.

The visual organ shows a definite unmistakable tendency to schematize, in that it merely notices striking irregularities. The same tendency manifests itself in details, as well as in the whole field. Otherwise, it would not be possible for a dark ground, treated in line or point fashion,

* Helmholtz, *Physiol. Optik.*

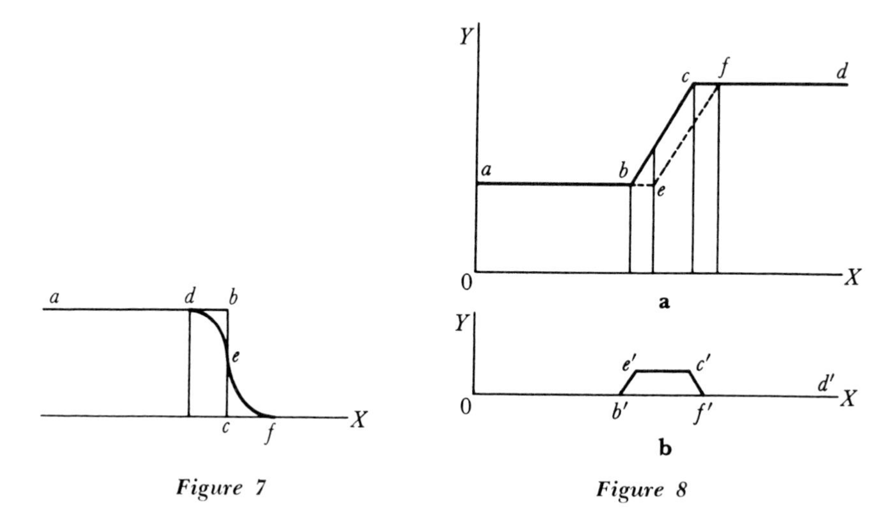

Figure 7

Figure 8

to be perceived as uniform as long as the details are still distinctly visible. Likewise, dotted figures could not be distinguished from the background as separate forms themselves. Forms, too, are schematized by the eye, as is evident from petroglyphs in all parts of the world.

Let us now try to get closer to the cause of the observed phenomenon. First of all, as we have already noted, there can be no doubt about its subjectivity. Its cause is not in the object, but in the visual organ. Places are seen as brighter or darker which are of equal intensity with their neighboring surroundings, or which, to mention intermittent light also, reflect in equal time equal quantities of light as their immediate surroundings.

Since it always is the surroundings which determine the effect on a particular place we can thus classify our phenomenon—for the time being—with contrast phenomena. And it is only a question of whether it belongs to successive or to simultaneous contrast.

Let *abcd* in Figure 8(a) be a light curve. Assume that the retinal image is shifted by a slight eye movement so that it now lies in the position *aefd*. Evidently, according to the direction of the eye movements there ought to be formed at one time a bright after-image, and at another time a dark after-image of the light curve $0b'e'c'f'd'$ which ought to respectively brighten or darken the whole strip *bc*. This is not the observed fact. We cannot ascribe our phenomenon to successive contrast due to eye movements, since the same rings on the disc would then at one time appear bright and at another time dark and, in addition, could not be as narrow as they really appear, and would only be visible piece by piece, corresponding to the direction of the eye movement.

In order to rule out eye movement completely I illuminated my photographed discs with electric sparks and observed them. Then, however, one either cannot see the rings at all or can see them only very weakly and indistinctly. On the other hand, the bright and dark stripes in Plate II-5 and 6 are seen also with electric spark illumination, appearing only as broad indistinct bands. In the latter figures the stripes are generally more distinct than in the photographs. Accordingly, it appears that a certain amount of time is necessary to bring about our phenomenon. Also, with rotating discs at slower rotations, so long as the discs still flicker, the rings appear brighter than with faster rotation, but are broader and more indistinct. It seems to me that the exact study of vision by means of illumination by electric spark is very promising. One might, in this manner, momentarily "surprise" the retina—so to speak—during many of its processes.

If the phenomenon were dependent upon eye movements (which, by the way, cannot be granted because of the reasons already mentioned), then it should disappear completely under illumination by the spark of the Leyden jar and, in addition, a brief illumination should make the rings smaller. In any case, we must be dealing with simultaneous contrast, if one can call this phenomenon contrast at all, nor can the name "induction" introduced by Brücke* be suitably applied to these cases.

It appears to me that the phenomena discussed can only be explained on the basis of a reciprocal action of neighboring areas of the retina. Indeed, this is indicated by the whole form of the law. I must, therefore, accept a viewpoint similar to that already put forth by Plateau. The reciprocal action of the retinal points does, however, require an anatomical connection. In fact, this appears to be confirmed by the most recent researches. Ritter's† data on the structure of the retina follows in his own words:

> The neural tissue of the retina forms a very regularly arranged, completely congruous structure, which is repeated with only slight variations in all vertebrates. From the nerve fiber, which runs inside the optic nerve and then enters the retina, to the rod layer there is one continuous connection; the manifold connecting links serve only to lead up to divisions of the single fiber, or to attribute a higher physiological value to the conducting fiber.
>
> The fibers of the optic nerve form, first of all, a small layer, out-

* Brücke, *Pogg. Ann.*, 84.

† C. Ritter, "Die Structur der Retina, dargestellt nach Untersuchungen über das Wallfischauge," (in Worpswede, Leipzig, W. Engelmann, 1864). See also: Helmholtz, *Physiol. Optik;* Wundt, *Physiologie,* p. 490; Kölliker, *Gewebelehre,* Leipzig, 1863, p. 661; Fick, *Anatomie der Sinnesorgane,* Jahr. 1864, p. 182.

side the limitans, which is thickest next to the entrance of the optic nerve, gradually gets thinner toward the periphery, and finally forms only a manifold perforated lattice work. Without making other connections, the fiber terminates as the inner process of the ganglion cell. As yet there is no research on whether only one nerve fiber, or several, terminate on each ganglion cell. But up to this time only one fiber per cell has been found. In every case, however, there is at least one fiber for every ganglion cell.

The ganglion cells are immediately outside the nerve fiber layer; they are found mostly in a single layer; in certain places (the yellow spot of man and ape) and in certain classes of animals (birds), which have very acute vision, they form a double and multiple layer. Toward the periphery the number of cells decreases in regular proportion; they no longer lie tightly against one another but become separated by larger and larger interstices filled with connective tissue fibers. And they finally stop completely a short distance from the *ora serrata.* The ganglion cells frequently send off processes toward the inner and outer sides; lateral connecting branches between the cells are seldom found. The inner processes are fibers of the optic nerve, the outer ones enter the fiber layer and form in the center of the retina a large and, toward the periphery, a decreasing part of it. There are always several outer processes in each place, only in the yellow spot of man is there the possibility of a connection of one cell with one outer filament, but even here this is not yet proven. Often several such processes arise from a thicker branch, which divides itself two or three times until in the terminal stage the branches have reached the smallest width of the outermost processes appropriate to each animal. The cell branches have their origins at very diverse angles, they penetrate the fiber layer in all directions, and only single ones on each cell run fairly radially. At the end of its path every process reaches a granular cell, and indeed only one process contacts one such cell.

The granular cells lie immediately outside the fiber layer. From the outer side of these small cells arise one or two fine fibers which probably divide into a certain small number of filaments and penetrate radially through the granular layer. Inside the filaments lie several granules; that is, round or oval clusters, possibly of a medullary substance. The filament continues then outward into the covering of the rods and cones and ends near their outer limit with a knob shaped swelling.

This interconnection of the nerve tissue is found in the retinas of all vertebrates.

According to Ritter's count there are about seven rods converging on and connected with one granular cell, and 13 granular cells with one ganglion cell. One optic nerve fiber connects with something like 100 rods. We find a systematic branching toward the periphery. If the rods are really the sensitive end elements, their various excitations must definitely undergo a series of reciprocal actions before they are transmitted to the fibers of the optic nerve. I would like to say that, in part, the retinal elements determine among themselves which sensations they will further conduct. I do not wish to hazard more definite conjectures.

I do not doubt that many physiologists would be inclined to explain the phenomena described in this paper in terms of unconscious conclusions and judgments, instead of in terms of the structure of the retina and its physical processes, if only some principle could be found whereby this could be done. I consider even this conception of the sense organs as somewhat of an advancement. Why should not the sense organs have a certain logic? Why should the ganglion cells of these organs behave differently than those of the rest of the nervous system and the brain? After one has explained conclusions by the sense organs as unconscious analogies of conscious processes, however, I cannot agree that one should search for antecedent conditions on which only conscious processes can be based, instead of searching for both the genuine antecedent conditions and the corresponding physical processes and organs in the sensory apparatus itself. Too much is expected of the eye if it should be expected to know that note paper is white, that the color of a body showing faintly through it is modified, that white itself is compounded of complementary colors, etc. All these things I know quite well as a physicist and yet I do not understand how the contrast phenomena continue to be the same for my eye, even when I am not aware of it. Where could the eye have obtained this knowledge of the science of color? And yet this judgment does take place in the eye, or else the experience of the phenomena would have to be modified through conscious reflection.

Until not too long ago, all things psychological were not accepted as facts; as far as their reality was concerned they were considered incommensurable with physical events. Only recently a very distinguished scholar said about my experiments: "Why bother with this? It must be only an illusion!" Those times are past. We know that even "illusions" are facts, and that laws underly them. Now we even make a little too much of this and forget, at times, that every psychical event should correspond to a physical event, and that it is very desirable to determine this correspondence.

In this connection, permit me to mention here a heuristic principle of psychophysical research* which I frequently apply, often implicitly, and perhaps not entirely without success: Every psychical event corresponds

* An indication of this principle is already contained in my *Compendium of Physics,* Vienna, 1863.

to a physical event and vice versa. *Equal* psychical processes correspond to *equal* physical processes, *unequal* to *unequal* ones. When a psychical process is analyzed in a purely psychological way, into a number of qualities *a*, *b*, *c*, then there corresponds to them just as great a number of physical processes α, β, γ. To all the details of psychological events correspond details of the physical events.

These hypotheses have led me to my view of the accommodation of the ear and the formation of the tone series, and to a way of thinking about the sense of time and spatial vision. If one would treat the science of color according to these principles, it would have to lead to the Young theory.* But then the basic colors would be red, yellow, green, and blue, for only in these can no other colors be distinguished by mere observation. In addition, a special physiological process would have to be postulated for the sensation white and black. For in white no other color is perceptible. Even if several excitations in the retina correspond to it, the last process in the physiological chain, which causes the *single* sensation of white, must—like the sensation—be thought of as single.

Let us examine another phenomenon with the help of our principle, which to my knowledge no one has yet discussed. White of a lesser intensity appears gray next to a brighter white. On the other hand, we are never in doubt whether we have before us a white or gray paper even under quite different conditions of illumination: in bright sunshine, overcast sky, in twilight, or by candle light, we have always almost the same sensation. What might be the cause of this? If the light intensity is 2-, 3-, or *n*-fold brighter, so then is the retinal image of the white paper 2-, 3-, or *n*-fold brighter, but so also is the rest of the visual field and the entire retina receives the 2-, 3-, or *n*-fold illumination. The relation of the quantity of light on the entire retina and the image of the paper remains constant under otherwise equal conditions. I think, therefore, that a process is initiated whose intensity depends on this relation, and which causes the sensation of white for the retinal image. The brightness of the retinal image is, so to speak, being evaluated in terms of the total excitation. This is a judgment, the psychological side of the matter. The physical side is the process mentioned. It has not yet been discovered.

Note that my proposition is based essentially on Fechner's basic formula. The fundamental discriminations of the sense organs occur in accordance with it, as Wundt correctly noted.

When the above facts are brought together with our ring phenomena, it leads, to some degree, to an explanation of the latter. It is not improbable that small parts of the retina behave in a manner quite similar to the behavior of the whole eye. As special and comparative anatomy

* Translator's note: Now generally known as the Young–Helmholtz theory.

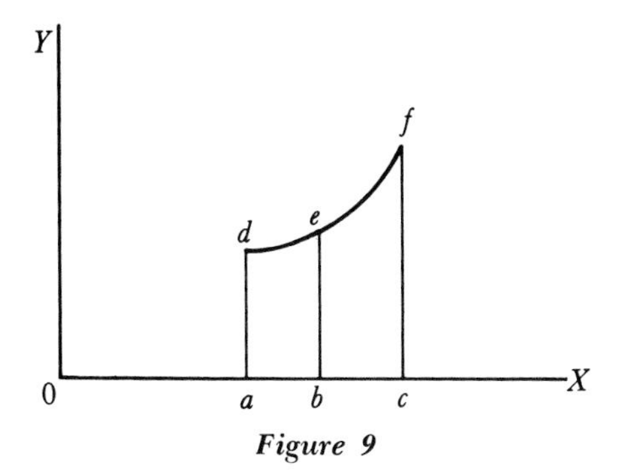

Figure 9

indicates more and more, from day to day, the whole organism is built according to a plan—a true homoeomeria. If we accept the idea that the brightness of a rod is evaluated in terms of the total brightness on an assembly of rods (something like 100 rods according to Ritter) as the previously mentioned retinal image is evaluated in terms of the whole retina (or in other words, if for each rod a process is initiated whose intensity depends on the relation of the quantities of light on the rod and on the assembly of rods), then we can understand our phenomena.

The rod *b* of Figure 9 would be affected by the light intensity *be* and the whole extent of rods *abc,* which we think of as being anatomically interconnected with *b,* by the part of the light curve convex to the axis of the abscissa. Obviously the brightness of the rod *b* must be less than average total brightness of the extent of rods *abc,* and it would thus be judged as darker, psychologically speaking. The reverse would be true if the light curve were concave with respect to the abscissa. I will restrict my analysis to these suggestions.

Finally, I would like to mention that my auditor, Herr Joseph Krizan, carefully prepared for the work the necessary laborious drawings and diagrams, and further that Herr Dr. Fr. Davidowsky, Director of the Handelsakademie in Graz, kindly made some of the photographs. Some especially fine and exact pictures were prepared for me by Herr L. Bude, photographer at Graz.

ERNST MACH

2. *On the physiological effect of spatially distributed light stimuli**

The aim of this paper is to supplement an earlier publication.†

Let us think of the retina as a plane surface and of its intensity of illumination as changing from point to point in any chosen manner. Let us then erect on each point an ordinate proportional to the light intensity and connect the terminal points of all of the ordinates; a surface is thus obtained which I will call the objective light intensity surface or *light surface.*

Now let us erect an ordinate on each point of the same retina which is proportional to the corresponding intensity of the sensation of light at this point; thus, there results another surface which I shall call the subjective light intensity surface or *sensation surface.*

In general, the two surfaces, the *light surface* and the *sensation surface* are different, although they

* Translated from: E. Mach, "Über den physiologischen Effect räumlich vertheilter Lichtreize (Zweite Abhandlung)," Sitzungsberichte der mathematisch-naturwissenschaftlichen Classe der kaiserlichen Akademie der Wissenschaften, 1866, 54/2, 131-144.

† Translator's note: The preceding paper in this series (Number 1).

resemble one another insofar as one represents a distorted image of the other. They are, therefore, similar, but not in the geometrical sense. Geometrically they could not be called *affinitive,* but only *collinear.*

There exist, nevertheless, quite simple relations between the two surfaces which physiology must determine. We notice first of all that, assuming the validity of Fechner's law, the ordinates of the light surface are proportional to the light intensity while the ordinates of the sensation surface are proportional to the logarithm of the light intensity. The latter, however, is true only approximately. A correction must be added which we will now consider.

In the previous work we investigated the special case where the light intensity on the retinal plane varied only parallel to it and only in one direction so that both the light surface and the sensation surface are transformable to a cylindrical surface. In this case we can restrict ourselves to the investigation of the two directrices and call the one belonging to the light surface the *light curve* and that of the sensation surface the *sensation curve.*

Experience has shown that the magnitude of the ordinates of the sensation curve depends not merely upon the corresponding ordinates of the light curve but also upon the curvature of the light curve at the corresponding points. I have already expressed a formula which represents the facts more concisely and plainly than one can with words, without, however, claiming quantitative exactness.

Let $i = f(x)$ represent the light curve. Then the ordinate of the sensation curve is

$$e = a \log \left\{ \frac{i}{b} \pm \frac{k \left(\frac{d^2 i}{dx^2} \right)^2}{i} \right\}$$

where a, b, and k are constants and where the upper sign holds for a negative value of $(d^2 i)/(dx^2)$.

As was said earlier, exact measurements cannot be carried out and the facts are about as well represented when one uses the expression

$$e = a \log \left(\frac{i}{b} - \frac{k}{\rho i} \right)$$

for the ordinate of the sensation curve where ρ signifies the radius of curvature of the light curve at the point concerned.

Both formulas are inexact, because they are no longer valid when $(d^2 i)/(dx^2)$ becomes very large or when ρ becomes very small.

The form of this law was verified on the following:

(1) Rotating discs and cylinders,

(2) Photographs of rotating objects,
(3) Surfaces ruled with fine lines, and
(4) Shaded surfaces.

Since then, I have employed another simple method for the same purpose. If one grinds a prism from a semitransparent body such as bone glass, with a cross section through the base as represented in Figure 1, and places it in an opening in the window shutter of a darkened room, then one sees a brighter line at the concave edge α and a darker line at the convex edge β. If the absorption of light in the semitransparent medium is considered, then this phenomenon is easily explained in terms of our law.

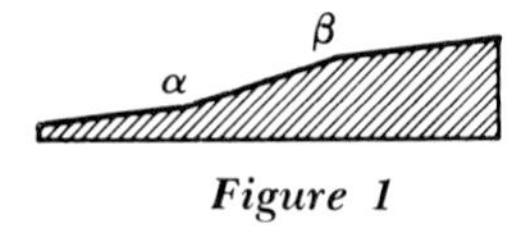

Figure 1

Let us now turn to the general investigation of light surfaces. One can produce these most easily if two cylindrical light surfaces are superimposed with their axes perpendicular. Figure 2 represents the retinal plane where we shall place a light surface whose equation is $i_1 = f(x)$ and upon it one whose equation is $i_2 = F(y)$. A new light surface is thus created whose equation is $i = f(x) + F(y)$ and which is no longer a cylindrical surface.

With the use of this basic idea I have found several simple methods in order to produce more complicated light surfaces experimentally. I will describe these briefly.

(1) A disc painted with black and white sectors is rotated. A ring of its surface is indicated by the dotted lines as shown in Figure 3. The center of the disc is at A. In front of this same disc rotates another disc provided with cutout notches, represented by solid lines, whose center is at B. Thus, at the part of the surface *abcd*, one sees the first rotating disc through the second. In each disc the light intensity varies only along the direction of the radius of the disc. However, in the part of the surface *abcd* it may vary in all directions.

The light, which is radiated from any one point of the part of the surface *abcd* during rotation, is the sum of the light that the second disc would give in front of a totally dark background and the light that emanates from the first, passing through the second. Thus, when the form of the sectors on the one disc and the type of notches on the other are known, one can easily calculate the light surface for *abcd*.

A disturbance results here from the so-called "spoke curves" coming

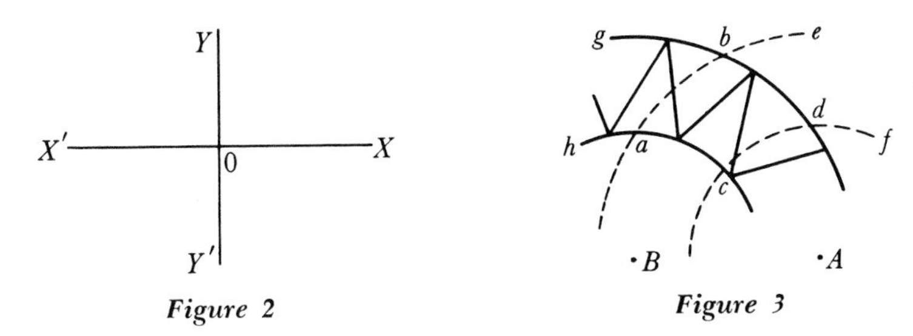

Figure 2 *Figure 3*

into play. They can be made to disappear if one disc is rotated much faster than the other. However, the experiment thereby becomes inconvenient, and I have given up its further pursuit.

(2) The difficulty is immediately eliminated if one replaces the rotating painted disc with a still photograph of the same. Then, "spoke curves" are impossible.

(3) Another method consists of superimposing the two painted discs by reflection from an unsilvered plane glass. Let *aa* and *bb,* in Figure 4, be two horizontal rotating discs, *dd* the cross section of a vertical-plane unsilvered glass. Then, looking through the plane glass from directly above *a,* one can see the disc *bb* and, superimposed on it, the reflected image *cc* of the disc *aa.* The light from the directly viewed disc and from the reflected disc simply add together.

(4) One can also superimpose photographs of rotating discs by reflection in a plane glass.

(5) One can photograph the rotating discs on transparent glass plates, then simply superimpose the plates and look through them.

(6) A convenient means by which any chosen light surface may be produced consists of the following:

A solid is formed from a semitransparent substance which is plane

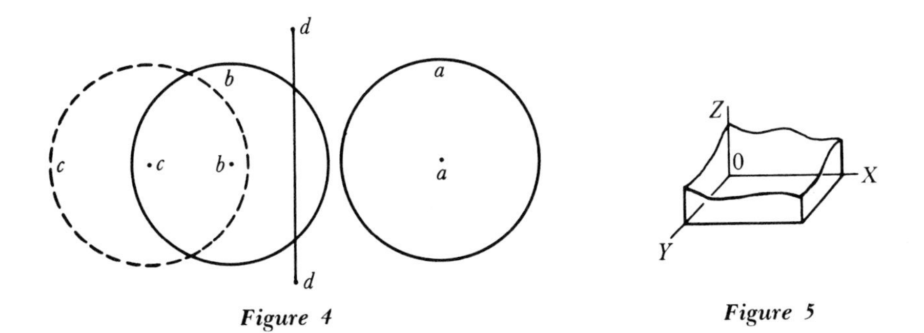

Figure 4 *Figure 5*

on one side and which is limited on the other side by any chosen surface. Let the plane coincide with the *XY*-plane of a coordinate system and let the equation of the irregular surface be $z = f(x, y)$ where z also represents the thickness of the plate at any one point. Such a plate placed in a window opening gives a light surface of the form $i = Ae^{-af(x,y)}$, where A and a are constants depending on the intensity of the illumination and on the absorption coefficient. I have had several simpler forms of this sort ground from bone glass.

I have made observations with all of these methods and have obtained results which agree with one another. Hence, I will confine myself in the following presentation to (5). For simplicity, the curvature of the discs was neglected, since only small annular pieces of the discs photographed on glass plates were superimposed.

In Plate I-1, *AA* and *BB* are two ring-shaped strips of a rotating disc photographed on glass plates where the two glass plates were superimposed as indicated in the figure. The strip *A*, where it projects to the left of the intersection, is portrayed with the sectors which it would show at rest; where it projects to the right represents the appearance it would have in rotation and on a photograph. The shading represents the darker appearing portion. The strip *BB* is represented in the same way, and the same holds for the subsequent figures. The strip *AA* shows a subjectively brighter line $\alpha\alpha$, as does *BB* at $\beta\beta$. At the intersection one sees the two lines cross one another at 0, without, however, there being a noticeable brightening at the point of intersection. Here the superposition results in four fields whose brightness is indicated approximately by the shading. In the crossed field the upper right corner is the darkest, and the lower left the brightest.

Plate I-2 is similar. In it the bright stria $\alpha\alpha$ crosses the dark one $\beta\beta$ at 0. One sees both striae at the point of intersection and neither one appears to cover the other. I am convinced that objective bright and dark fine lines, too, do not interfere with one another when one superimposes them by means of a plane glass. One either sees both at the same time at their intersection, or one after another, depending on the direction of attention. It is even possible to superimpose whole linear drawings without mutual interference. This seems very strange to me.

In Plate I-3, the upper part of the stripe *AA* would appear brighter where it borders on $\alpha\alpha$, while the part below $\alpha\alpha$ would appear darker, so that $\alpha\alpha$ forms a border between dark and light. In the stripe *BB*, $\beta\beta$ forms the right border of a brighter field and the left border of a darker field. By superimposition four fields result whose subjective illumination is represented by shading. The shading is correct only for the regions in the immediate vicinity of 0. For it is clear that the lower-right corner

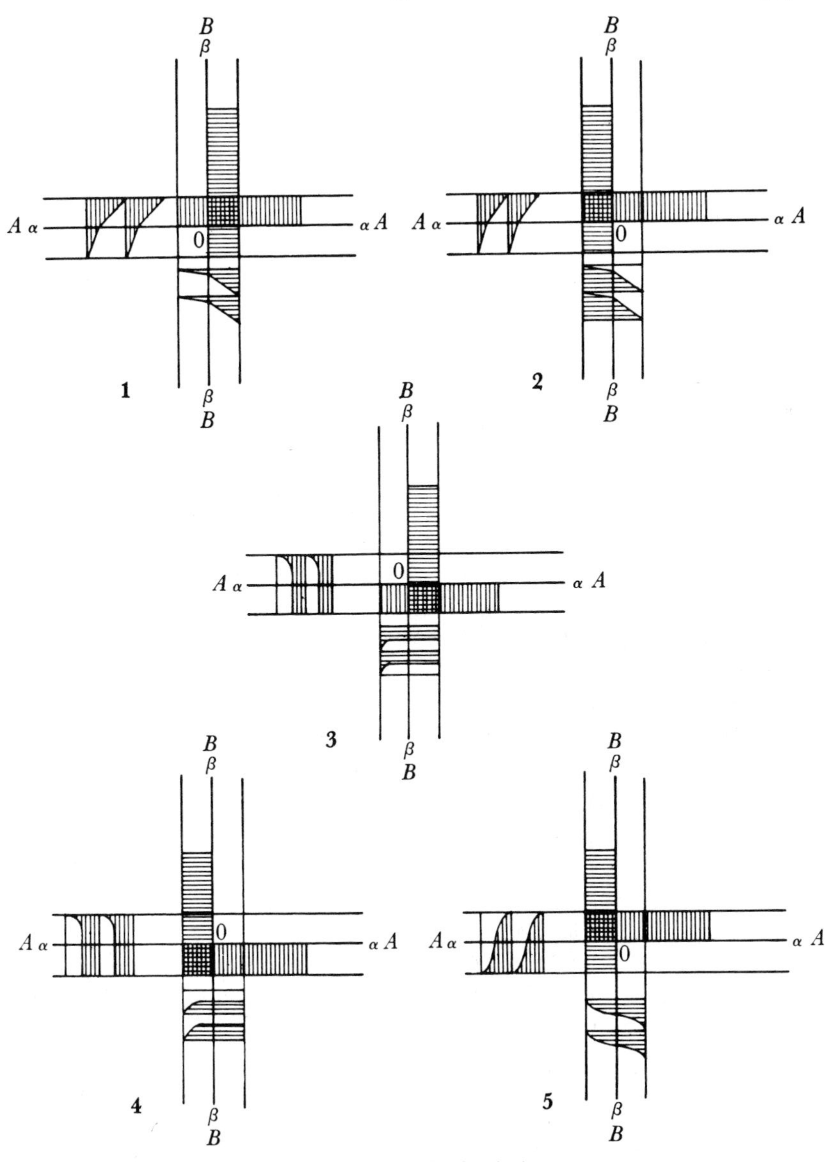

Plate I—1, 2, 3, 4, 5

of the crossed field must be the brightest region, the upper-left the darkest region. The shading, naturally, is exaggerated in order to show the light distribution distinctly.*

It is to be noted that the division into four fields is visible, even with-

* The curved lines on the sectors in Plate I-3, 4, and 5 are circular arcs, all having the same radius.

out drawing the lines $\alpha\alpha$, $\beta\beta$. It becomes more distinct when these lines are made very fine. The whole phenomenon disappears when the lines are thickened.

Similar phenomena are illustrated in Plate I-4 and 5.

We knew previously that when a light surface is curved convex or concave in only one direction with respect to the plane of the retina, the ordinates of the corresponding point of the sensation surface are either decreased or increased.

From the experiments cited above, we learn that two convexities of the light surface which are perpendicular to one another reinforce each other so that the ordinates of the sensation surface become even smaller. The reverse is true in the case of two concavities perpendicular to one another. A concavity is compensated for, however, by an equal convexity perpendicular to it. The ordinate of the point in question on the sensation surface behaves as if the light surface were plane at that point.

We will denote a light surface for any point on the basis of its curvature in two perpendicular directions with respect to the surface of the retina. The expressions convex–concave, plane–concave, and so forth then become immediately understandable.

Therefore, in Plate I-3, the light surface for the right-upper field is plane–concave close to point 0; for the right-lower field, plane–plane; for the left-upper field, concave–concave; and for the left-lower field, plane–concave. Accordingly, although the light intensity itself nearby point 0 is equal for all fields, the left-upper field appears the brightest at that place.

In Plate I-4 we find that the crossed field at 0 is plane–concave in the right-upper portion, plane–plane in the right-lower, convex–concave in the left-upper, and plane–convex in the left-lower. The left-lower field is, therefore, the darkest. Plate I-5 is similar.

Briefly, points of the light surface with stronger concavities or convexities always correspond with bulges or depressions, respectively, in the sensation surface.

I next tried to determine if, by suitable choice of the light surface, certain points on the sensation surface might not be made more distinct by their brightness or darkness.

If, as indicated in Plate II-6, one stretches a rather long paper belt, painted with black sectors, over two wooden rollers, sets it in rotation and photographs it, a rectangular picture with a completely black midline is obtained, from which the light increases toward both sides. If one rotates this picture about a point of the midline, one obtains a circle, Plate II-7, whose midpoint is completely dark, whose periphery is completely white, and whose light intensity increases linearly from the midpoint to the periphery.

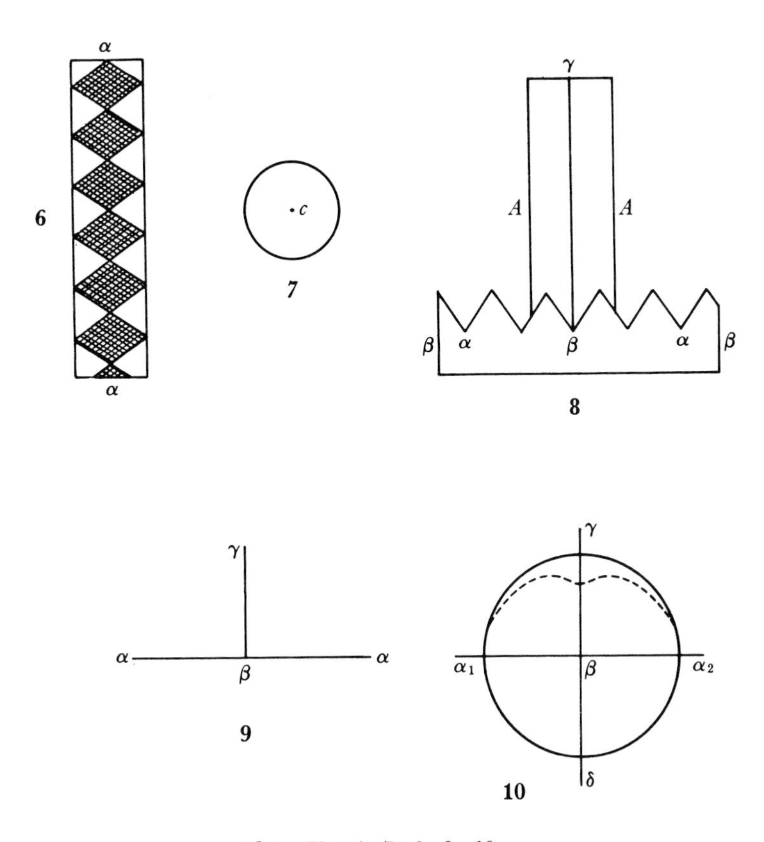

Plate II—6, 7, 8, 9, 10

The light surface may be represented by the surface of a cone with a circular base, whose apex rests on the retina, and whose axis is normal to the retina. Now, the midpoint of the circular image attracts attention, to be sure, because of its darkness, but it corresponds not only to a distinct convexity of the light surface, it is also actually the darkest point. Thus, the experiment does not permit one to draw any special conclusions.

We must obtain a light surface which has a point of light intensity equal to that of its immediate surroundings, yet with a distinct concavity or convexity.

In Plate II-8, *AA* represents the photographic image of the rotating belt of Plate II-6. We let a white disc with cut-out sectors rotate in front of this photograph as is indicated in the sketch, obtaining the image represented in Plate II-9. Below $\alpha\alpha$ everything is white. From $\alpha\alpha$ upward the darkness increases, faster going up from β, slower proceeding from a point on the line $\alpha\alpha$ which is farther from β. The line $\alpha\alpha$ is distinct from its surroundings by its brightness because it corresponds to a flection or bend in the light surface. In the line $\alpha\alpha$, β is the brightest point, since it corresponds to the most pronounced concavity.

The form of the light surface which is thus obtained can be illustrated approximately as follows. We form a plane through point β parallel to the retina (Plate II-10) and inscribe in it a circle around β. We then draw a line $\alpha_1\beta$ through β and a point on the circumference of the circle, rotating this line and leaving one end at β and tracing the other end through the semicircle α_1, δ, α_2. As soon as we come to $\beta\alpha_2$, however, continuing with the rotation, we lower the peripheral end of the line more and more below the plane the greater the angle of rotation becomes. The inclination below the plane reaches its maximum at the position $\beta\gamma$ and from there on we lift the line and return it to the position $\beta\alpha$ again. In this way we have formed a conical surface which corresponds approximately to our light surface.

Thus, in an illuminated surface, single lines, areas of surface, and points can be prominent by means of their apparent brightness, without being objectively brighter than their immediate surroundings, if "outgrowths" or "bulges" are formed on the sensation surface which correspond to stronger curvatures of the light surface.

We can reduce all our assembled results to a mathematical expression which qualitatively represents the phenomena.

If $i = f(x, y)$ is the equation for any chosen light surface, then we obtain the equation for the corresponding sensation surface whose ordinates are represented by e:

$$e = a \log \left[\frac{i}{b} - \frac{k}{i} \left(\frac{1}{\rho} + \frac{1}{\rho_1} \right) \right],$$

where ρ and ρ_1 represent the radii of curvature of two normal sections through the light surface, perpendicular to one another at the corresponding point.

If the light surface becomes cylindrical then we can place the normal section so that $1/\rho_1$ equals 0, and we pass to our old formula.

As noted, our formula expresses the facts only approximately, but quite distinctly. It is still incomplete in one respect, which must be emphasized. The formula represents the phenomena as if the ordinate of a point on the sensation surface were merely dependent upon the corresponding point a of the light surface and upon the next infinitely close neighboring points. One can show by experiment, however, that this is not the case.

In Figure 6 *abcd* is the unrolled surface of a cylinder painted with

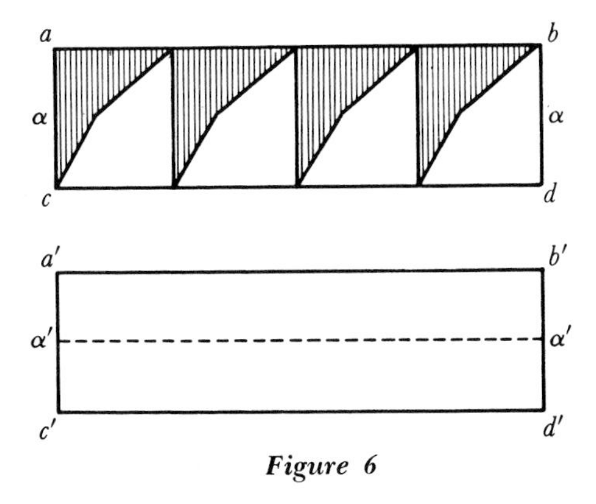

Figure 6

black sectors. In rotation it forms an image $a'b'c'd'$, which is darkest at $a'b'$ and brightest at $c'd'$. A washed-out brighter strip $\alpha'\alpha'$ corresponds to the flection of the sectors $\alpha\alpha$. The strip could not appear washed-out if only the point of flection of the light surface were brought into prominence in the sensation surface. Therefore, neighboring parts must also become prominent. The bend in the light surface thus also affects those parts of the sensation surface which are located at finite distances from the point which corresponds to the bend.

A second experiment shows the same thing. If one decreases the cylinder surface $abcd$ more and more, by cutting off strips from both sides so that the line $\alpha\alpha$ always remains as the midline while the rectangle $abcd$ becomes smaller and smaller, then, in rotation, the bright strip $\alpha'\alpha'$ becomes continuously weaker and finally disappears altogether.

If one continues to decrease the width greatly, then the phenomenon takes on another characteristic. One no longer sees the bright stria at $\alpha'\alpha'$ during rotation, but $\alpha'\alpha'$ forms the border between two uniformly bright bands sharply separated from one another: i.e., a darker upper one, $a'b'\alpha'\alpha'$, and a brighter lower one, $\alpha'\alpha'c'd'$.

The sensation of brightness at a particular retinal point thus depends upon the illumination of a large retinal region surrounding this point of the retina. Naturally, the points in this region closest to the point in question have the greatest influence on it and in this respect the above-mentioned formula always approximates the main features of the phenomena.

If one places a fine black line over the bends in Figure 6 it appears, in rotation, enclosed by a brighter shimmer. Only when the line is drawn heavier does the phenomenon disappear. This also illustrates the influence of more distant retinal points upon one another.

All of the previously described phenomena are equally distinct in monochromatic light of any chosen color. Likewise, they are seen in white light. Never does a coloration appear in experiments with white light. From this it follows that the laws mentioned above hold for every particular color in the same manner and to the same degree. Always, under the same conditions, all colors are subjectively strengthened or weakened to the same degree.

If, instead of black sectors, one uses sectors of the color A, and, instead of white sectors, sectors of the color B, there results in place of each darker point a prominence of the color A, and in place of each brighter point a prominence of the color B. The phenomena are not as striking with this combination, however, as with black and white, since most of the colors contain some white and, therefore, the other color as well.

It seems to me as if almost all of the previously known phenomena of simultaneous contrast could be described as special cases of the phenomenon under discussion, for which I would like to propose the name *influence-phenomena.*

In the earlier work I tried to give a theoretical conception of the phenomena discussed. I will once again consider this point.

It has already been determined that the character of the sensation of a retinal image stays the same over a wide range if the light intensity relations of this image and of the entire retina are not altered.

One can also convince oneself that the total light which falls on the retina, or the average light-per-unit area of the retina, is not a mere mathematical quantity, but has a physiological value.

The diameter of the pupil depends on this total, or average, light. The pupil diameter depends only on the total light and, within a wide range, is independent of the distribution of light on the retina.

To verify this I have carried out a simple experiment. A large disc painted with black and white sectors is placed vertically and set in rapid rotation so that it appears uniformly gray. One takes a position so near to it that the disc fills the entire visual field. The rotating disc is now suddenly halted so that in place of the gray image a black-and-white spotted image appears. There now results not the slightest noticeable change in the observer's pupil diameter.

One can verify this by direct observation of the eyes of another observer, but also very easily by observing one's own eyes as follows:

I wear weak concave spectacles. If I stand in such a way that while I observe the disc some light falls on my spectacles from behind and from the side, I always find several strongly illuminated dust particles on them which create dispersion circles in my eye and which correspond in size to the width of the pupil.

2.

The dispersion images I see become distinctly larger when I cc eye or otherwise decrease the light intensity. They show no alteration, however, when the rotating disc is suddenly stopped.

If I look at the disc through a small opening in a metal plate I can thus superimpose the edge of the iris on the edge of the disc. If the rotation of the disc is stopped, the two edges remain in coincidence.

The average light on the retina thus has a physiological significance, because the diameter of the pupil depends upon it and the units of light on the retina may be evaluated in terms of it.

It is therefore probable that the average illumination on smaller retinal areas plays a similar role in their sensory processes. According to our results, however, it appears that two retinal points have a smaller reciprocal action on one another the farther they are from each other.

The light on a single point is thus evaluated in terms of the light on all other points. In our calculation the effect of a point should be given a lesser weight the farther it is from the point under observation.

If we let j represent the light intensity on the observed point and e its sensation intensity; and let $i_1, i_2, i_3 \ldots$ represent the intensity on the other points and $r_1, r_2, r_3 \ldots$ their distance from the observed point, then, approximately, the following computational formula results:*

$$e = \left(\frac{\dfrac{j}{i_1/r_1 + i_2/r_2 + i_3/r_3 + \cdots}}{1/r_1 + 1/r_2 + 1/r_3 + \cdots} \right) = j \frac{\Sigma \dfrac{1}{r}}{\Sigma \dfrac{i}{r}}.$$

Or if, because of the continuous illumination of the surface elements, we may introduce dv and integration:

$$e = j \frac{\int (dv)/r}{\int (i\, dv)/r}.$$

I do not believe that there is, among the contrast phenomena and influence-phenomena observed by others and by myself, a single one which is not explainable in terms of this principle.

Once more I must emphasize that the so-called "unconscious inferences" seemed to me to be increasingly without foundation, the more I dealt with these phenomena. With their help one can explain one phenomenon almost as well as its opposite. Also, there are phenomena which would lead to an acceptance of the hypothesis of unconscious chains of conclusions.

* Translator's note: In the original text $1/r_1 + 1/r_2 + 1/r_3 + \ldots$ appears as $1/r^1 + 1/r^2 + 1/r^3 +$. Apparently this was a typographical error in the original.

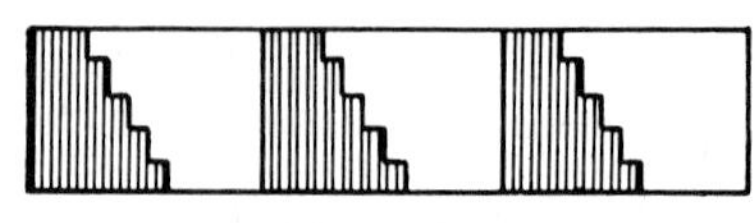

Figure 7

I will describe one such case. The cylinder surface shown in Figure 7 would have to result in a series of stripes when rotated, provided the light sensation always corresponds to the light intensity. The upper ones would be brighter, the lower ones darker. Each stripe, however, would have to be equally bright throughout its whole extent.

As is well known, however, each stripe appears darker at its upper edge and brighter at its lower edge. This would thus be a false inference. Moreover, the stripes appear as if hollowed out, which would obviously be a false inference following from the first one. If the stripes were concave and were illuminated from above, then they would in fact have the objective light distribution which is subjectively ascribed to them. I shall say more about phenomena of this type later.

For simplicity's sake I have thus far always spoken as though only a particular sensation surface should always correspond to a particular light surface. This is only approximately true insofar as all persons see the described phenomena in almost the same way. Even for the same person, however, the phenomenon changes according to his disposition—within narrow limits, to be sure. Thus, it only follows that a series of circumstances is still involved, which probably lie in the retina and deeper in the nervous system.

When we observe any object we: (1) place the visual axis of the eye on the fixated point; (2) accommodate on this point; and (3) turn our attention to the retinal image. Now, if the series of processes should come to an end in the retina, the physical events should suddenly become transformed to psychical events—i.e., the light should become a sensation. From here on, the phenomena are too complicated for me to believe this. I would like to express myself figuratively. I believe that one layer of the retina can, so to speak, regard another, turn its attention to it and turn away again.

We shall never ascertain what these processes are if, from the very beginning, we conceive of them in too simple a manner.

ERNST MACH

3. *On the physiological effect of spatially distributed light stimuli**

Here I present some further investigations of the phenomena discussed in the two earlier papers.

I. The perspective images of curved monochromatic surfaces such as uniform white yield various light surfaces depending on the type of illumination and the form of the surface.

It is worthwhile to investigate further the relationship between the form and type of illumination of a uniform surface, the light surface of its perspective image, and the corresponding sensation surface.

The light intensity of an element of an illuminated surface is proportional to the intensity of the light source and is also dependent on the material of the surface. It is inversely proportional to the square of the distance of the element from the source and directly proportional to the sine of the angle of inclination of the light rays on the element.

The light intensity of the perspective image of each such surface element on the retina is simply

* Translated from: E. Mach, "Über die physiologische Wirkung räumlich vertheilter Lichtreize (Dritte Abhandlung)," Sitzungsberichte der mathematisch-naturwissenschaftlichen Classe der kaiserlichen Akademie der Wissenschaften, 1866, 54/2, 393-408.

proportional to the light intensity of the element. It does not depend, however, on the distance from the eye to the element. While it is true that the quantity of light which reaches the retina from the element decreases in relation to the square of the distance, the surface of the image of the element decreases in the same way. I mention this partly to state my assumptions exactly, and also because some of the points in question are incorrectly stated in current books on illumination.

Let us imagine, according to the assumptions stated, a surface $z = F(x, y)$ illuminated by parallel rays as in sunlight. The light is incident along the direction of the X-axis. Instead of the perspective image let us consider the orthogonal projection of the XY plane and take the illumination of the projection as equal to those of the projected elements. Thus, we easily obtain the equation for the light surface of this projection:

$$i = \frac{-dz/dx}{\sqrt{(dz/dx)^2 + (dz/dy)^2 + 1}}$$

where i signifies the light intensity which, for perpendicular incidence, we set equal to 1.

On the other hand, if the light surface $i = \varphi(x, y)$ is known, then the form of the curved surface, which is illuminated by parallel rays along the X-direction, may be found by integration of the partial differential equation:

$$\varphi(x,y) = \frac{-dz/dx}{\sqrt{(dz/dx)^2 + (dz/dy)^2 + 1}}$$

It is seen at once that the first problem is determinate, the second indeterminate; i.e., many curved surfaces may correspond to one light surface even if they are illuminated in the same manner. This explanation and that which follows hold true only under the assumption that no part of the surface may reflect light to, or cast a shadow on, any other part. In actual practice, the fact that every real surface is rough must also be taken into consideration. Thus, if light falls nearly tangential to an element, then it will not appear uniformly illuminated, but speckled, since projecting small parts will cast shadows on the other parts.

Let us now suppose the illuminated surface to be that of a cylinder with the vertical axis of the cylinder parallel to the Z-axis. Let the directrix of the same be $y = f(x)$, and let the X-axis again denote the direction of the light. Then the light surface is also cylindrical and the equation of the light curve is:

$$i = \frac{dy/dx}{\sqrt{1 + (dy/dx)^2}}.$$

If the light curve is given by $i = \varphi(x)$, we then find the corresponding cylinder by integration of the equation:

$$\frac{dy}{dx} = \frac{\pm\varphi(x)}{\sqrt{1 - \varphi(x)^2}}.$$

The nature of the surface is not changed by the integration constant. On the contrary, the double sign indicates that two congruent cylindrical surfaces, or—what is the same thing in this case—two cylindrical surfaces symmetrical to each other, yield the same light curve. When the light falls from the right toward the axis of the abscissa, one cylindrical surface yields the same light curve as the one symmetrical to it in relation to the XZ-plane when the light falls from the left. Or one cylindrical surface, when the light falls on it from the right, gives the same light curve as does a negative cast turned upside down, when the light falls from the left.

Flections in the directrix of the cylinder reveal themselves as discontinuities in the light curve. Where the ascending curve of the directrix has a flection, a similar flection will also be found in the light curve.

If we take as a Z-axis the axis of a right cylinder with a circular base, then we can easily calculate that, with light falling towards the X-axis, the light curve is a straight line. The light surface thus becomes a plane inclined to the plane of the retina. Inversely, a plane light surface can always be represented by an illuminated right cylinder with a circular base whose axis is parallel to a line of section through the light surface and through the retina.

If the directrix of a cylinder is $y^2 = 2rx - x^2$, then the light curve is $i = (-x/r) + 1$ when the intensity of a perpendicularly illuminated element is set equal to 1. The light curve extends only from $x = 0$ to $x = r$, since the other half of the cylinder is assumed to be unilluminated.

We can now also use the curved surfaces for the purpose of testing our law on the relation of the light surface to the sensation surface.

In Figure 1(a) a circular curve *ab* of about 60° is inscribed about the point *c*. At *b* we draw the tangent *bd* on the circle. The curve *abd* thus begins with a circular curve and continues without a flection into a straight line. If we now cut a cylinder from wood with a base *abde*, cover the curved surface with white paper and let light fall on it in the direction indicated by the arrow, then, according to the above, the corresponding light curve is as given in Fig. 1(b). The flection at *g* corresponds to the point *b*. According to our law we ought to perceive a dark stripe corresponding to *b*, and such is the case.

One can see the stripe in direct sunlight without special arrangements. It is interfered with somewhat, however, by any diffuse light which falls

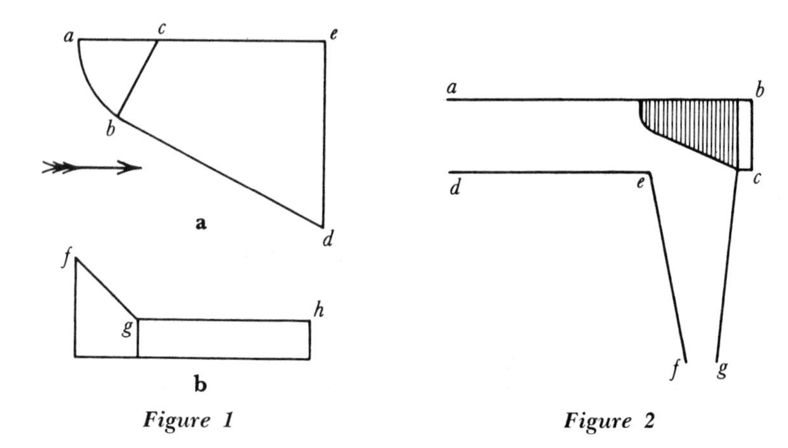

Figure 1

Figure 2

on the cylinder. The phenomenon is more striking if one places the cylinder in a box blackened on the inside as in *abcgfed* of Figure 2 so that the diffuse light is excluded and there are only two openings, one at *ad* for the entrance of the direct sunlight and another at *fg* for the eye of the observer.

Also, other cylinders placed in the box always show the theoretically predicted phenomena. Thus our law finds its verification here.

The relation between curved illuminated surfaces and their light surfaces is noteworthy in one other respect. In the preceding paper I have said that some rotating discs appear quite plastic, sometimes appearing as if they were modelled out of gypsum. One notices the same thing on translucent photographs of the rotating discs taken on glass plates.

One can now demonstrate through systematic experiments that the light curve of any chosen cylinder illuminated from the side, when transferred as a sector on a rotating disc, always appears plastically to the eye as the corresponding cylinder surface—if one causes the light to fall on the rotating disc in the same way that it fell on the cylindrical surface for which one has constructed the light curve. If the light falls on the disc from the opposite direction, then one sees plastically the negative cast of the corresponding cylindrical surface.

Thus, the eye reconstructs the form of the illuminated surface from the light surface. The result of this construction is no mere conception, but is a perception of space. The elements given to the eye are quite sufficient to realize this construction. If we have a cylindrical surface with a vertical axis before us, with the light falling on it from the left, then, since those parts situated on the right side of the surface are dimly illuminated, they must be closer to us than those situated on the left side. Furthermore, such a surface on which the illumination increases toward the right can only be concave toward us, and one on which the illumination decreases toward the right can only be convex toward us. In this manner, incidentally, the form of the surface is determined.

Now, how does the eye carry out this construction? By the process of inference? I do not believe that this would correctly account for the facts.

Let us imagine for a moment that every retinal point could generate sensations of depth of different intensity in addition to light sensations of different quality and intensity. It would now require nothing more than a simple reflex mechanism, which would trigger the depth sensation simultaneously with the light sensation, for this phenomenon to be understood. Three successive retinal elements, from right to left, of which the left is always more strongly illuminated than the right, would always generate in themselves three depth sensations, which would increase in the opposite direction, but in such a way that the middle element would produce a somewhat greater depth sensation than the average depth sensation of the two neighboring elements. This holds true under the assumption that the light is incident from the left, which circumstance distinctly expresses itself in the retinal image.

If, however, such a reflex mechanism was not already provided for in the retina, then the same thing would have to develop in the process of seeing. The perception of depth also arises from another source, namely, through binocular vision, and the same light distribution always corresponds to the same distribution of depth sensation. An adjustment of the reflex mechanisms as Wundt perceives it seems to me to be unavoidable. If the Darwinian theory is correct, then the mechanism is inherited—that is, it develops under favorable circumstances in descendants more easily than in their parents.

In the evening I often sit at the piano and chat about various things without thinking in the slightest of what my hands are rambling over on the keys. Yet it almost never happens that I strike a false chord or resolve incorrectly. How does the left hand know about the right? How does one finger find out what the others are doing? Under the influence of the theory of music and the ear, the fingers and hands have become accustomed to a certain collaboration and they keep this custom even when the theory of music and the ear are absent. Here, one could also think of unconscious conclusions. The reflex mechanism is simpler, however. I would even like to admit that the fingers act logically, but their premises are not based on the ear or the thoroughbass, of which they know nothing, but merely on the accustomed sense of touch. It is probably the same with the eye. The retina knows nothing about perspective, nor about the workings of illumination, which belong to the conscious thought processes, and therefore cannot draw any conclusions from these, yet these things can so easily be represented as though, in the one case, the conclusions are drawn from the theory of music and, in the other, from the perspective.

The plastic monocular effect of the rotating discs has led me to construct binocular situations of this type using rotating cylinders and to observe them under a stereoscope. If I move a vertical straight line as directrix through a sinusoid, a wavy cylindrical surface results. This I illuminate from the side and provide for the two eyes two such illuminated surfaces next to one another on the same rotating cylinder. In this case all light intensities are continuous from one level to another. Each image alone gives the impression of the plastic cylindrical surface referred to above. They appear even more plastic when I superimpose the two images by crossing my eyes. In this way, the stereoscopic images can be constructed without any contours.

II. If one rotates a disc with a star-shaped cutout with a uniform plane as background, two rings are observed in accordance with the already known causes, one at the re-entering angle and the other at the salient angle of the star. If the star is brighter than the ground, then we find the first ring brighter and the second ring darker than the surroundings. The reverse is observed when the star is darker than the ground. With equal brightness of the star and ground, the star, upon rotation, disappears completely into the ground. The rings appear to gleam if the planes of the star and of the ground are quite far apart, and also if they move. Similarly, the bright and dark lines gleam on a shaded surface if one moves the shadow. This reminds me of stereoscopic luster and of another phenomenon of which I have spoken earlier. (Reichert and Dubois' Archiv. 1865.)

III. If I look sharply at Plate II-5 or 6 of my paper in Vol. 52 of the Proceedings* and quickly turn it back and forth a while in its own plane, the parallel lines appear to curve peculiarly. With prolonged observation I have noticed that they all seem to be undulating and inflated, with nodules and outgrowths, and that this appearance does not disappear until the eye is completely rested. It appears almost as if, with fatigue, the perception of space gets into disorder just as the perception of light gets disordered when the visual field is full of after-images and a uniform field appears mottled. After-images of movements are known. The waves and swellings on lines have already been observed in the very fine closely spaced lines of micrometric scales and, as is known, have been

* Translator's note: The first paper in this series.

ascribed to the retinal elements. Since they also appear on much thicker lines, however, it is very doubtful if the retinal elements play a principal role in this phenomenon at all.

According to the usual manner of speaking, one would include these phenomena under the heading of sense delusions. It would, however, be most suitable to banish this term completely from science. The senses never delude and never indicate correctly. We actually know nothing except that the senses act differently under different circumstances. When it appears that a different performance results under the same circumstances, then this is the case only because, under the same external circumstances, the internal circumstances within the organs can still be different.

IV. On the occasion of these experiments I tired of painting sectors and devised a simple device by means of which one can at least represent a very great number of different light curves. This is based on the Fourier series. Let us designate as x the direction on the surface of a rotating cylinder parallel to the axis and the light intensity as i. The light curve may thus be represented in the form:

$$i = a \sin rx + b \sin 2rx + c \sin 3rx + \cdots.$$

We can therefore represent any light curve by mere addition of sine sectors. It is simply a question of making the values of the amplitudes $a, b, c, \ldots$ variable.

One finds easily that

$$m \sin rx + m \sin (rx + \xi) = m\sqrt{2(1 + \cos \xi)} \sin (rx + \eta)$$

where

$$\operatorname{Tg} \eta = \frac{1 + \cos \xi}{\sin \xi}$$

which is to say that two sine sectors of equal amplitude, displaceable with respect to one another, yield a sine sector of variable amplitude. The value of the expression $m\sqrt{2(1 + \cos \xi)}$ can change continuously from 0 to $2m$.

On the surface of a cylinder I place two paper rings ($\alpha\alpha$ and $\beta\beta$ in Figure 3). Under these are the sine sectors, made of paper strips which are movable in the direction of the axis of the cylinder (the direction of the arrow). The figure shows the first two pairs. With the arrangement sketched in Figure 3, the cylinder yields a uniformly gray surface. This apparatus may also be used to represent many mathematical and physical phenomena.

If one could now also make the displacement of the pair of sine sectors dependent upon the angle of rotation in a simple way, then not only cylindrical surfaces but also light surfaces in general could be represented in this way.

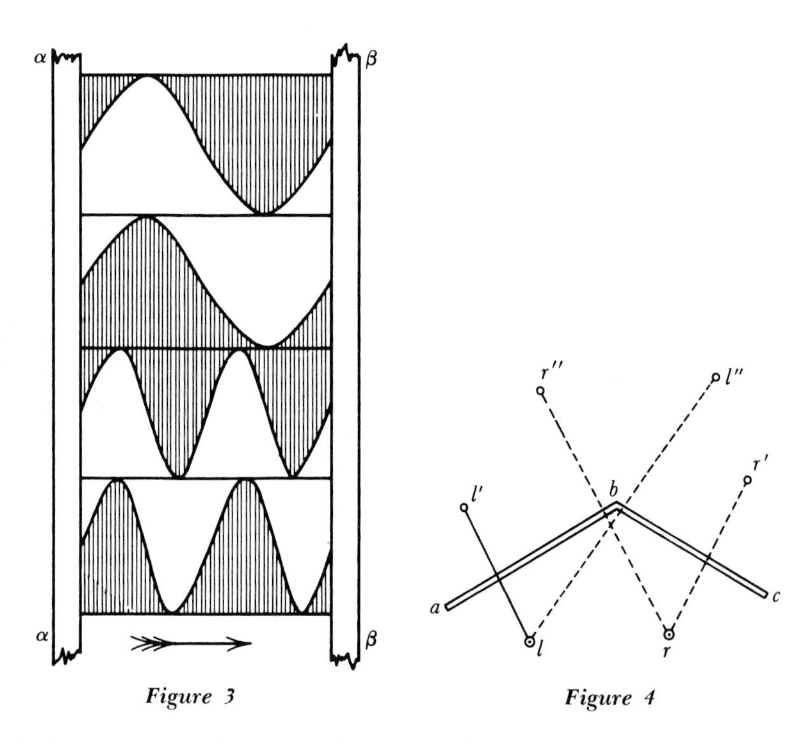

Figure 3 *Figure 4*

V. The stereoscopic effect, which is produced by a certain distribution of light on one retina, led me to some experiments on stereoscopic vision which, as is known, depends upon a certain inequality of the distribution of light on the two retinas.

In his telestereoscope Helmholtz had made the first attempt to modify the conditions under which the usual binocular vision of an object takes place. As Helmholtz himself has already suggested, one can carry out not only these types of experiments with simpler means, but carry them out still further.

I make use of a large angular mirror *abc* with a variable angle (Fig. 4). It is readily apparent that an eye sees every object in the mirror in such a way that the mirror image of the eye would see the actual object, only the mirror image is not congruent but symmetrical to the object in relation to the plane of the mirror. This is sufficient in order to understand the principle involved. If now I bring the angular mirror in front of my face, as indicated in the figure where l represents the left eye and r the right, I then see two images of my face whose perspectives are much different than they actually can be for the two eyes not displaced. When these two images are now superimposed by fixating the right image with the right eye and the left image with the left eye, I obtain the impression of a solid object which, initially, is not striking. With longer observation, however, the relief grows gradually from one moment to the next, the eyebrows move far in front of the eyes, the nose appears to become as long as a shoe, the mustache leaps like a fountain from the lip, the teeth appear unattainably far behind the lips, and so forth. In fact, the two perspective images in the mirrors correspond to the interocular distance of the mirror images of l, r, or, in the case of unchanged interocular distance, to an object with far greater relief. Only the gradual development of the perception of relief is noteworthy. One finds a similar effect in observing ordinary stereoscopic pictures. If such pictures are drawn freehand, the development takes longer the rougher and more dissimilar the corresponding lines of the two pictures are. Once the sensation of relief has developed, it persists for some time, even with poor pictures; one can turn the eyes away, and, upon returning the view to the pictures, still see them as before.

As regards our research with the mirrors, the fact is to be stressed that there are an infinite number of geometrically related objects (actually surfaces), to all of which belong the same pair of perspective images in relation to the two eyes. These surfaces form a continuous series and produce more relief the farther they become removed from the eye. Thus, in an experiment where only the perspective images were decisive, I could see a smaller and nearer face that was geometrically similar to my own. It follows, then, that the estimate of distance and size depends upon still other features than the perception of relief. In any case, the angle of convergence of the axes of the eyes plays only a very subordinate role, since two opaque stereoscopic images always give the same impression of relief, size and distance, whether I superimpose them by convergence, by parallel position, or even by divergence, provided that the same image is always assigned to the same eye.

If I observe in the angular mirror the left image with the right eye and the right image with the left eye, then the appearance differs according to the position of the mirror images of the eyes, which in turn depends upon the inclination of the mirror and its distance from the face. If l'' is to the left, and r'' nearby but toward the right, then I see my face strongly flattened. However, if l'' and r'' are crosswise over one another, as in Figure 4, the left eye thus takes the role of the right and vice versa and my face appears pseudoscopic—that is, the hollows are elevated and the elevations hollowed.

Pseudoscopy with interchange of the two pictures in the stereoscope from right to left is well known. The phenomenon does not manifest itself equally well, however, with every type of picture. Geometric figures show it without difficulty, while landscapes often show it only weakly in separate parts of the picture and often it is not manifest at all. I have a stereoscopic picture (a view from China) which for a long time has given me a very good stereoscopic effect. However, a small speck which appeared to be floating in the air disturbed me. It similarly affected many other observers to whom I showed it. More exact observation revealed to me, however, that in this case the left-hand picture had by mistake been pasted in place of the right-hand one. The idea occurred to me to turn the whole picture from top to bottom. The pseudoscopic effect then appeared quite distinctly. I now find that all landscape pictures generally show pseudoscopic effects as distinctly as do geometric figures if one interchanges the pictures and inverts the whole.

What are the causes that make pseudoscopic vision of upright landscapes so very difficult? I believe I can name several. First of all, we know that the monocular picture of a landscape already has quite a significant relief due to perspective and illumination. Both pictures together (provided they are arranged for pseudoscopy) thus require of the eyes the reverse of what each one does alone.

For a complete explanation it is necessary to know the elements of the mechanism by which light causes the perception of relief. These I cannot specify, except to say that one major difficulty appears to me to lie in pictures of the ground in landscapes. The higher parts in pictures of the ground in landscapes are, in the overwhelming majority of cases, the cause of a greater sensation of depth. Pseudoscopy requires the opposite. I succeed only with the greatest effort in seeing the upright landscape of the earth pseudoscopically if I visualize it quite vividly the way it should appear. The influence of the central nervous system upon the sense organs is thus, in these matters at any rate, a very limited one.

I do not question that the eye has acquired for itself a kind of knowledge and certain manners according to which it behaves in such cases, since I have seen how animals with their brains removed still show characteristic behavior which they obviously have become accustomed to under the influence of their mode of life. This only indicates, however, the direction in which the explanation might be sought.

One can also view solid bodies pseudoscopically and, in general, encounter thereby the same difficulties as with two-dimensional pictures.

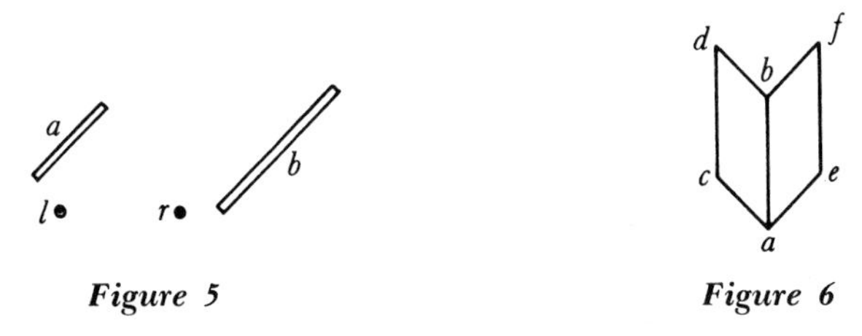

Figure 5 *Figure 6*

Figure 5 illustrates the very simple arrangement of this experiment. Here one observes an object directly with the right eye *r*, and, with the left eye *l* observes the same object through the two mirrors *a* and *b*. The right and the left eye thereby exchange their roles. Consequently, pseudoscopy occurs.

Since an object is nothing more than a perspective image for one eye, a series of elegant stereoscopic experiments may be carried out with two congruent objects. If, for example, one takes two plaster casts of the same form, places them next to one another and then observes the one cast with the one eye, and the other cast with the other eye, the stereoscopic impression is very striking. One can rotate the figures so that they appear flatter than under usual circumstances, in greater relief, or even pseudoscopically. The latter occurs when one sees more of the left side of the right figure with the right eye and more of the right side of the left figure with the left eye.

It is well known that one can see a perspective image in two ways in a plane such as Figure 6. If I imagine that I am looking down at a roof from above, then the corner *ab* appears to me to project outwards. If, however, I think of myself under the roof, then the same corner projects inward. Now each time it requires some effort to turn the roof about and this happens to an even greater extent with complicated sketches. In the above-mentioned pseudoscopic landscape I have, in the beginning, seen the roofs just as distinctly elevated as they were later hollow. I can thereby think of only a depth sensation which is caused by the perspective.

I find it very instructive to observe solid objects with one eye and (as in Fig. 6) to reverse my perception of them. After some practice one soon overcomes the difficulties which, to be sure, are somewhat greater here than they are with plane drawings. For this reason, the result of the experiment is indeed very noteworthy.

If I fold a rectangular piece of stiff paper along a straight line to form two congruent rectangular parts and place it on the table in front of me so that when vertical it has the projecting side turned toward me, I obtain the image shown in Figure 6. The light should fall from the left, and the right side will thus be somewhat darker. If I then close one eye, the sensation is almost completely unaltered. If I try to see the paper as recessed, however, I succeed after some effort. The left side thereupon appears to become much brighter and the right side much darker. Light and shade appear as if painted upon it. Moreover, I notice a different color tone on the right and left side which had not been noticeable to me earlier. Furthermore, the form of the paper has changed. The lines *bf, bd* have become longer than *ae, ac,* the lines *cd* and *ef* shorter than *ab*. Finally, the corner *ab* no longer remains vertical, but the paper lies like an open book on a lectern before me.

These simultaneous alterations of the sensation of depth, the sensation of form, and the sensation of light which occur without the slightest theoretical deliberation, indicate how quickly these things, through well-regulated reflexes, transform themselves into one another. It thereby appears that the sensation, through which another becomes elicited, itself diminishes in the same proportion as it elicits the other.

I recall very well that at the age of about three all perspective plane drawings appeared to me as caricatures of the subject. The perspective of the images of real objects on my retina were immediately transformed into sensations of form and, as such, did not enter into consciousness. Likewise, all lights and shades in plane pictures appeared to me as unessential patches. On the other hand, I did not notice the shadows on solid objects. At that time Chinese paintings without shadows would have been more pleasing to me. Through these experiments I now understand far better the taste of the Chinese, who, as it appears, have remained in this childlike stage in their artistic outlook. Strange to say, the very same people have not gone beyond the five-tone scale in their music.* By a continuation of the experiments, one may be convinced that the reversal of monocular images is more difficult and uncertain with curved instead of straight contours. Let us investigate the basis of this phenomenon.

If we fixate any doubly bent curve in space with both eyes, and if straight lines are passed through the two nodal points of the eyes and moved along the curves, we thus obtain a perspective image on each retina. The intersections of the moved straight lines with the retinas give the images. If, on the other hand, the two images are given, one needs merely to use them as the directrices and, through the nodal points as vertices, to construct conical surfaces. The intersection of the two surfaces is the curve.

Thus, an infinite number of spatial forms correspond to one monocular image and the spatial interpretation must be of the greatest un-

* Some remarks on perspective and illumination in the Egyptian, Assyrian, and Chinese painting will follow later. [Translator's note: See Mach (1910, p. 66).]

certainty. The eye has free choice among all the forms which lie in that one conical surface so long as the other is not added to it.

One curve in space always yields a curve image on each of the two retinas. Only a plane curve yields in a single case one straight-line image on one retina and a curved image on the other (if, that is, the plane of the curve passes through one nodal point). Only in the even more special case—in which the plane of the curve passes through both nodal points —do we obtain two straight-line images.

On the other hand, one straight line always yields two straight lines— one on each retina. Thus, when one retina receives a rectilinear image the other retina will also almost always be led to the perception of a straight line in space. The reflexes must therefore so regulate themselves that a rectilinear image from one retina would be seen, with predilection, as a straight line in space.

Since the straight line surrounds civilized man always and everywhere, one can well assume that each straight line which is possible on the retina has been seen in space innumerable times and in all possible ways as a straight line. Therefore, the ability of the eye to interpret straight lines should not surprise us.

Let us now consider a special example. Let *abcd* in Figure 7 be a plane sketch and *k* be the nodal point of the observing eye outside of this plane. According to what has been said above, the straight line *ab* can represent all straight lines in the plane $\alpha k \beta$, and the straight line *ac* can represent all straight lines in the plane $\alpha k \gamma$, and so forth. Now, however, it is clear that the eye itself will not without special inducement make the effort to develop three distinct sensations of depth at the corner *a*: for example, one for the end point *a* of the line *ca*, one for the end point *a* of *ba*, a third for *da*. The lines would, therefore, also

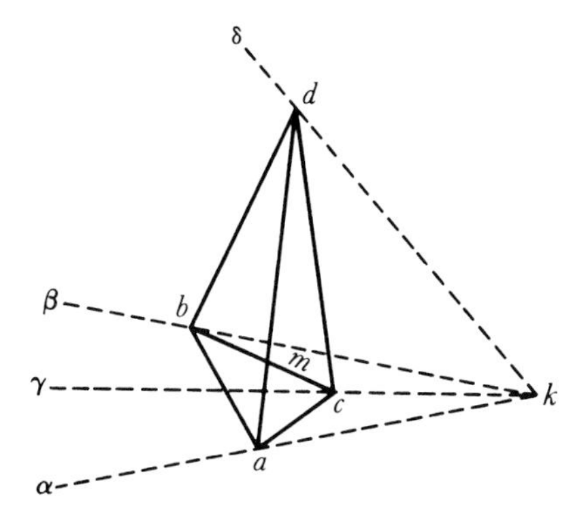

Figure 7

be taken as being at the same distance where they intersect, so long as one unconstrained eye alone observes the drawing.

The first and simplest case is that the plane drawing would be regarded as plane. If we now develop, with effort, two sensations of depth for the point of intersection *m*, by conceiving the line *ad* to be nearer to us than *bc*, a three-sided pyramid is thus formed with the corner *a* nearest. If, on the other hand, we conceive *bc* at *m* to be nearer than *ad*, we obtain a three-sided pyramid, in which the corner *a* is farthest. If we consider *m* as the intersection of four lines and as the nearest or farthest point, we thus obtain a four-sided pyramid.

The intersection *m* is the point that is important in the reversal. In Brewster ("On the Stereoscope," p. 228) one finds the erroneous view that the fixated corner in the drawing of the cube is decisive.

In all such cases, the eye appears to act according to the principle of least effort and to do no more than is imposed upon it—either by the other eye or by the central nervous system. Using this principle it could also be directly explained why, with predilection, we see a straight retinal image as a straight line in space. The eye develops a minimum of depth sensation differences.

It appears to me that every retinal point must also be capable of developing, aside from a variable sensation of light, a variable sensation of depth and a sensation of height and width proportional to it. While it is true that the sensation of depth results originally from the reciprocal action of the two retinas, by the gradual building up of reflex mechanisms it can also develop from the light sensation of a single retina.

I need not further explain how far I hereby agree with the views of Hering.*

* Translator's note: An English translation of Hering's major work on vision is now available. See Hering (1964).

ERNST MACH

4. *On the physiological effect of spatially distributed light stimuli*[*]

It was shown in the three preceding works that a rather large number of phenomena can be explained very simply if one assumes that an analog of Fechner's psychophysical law holds for smaller parts of the retina.

This idea, which has so far merely been indicated along general lines, shall now be worked out more exactly. First, however, the psychophysical basis itself will be examined.

It has already been much disputed whether the psychophysical law is of a physical, psychological, or psychophysical nature. The supposition that it is of an organic nature, which I take to be the correct one according to the present state of the question, has, so far as I know, not appeared up to now.

Fick has shown that the nerve excitation produced is proportional to the stimulus. Thus the law probably cannot be physical.

According to Wundt the law is supposed to be psychical, since it governs the process of compari-

* Translated from: E. Mach, "Über die physiologische Wirkung räumlich vertheilter Lichtreize (Vierte Abhandlung)," Sitzungsberichte der mathematisch-naturwissenschaftlichen Classe der Kaiserlichen Akademie der Wissenschaften, Wien, 57/2, 1868, pp. 11-19.

son. This process should, however, be further divisible into parts. And, if we think that the physical and psychical are closely interconnected with one another, then parts of the physical process should correspond to parts of the psychical. Conversely, one can also assert that if the law is psychical, it must then probably also be physical.

A psychophysical law, that is, a law which stands with one foot in the physical and with the other in the psychical, will not properly suit Herr Wundt. It does not suit me either, but merely because of its form. This form appears to me to show that the two members which the law connects are the ends of a series. The final nerve excitation and the sensation, which unalterably go with one another, cannot very well be other than proportional to each other.

My opinion is that the law is an organic one; that is, it is based on organization. This is obvious where it stands out most clearly—in the realm of sound. It is possible to imagine an ear for which not the relationships but the differences in frequencies would be controlling.

I will be brief. The psychophysical law holds not for the relation between stimulus and nerve excitation in a single nerve, nor for the relation of nerve excitation and sensation in a single nerve, but for the relation of the primary stimulus and the last nerve excitation with which the conscious sensation goes. Indeed, this is precisely because the excitations in the sense organ are filtered through a complicated web of nerves.

We can, therefore, call the law organic-physical, or also organic-psychic, since the filtration process referred to can be regarded as a physical process as well as a psychical process.

Permit me to illustrate this by a few observations on the eye, which, it is true, I do not regard as exhaustive, but which are, nonetheless, very useful.

Let us first ask how we would find our way in the visual world if we would perceive, not relations of, but only differences in, illumination. One and the same thing in the same surroundings would become immediately unrecognizable with the slightest alteration of light intensity, such as when a cloud covers the sun. Should we still want to find our way, we would then have to habituate ourselves to maintain equal levels of light intensity, for instance by closing and opening the eyes. In fact, if this god of the psychophysical law were non-existent, the organism itself would have to devise it and, if the Darwinian theory is correct, it has devised it. The seeing of light intensity relations, within certain limits, is necessary for the existence of organisms.

Let us now consider those functions of the organism which could possibly serve for the maintenance of the psychophysical law.

First of all, we find the iris, which, with the help of its muscles, can hold the intensity of the retinal image at a constant level, within certain limits, during variations in the external light intensity.

The iris cannot accomplish everything, however. Should not the remainder then be taken care of by similar regulators?

Let i be the light intensity of an object and f the area of its image on the retina. Similarly, let i' be the intensity of the surrounding background, and f' the area of the image. Call the area of the pupillary opening W. If the iris had the ability to always allow the same total amount of light C to reach the retina, then the following equation would hold:

$$W(if + i'f') = C \quad \text{or} \quad W = \frac{C}{if + i'f'}.$$

The light intensity of the image is now

$$I = iW = i\,\frac{C}{if + i'f'}.$$

Thus, the illumination of the object and the background could become 2, 3, . . . , n times greater, yet the intensity of illumination of the retinal points would not change and we would have the same sensations.

It may be that still other types of regulators exist. It is not improbable that the light on a single retinal point could be evaluated in comparison with the light on the entire retina. In other words, more or less of the excitation of a point can be discharged into the sensorium, the less or more, respectively, that the entire retina is excited. The excitations of two points reciprocally obstruct their discharge to the sensorium.

Let us first assume that all retinal points participate in an equal reciprocal action. Let E be the excitation discharged from one point to the sensorium. We then have

$$E = iW\,\frac{i(f + f')}{if + i'f'} = i^2\,\frac{C(f + f')}{(if + i'f')^2}.$$

Accordingly, the excitation discharged from one point to the sensorium would again remain the same so long as the distribution of illumination itself is not changed. By this hypothesis one would do justice to the facts of contrast. One may not, however, regard the reciprocal action of the retinal points as independent of their separation but must ascribe a greater reciprocal action to retinal points which are closer together.

If one places a white square *abcd* on an unbounded black ground, this shows a certain contrast brightness. If one now cuts from this same square *efgh* and places it close by at *iklm*, the total brightness of the visual field remains the same. The brightness of the white increases,

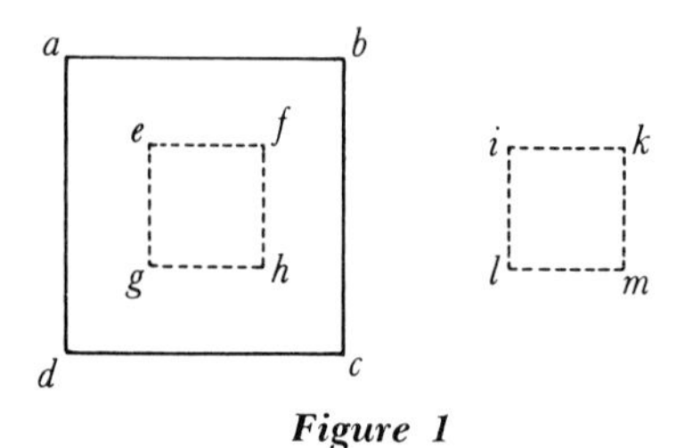

Figure 1

however. This points to the reciprocal action of the retinal points and, indeed, to a stronger reciprocal action the nearer the retinal points are to one another. Nothing happens in the experiment other than that some black points move closer to some white ones.

In the above I wished to show only that it is possible to combine Fechner's law and Fick's observation of the proportionality of stimulus and excitation without making a wild leap into the psychic. One can set the sensation proportional to the stimulus and assume that from two compared stimuli equal excitations are discharged into the sensorium if the two stimuli always stand in the same relation.

Naturally, this is not the whole truth. The absolute magnitude of the stimuli is not irrelevant, or else we would not be able to distinguish sunlight from candlelight.

When the octave follows after a tone, a part of the earlier sensation repeats itself in the partial tones. This obviously depends on the organization of the ear, which receives the partial tones separately. With this, however, the significance of frequency relations is established.

Thus, I assume that an equal excitation always occurs (in part, at least) when the stimuli remain in the same relation. The analogy supports the idea that this is due to the organization of the senses. It can be presumed that we are not dealing with such a rigid mechanism as we are supposing here for simplicity's sake, that attention, for example, can bring some points of the retina into closer relationship than others.

I will now attempt to explain my contrast phenomena according to the principle suggested.

Let us set up in the retinal plane a coordinate system (XY). Let us think of the width of the pupil as constant and the distribution of light on the retina given by

$$i = f(x, y).$$

Two retinal points stand in a reciprocal relation, which is determined by a function of their separation $\phi(r)$. The excitation, which a point illuminated with the intensity i discharges into the sensorium is, therefore

$$e = i \frac{i \Sigma \phi(r) \Delta v}{\Sigma i' \phi(r) \Delta v}.$$

In the numerator under the summation sign the distance function of all retinal points from the i-point are to be thought of as multiplied by their elements of surface Δv; in the denominator every point appears with its own intensity i'.

The explanation of the bright and dark striae I observed is now already yielded without an exact knowledge of the function $\phi(r)$. That is, it becomes evident from the phenomena that the points nearest to one another exert the predominantly greatest influence upon one another. If we represent $\phi(r)$ as a curve diagrammed with r as the abscissa, this yields something like the appearance of Figure 2.

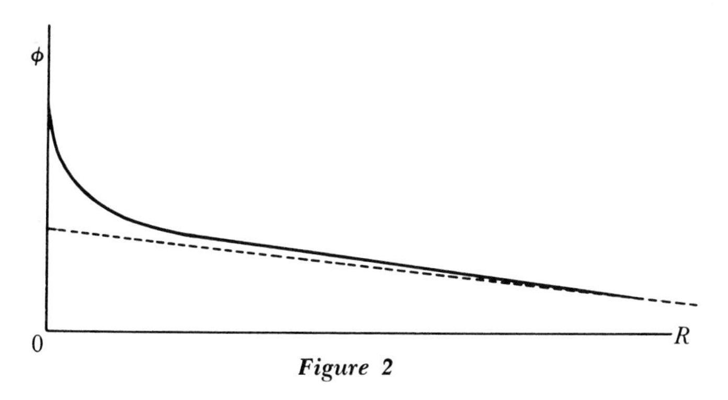

Figure 2

One can think of this curve $\phi(r)$ as the result of the superimposition of two curves, as indicated by the dotted line. One of them, $\varphi(r)$, approaches the axis of abscissae rapidly with increasing r, while the second, $\psi(r)$ progresses rather levelly.

Let us consider next the predominant influence of the nearest points, which expresses itself in $\varphi(r)$. We have

$$e = i \frac{i \Sigma \varphi(r) \Delta v}{\Sigma i' \varphi(r) \Delta v}.$$

The intensity i' of one of the points neighboring the i-point, however, is

$$i = f(x + h, y + k) = i + \left[\frac{di}{dx} h + \frac{di}{dx} k\right] + \frac{1}{2}\left[\frac{d^2i}{dx^2} h^2 + 2 \frac{d^2i}{dx\, dy} hk + \frac{d^2i}{dy^2} k^2\right] + \cdots.$$

If we wish to consider all of the points surrounding i, we have to form the functions

$$f(x+h, y+k), \quad f(x-h, y+k),$$
$$f(x+h, y-k), \quad f(x-h, y-k).$$

For $\varphi(r)$ substitute $\varphi(\sqrt{h^2+k^2})$ and for Δv substitute $dh\,dk$. We obtain:

$$\sum \varphi(r)\,\Delta v = 4\iint \varphi(\sqrt{h^2+k^2})\,dh\,dk,$$

$$\begin{aligned}\sum i'\varphi(r)\,\Delta v = &\iint f(x+h, y+k)\varphi(\sqrt{h^2+k^2})\,dh\,dk \\ &+ \iint f(x+h, y-k)\varphi(\sqrt{h^2+k^2})\,dh\,dk \\ &+ \iint f(x-h, y+k)\varphi(\sqrt{h^2+k^2})\,dh\,dk \\ &+ \iint f(x-h, y-k)\varphi(\sqrt{h^2+k^2})\,dh\,dk\end{aligned}$$

or:

$$\begin{aligned}\sum i'\varphi(r)\,\Delta v &= \iint (4i+2)\left(\frac{d^2i}{dx^2}h^2 + \frac{d^2i}{dy^2}k^2\right)\varphi(\sqrt{h^2+k^2})\,dh\,dk \\ &= 4i\iint \varphi(\sqrt{h^2+k^2})\,dh\,dk + 2\frac{d^2i}{dx^2}\iint \varphi(\sqrt{h^2+k^2})h^2\,dh\,dk \\ &\quad + 2\frac{d^2i}{dy^2}\iint \varphi(\sqrt{h^2+k^2})k^2\,dh\,dk.\end{aligned}$$

Now, since $\varphi(\sqrt{h^2+k^2})$ vanishes for appreciable values of h and k, we can thus simply carry out the integration from 0 to ∞.

Now we set

$$\int_0^\infty\int_0^\infty \varphi(\sqrt{h^2+k^2})\,dh\,dk = m$$

$$\int_0^\infty\int_0^\infty \varphi(\sqrt{h^2+k^2})h^2\,dh\,dk = \int_0^\infty\int_0^\infty \varphi(\sqrt{h^2+k^2})k^2\,dh\,dk = n.$$

Thus we obtain:

$$e = i\,\frac{4mi}{4mi + 2n[(d^2i)/(dx^2) + (d^2i)/(dy^2)]}$$

and set

$$\frac{2n}{4m} = \frac{k}{2},$$

$$e = i\,\frac{i}{i + \dfrac{k}{2}\left(\dfrac{d^2i}{dx^2} + \dfrac{d^2i}{dy^2}\right)}.$$

This formula, derived from the assumptions given, represents the phenomena quite well. If we also introduce the diameter of the pupil W, we then have:

$$e = Wi \frac{i}{i + \frac{k}{2}\left(\frac{d^2i}{dx^2} + \frac{d^2i}{dy^2}\right)}.$$

(1) If all the intensities of illumination are increased p-fold, then the formula yields

$$e' = \frac{W}{p} \cdot pi \frac{pi}{pi + p\frac{k}{2}\left(\frac{d^2i}{dx^2} + \frac{d^2i}{dy^2}\right)} = e.$$

The pattern and intensity of the excitations remain the same. The sensation being supposed proportional to the excitation, nothing changes in the sensation. This corresponds to the observations in the first paper.

(2) All intensities of illumination shall increase by the amount a. We then have:

$$e' = \frac{Wi}{a + i} (a + i) \frac{a + i}{a + i + \frac{k}{2}\left(\frac{d^2i}{dx^2} + \frac{d^2i}{dy^2}\right)}.$$

As a becomes very large, the influence of the term $(k/2)[(d^2i)/(dx^2) + (d^2i)/(dy^2)]$ diminishes completely, as the observation also shows.

(3) If the term $(k/2)[d^2i)/(dx^2) + (d^2i)/(dy^2)]$ is positive, i.e., if the *light surface* is predominantly curved convex toward the retina, then the excitation at the corresponding point appears diminished. The converse is true in the opposite case.

Of course, one could determine by observation the value of the constant k and the form of $\varphi(r)$, if sufficiently exact measurements were feasible.

I have repeatedly stressed that the theory is also applicable to the phenomenon of color contrast. One can carry out the experiments relating to this in a very simple manner, as I will indicate briefly. I make use of the disc provided with the cut-outs (Figure 3). This is covered on one side with white paper and on the other with black paper. A colored background is observed through the cut-outs of the rotating disc. A red background shows a dark line at α and a bright line at β, if the observer stands on the black side of the disc. When the black is illuminated a little so that it appears gray, one then sees at α a complementary greenish ring. The white side can either be used directly or with colored illumination. The phenomena do not present anything which is not predictable in terms of the foregoing explanation.

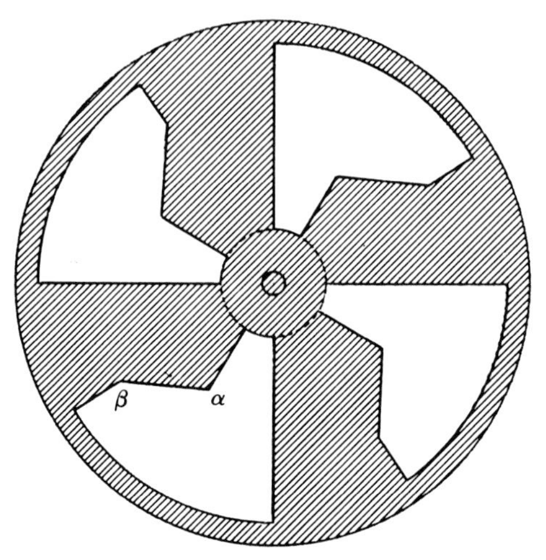

Figure 3

What appears to me to arise mainly from these phenomena and observations is, above all, that perception and even sensation are the result of countless individual organic forces and, that we must regard the retina as more vital and more independent than we have been accustomed to doing.

In recent times the physical view has passed through a not dissimilar change. In place of the concept of a gas there has appeared the concept of an animated confusion of molecules whose uniform actions only arise from the laws of probability. The concept of a liquid appears to be changing similarly, and soon one will find that crystals cannot be regarded as being overly simple and uniform.

Since every retinal point perceives itself, so to speak, as above or below the average of its neighbors, there results a characteristic type of perception. Whatever is near the mean of the surroundings becomes effaced, whatever is above or below is disproportionately brought into prominence. One could say that the retina schematizes and caricatures. The teleological significance of this process is clear in itself. It is an analog of abstraction and of the formation of concepts.

Mechanics, as is known, always leads especially to problems of minima and maxima. The significance of these minimum principles, however, goes far beyond the special hypotheses of mechanics. They come into play wherever several factors act together, partly facilitating one another, partly inhibiting one another. That the eye is also controlled by such minimum principles in the case of form vision, has already been indicated in the third paper, and shall be enlarged upon in the next one.

ERNST MACH

5. *On the dependence of retinal points on one another**

The expression "sense-illusion" shows that we have not yet become conscious of the fact that the senses neither falsely nor correctly manifest external events, or that we at least have not yet found it necessary to demonstrate consciousness of this fact in our terminology. The only exact thing we can say about the sense organs is that under different circumstances they produce different sensations and perceptions.

Since these "circumstances" are of such a great variety of types, partly external (situated in the object) partly internal (located in the sense organs) partly central (occurring in the central nervous system), that, to be sure, one can obtain the impression when one considers only the external circumstances that the organ produces unequal effects under equal circumstances. The more unusual effects we are accustomed to call "illusions."

It is true that we have now begun to consider all these circumstances. It appears to me, though, that there is a tendency to consider the sense organs as

* Translated from: E. Mach, "Über die Abhängigkeit der Netzhautstellen von einander," Vierteljahresschrift für Psychiatrie in ihren Beziehungen zur Morphologie und Pathologie des Central-Nervensystems, 1868, 2, 38-51.

rather simple mechanisms which under equal external conditions affect the central nervous system in fairly equal ways. Consequently, the "sense illusions" occasionally met with we prefer to regard as "errors of judgment."

I now have grounds to believe that the majority of the phenomena which we have believed to be errors of judgment (i.e., essentially due to processes in the central nervous system) actually have their basis in a more autonomous behavior of the sense organs. I will describe a series of observations that led me to the view that is already becoming familiar in comparative anatomy, namely that the sense organs are to be considered as subordinate central organs.

Figure 1 represents the unrolled surfaces of a cylinder made of paper and painted with black sectors as shown in the sketch. When the cylinder is wrapped in the paper shown in Figure 1(a)* and is rotated about its axis, the resulting appearance is familiar to everyone. The surface appears divided into two unequally bright stripes. The stripe below *ab* is about twice as bright as that above *ab*, following the law formulated by Plateau and Talbot.

If we now rotate a cylinder with the surface shown in Figure 1(b) we obtain a single stripe which is brightest at the lower border, darkest at the upper, and from bottom to top is of uniformly decreasing brightness, since that part of the white which is mixed with the black by rotation decreases steadily toward the top.

Now, one might expect the same with the surface shown in Figure 1(c), since here the white also decreases steadily toward the top, but slower to the midline *ab*, and then more rapidly. According to Plateau's law the midline *ab* should appear brighter than the lower half and darker than the upper half, just as *ab* in Figure 1(b). Instead, when the experiment is carried out, we see the midline as a prominently bright, somewhat washed-out streak. The bends in the sectors, which correspond to an alteration in the rate of decrease in the amount of white, appear brighter during rotation.

The surface in Figure 1(d) shows a dark streak corresponding to the bends at *ab*.

Let us seek the law explaining these phenomena. We succeed very easily if we consider that the form of the white sectors on the surface of the cylinder directly determines the distribution of the light intensity. Let us imagine a strip of paper on which the intensity of illumination changes from place to place, but only along the longitudinal direction. We represent the distribution of the light by choosing the longitudinal

* So that the line *ab* forms a circle whose midpoint lies on the axis of the cylinder.

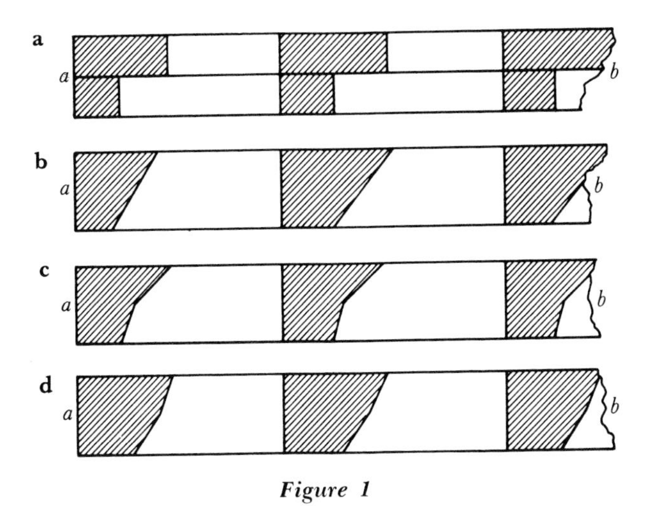

Figure 1

direction as the axis of abscissae (X-axis) and the light intensities as the ordinates. We would thus obtain something like the curve in Figure 2, where, in each abscissa, OA represents the distance of a point on the strip from one end and the appropriate ordinate AB the corresponding light intensity. Our phenomena now show that those places where the light intensity curve bends concave to the axis of abscissae (as at a and b) appear darker and those places where the bends are convex (as at c and d) appear brighter.

After I observed these phenomena, I asked myself first if their form could be attributed to the intermittent light produced by the rotating cylinder or if only the nature of the light distribution caused them.

I have since provided myself with surfaces of arbitrary light distribution illuminated in various ways with steady light.

I first photographed my cylinders during rotation. The photographs turn out to be quite similar to the rotating originals, since every point which appears brighter to the eye also, at the same time, sends more light to the sensitized plate. Without doubt, the bends in the light curve

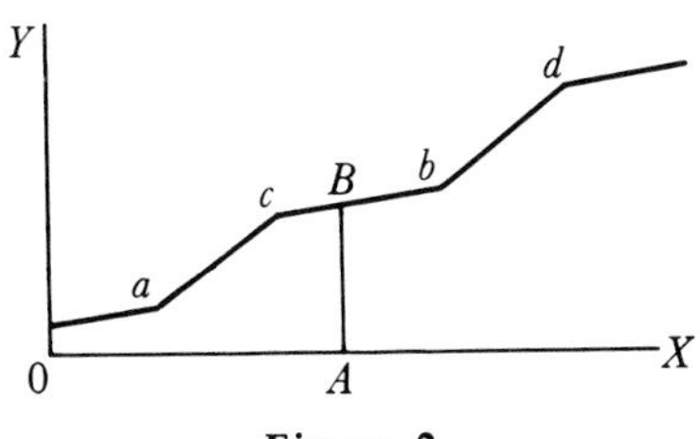

Figure 2

of the photographs correspond to those in the light curve of the rotating originals. The photographs now show the same bright and dark striae as do the originals. Thus, the phenomenon depends merely upon the distribution of the light.

If one draws some fine regular lines on paper, with their thickness changing according to a certain rule, one easily obtains the same distribution of light as that provided by rotating cylinders. If the paper is removed to such a distance that the lines disappear and the paper appears in various shades of gray to the eye, then the bright and dark striae soon appear as before.

If I grind a prism from a semitransparent material such as bone glass, with a cross-section as represented in Figure 3(a), and place it in the window shutter of a darkened room, the thickest parts transmit the least light. The corresponding light curve is represented in Figure 3(b). At *a* we see a bright stripe, a dark one at *b*.

If I let the shadow cast by the edge of a house in sunlight fall on a piece of paper, then the light distribution on the paper is given by Figure 4. From *a* to *b* is the shadow, from *b* to *c* is the half-shadow which increases in brightness toward *c*, and from *c* to *d* the paper is illuminated by the entire sun. At the border *b* of the full-shadow and half-shadow we see a dark line, whereas at *c* we see a bright line.

Figure 5(a) shows the cross-section of a cylinder with its surface *abc* covered with white paper. Sunlight falls on it from the direction indicated by the arrow. It is then easily shown that the illumination curve of the image of the cylinder on the retina can be represented by Figure 5(b), in which the intensity is greatest for each part of the cylinder's surface which is most perpendicular to the sun's rays. Once again one sees a dark stripe on the cylinder corresponding to the bend *b*. In all six of these cases, with the same distribution of light we have the same phenomena, no matter whether we use continuous or intermittent light as the means of illumination. Generally, therefore, a darkening and a

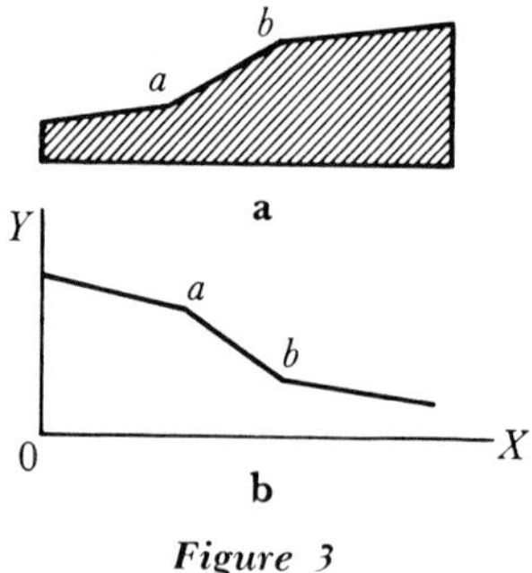

Figure 3

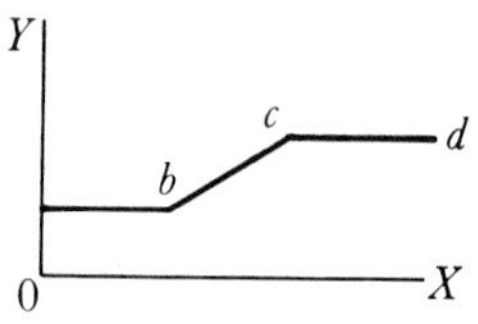

Figure 4

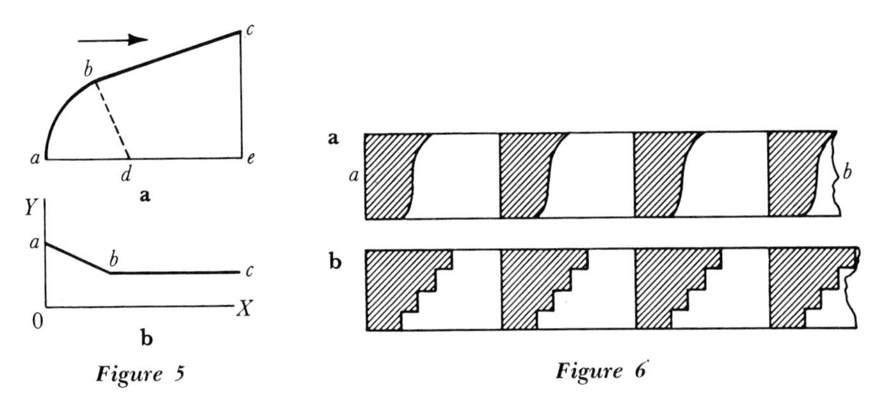

Figure 5

Figure 6

lightening correspond, respectively, to bends in the light curve convex and concave to the axis of abscissa.

Let us determine now if this law is not a special case of a more general law. The thought is obvious. A bend is nothing more than a very sharp curve. Will gradual changes in the light curve perhaps give effects similar to the sharp bends? One can easily answer the question by experiment. The research confirms the supposition.

As we already know, intermittent light has the same effect on the eye as continuous light, so we choose the rotating cylinder as the easiest means to our goal. According to Plateau's law, the cylinder surface in Figure 6(a) should appear as a gray stripe upon rotation—brightest at the lower edge and darkest at the upper edge and decreasing regularly in brightness from top to bottom. The facts, however, are otherwise. We do not notice at all the slight decrease of the white toward the top. We see instead the stripe divided at the midline into two unequally bright stripes, a brighter upper one and a lower darker one. The concave curvature of the light-curve completely overcomes the decrease in the objective brightness, while the convex curvature in the lower half causes the brightness to appear less. For the eye, the transition point from convex to concave forms an almost sharp border between bright and dark.

Our hypothesis, however, has been confirmed and can be stated as follows: *Everywhere that the light curve is convex with respect to the axis of abscissae and concave with respect to the axis of the abscissae we find a decrease and an increase, respectively, of the brightness.*

This principle includes the earlier cases of bent sectors as special cases and, likewise, a long-known contrast phenomenon. When rotated, the surface of Figure 6(b) appears, of course, as four stripes of graduated brightness, of which the lower is the brightest, the upper the darkest. Moreover, each stripe is darker on the lower side and brighter on the upper side. It should be thus, however, according to our principle, since on the border of each stripe convex and concave flections of the light curve fall immediately adjacent to one another.

Following this preliminary work, it no longer appeared doubtful to me that the principle had further generality. In fact up to this time we have only investigated illuminated surfaces whose intensity of illumination merely varied in one direction. Let us now consider other surfaces whose intensity of illumination is changed in all directions from place to place.

In order to discuss the resulting phenomena we must first come to an understanding as regards a brief characterization. I think of the retina, for simplicity's sake, as a plane on which the image of the observed surface is formed. Now, if I erect on each point of the retina a perpendicular line whose length represents the intensity of illumination on that particular point, and if I connect all the end points of these perpendicular lines, a surface is obtained which will be called the *light intensity surface*, or *light surface*.

More strongly illuminated points, as we have already seen, do not necessarily result in sensations of greater intensity. Therefore, if on every point of the retina we erect a second perpendicular line, which represents the intensity of the sensation at that point, and connect all the end points, we obtain a second surface which will be called the *sensation intensity surface*, or *sensation surface*.

Everyday experience teaches us, however, that elevations of the light surface also correspond to elevations of the sensation surface; that is, in its gross features the sensation surface is a copy of the light surface. However, as we will see—and have already seen in part—this is not true for

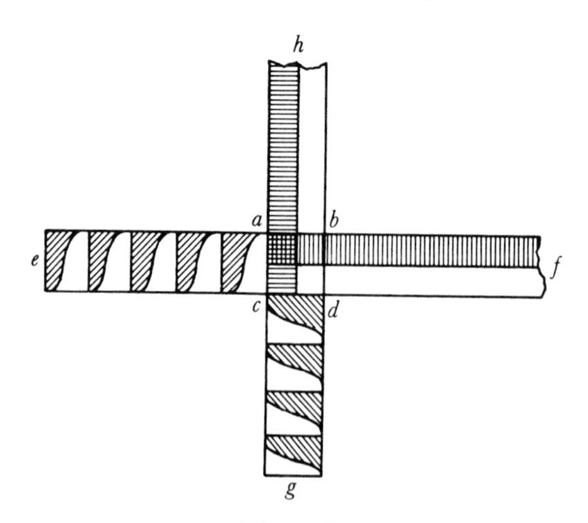

Figure 7

the finer details of the two surfaces, but only for the more gross features. Although the light and sensation surfaces have a similar physiognomy, the one is a caricature of the other.

I have obtained in various ways surfaces on which the illumination intensity varies in a number of directions. All of these surfaces have, on observation, given corresponding results. Because of this I shall present only the easiest and the clearest method.

When I set a cylinder in rotation whose surface is painted like *eac* in Figure 7 and photographed it on a glass plate an image was obtained like *bdf*. Similarly *cdg* photographed during rotation gave the image *abh*. If the two glass plates are then laid one on the other so that the stripes cross each other perpendicularly (held against a uniform ground), one obtains the crossed field *abcd* whose approximate appearance is indicated by shading in Figure 7.*

Figure 7 gives a complete survey of the experiment. The horizontal strip at rest is shown on the left, in rotation on the right. Similarly, the vertical strip is at rest below, in rotation above, and the crossed field gives the appearance of the photographs placed across one another. It should be noted that the shading is exaggerated for the sake of clearness, and that it is correct only for those places which are next to the midlines of both stripes since, due to strong curvature, the corner *a* of the crossed field *abcd* is the brightest, and the corner *d* the darkest.

In Figure 8 the apparent shading of the crossed field *abcd* is somewhat more exactly represented. Although the shading is again exaggerated, it clearly illustrates the phenomenon. In the corners *abcd* the objective illumination of the fields predominates, whereas in the neighborhood of the midpoint *o* and in the neighborhood of the midlines *mnpq,* where objectively rather equally illuminated regions border on one another, the curvature of the light surface shows its effect and the subjective illumination stands out distinctly.

After having described the phenomenon exactly, we shall next see what we can learn from it. The form of the light surface of the crossed field is given when the two ordinates of the light surface, one corresponding to each strip, are summated. Then the light surface *pon* is concave toward *on,* convex toward *op* (concave–convex). Similarly, in the field *moq* the light surface toward *oq* is concave, toward *om* convex (concave–convex). In the field *noq* there is a concavity toward *oq,* as there is toward

* Translator's note: From the discussion which follows it appears that part of the figure shown here may be the negative of the one Mach intended to use. The representation of the objective distribution of illumination in the field *eac* in Figure 7 is just the reverse of that shown in Plate I-5, Paper Number 1, page 277, which yields the same effect.

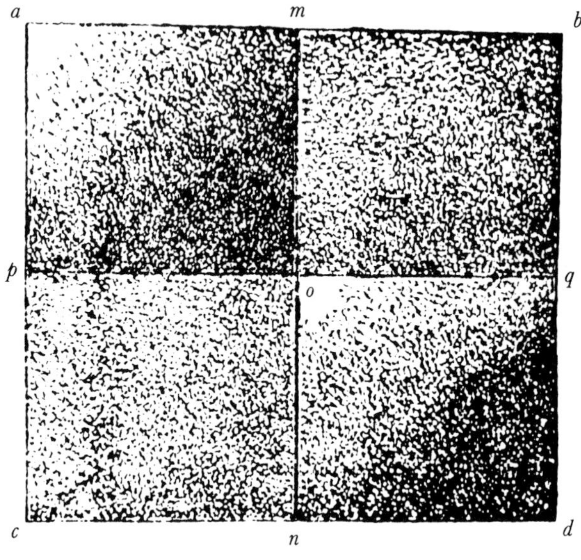

Figure 8

on (concave–concave). Finally, in the field *mop* there is a convexity toward *om*, and also toward *op* (convex–convex).

We thus see that in a convex–convex region of the light surface there is an apparent decrease in brightness, and in concave–concave regions an apparent increase in brightness. Provided that the concavity and convexity are equal, concave–convex regions show neither an increase nor a decrease in brightness.

If the objective and subjective brightness were identical, the crossed field *abcd* should simply appear as represented in Figure 9. This is what one would expect, a priori, on the basis of Plateau's law. As we have shown, however, the appearance is quite otherwise.

I have conducted a great number of similar experiments with many variations, and will give here only the results obtained from them.

Where the light surface, on the average, is concave with respect to the retina there appears an increase in brightness, and, on the average, the opposite where it is convex.

The sensation surface follows, in its gross features, the light surface. However, to the concave curvature of the light surface with respect to the plane of the retina there corresponds a greater elevation of the sensation surface. To the convexities on the other hand there corresponds a greater depression of the sensation surface.

This law holds not only for white light but also for monochromatic light. It holds equally well for all colors, since in experiments with white light a subjective coloration never appears.

That the law holds for any combination of colors, I am equally convinced. For example when I replace the black sectors of my rotating cylinder with red, and the white with yellow, I see in place of the black stripes only red, in place of the white stripes, green. Every color behaves in this manner. If one regards the sensation of white as compounded of the primary color sensations, then the law holds for every primary color sensation.

There can hardly be any doubt that we are concerned here not with physical but with physiological phenomena, in which areas of illumination of undoubtedly equal physical intensity appear unequally bright. That a photograph of the rotating cylinder appears just like the original should not lead us to interpret the phenomenon as physical. For we view the photograph with our eyes also, just as the original. It must be, then, that when the eye converts the physical intensity to physiological and alters it, this occurs in the same way in the case of the photograph as in the case of the original.

The only question is: What kind of physiological phenomenon is it, and in what known realm can it be classified? I would regard the phenomenon as a contrast effect, and, indeed, as a simultaneous contrast rather than a successive contrast phenomenon. The phenomena do not

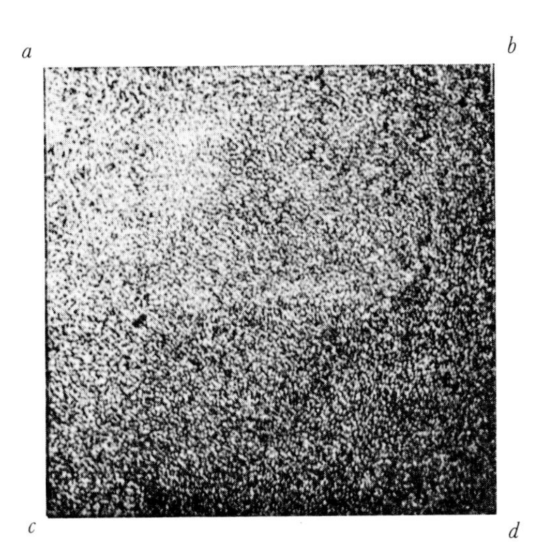

Figure 9

result from eye movement, since they still appear when eye movement is eliminated, as is the case when an object that shows the stripes described is observed when illuminated by an electric spark. One then still sees the stripes.

Let us now investigate the physiological significance of our law. The intensity of sensation of an area of the retina can be different for equal intensities of illumination of this area, depending on the illumination of neighboring areas. We cannot speak of concave and convex distributions so long as we consider a single point. Only with lines or surface areas does this have any meaning, as when we consider a series of retinal points and their illuminations. From our law it is quite evident, therefore, that neighboring retinal elements have a physiological relation to one another and that the sensation arising from each one is influenced by all of its neighbors.

To be sure, one could offer various objections. These phenomena could be ascribed to errors of judgment. The particular judgments, however, do not fall within the realm of the conscious. They are what we ordinarily call unconscious judgments. Is it plausible, then, that such unconscious judgments would first occur in the central nervous system? Or is it more plausible that processes similar to the judgments should already occur in the retina, which in its structure is so similar to the brain? Why this retinal structure, if it has nothing else to do but to transmit the sensation unaltered? It might well be very difficult, also, to specify the influences which could lead the judgment astray in one direction or another.

Let us for the time being hold to the more scientific view that the light stimuli are already sorted out and organized in the retina and that, thus already sorted out and organized, they enter consciousness.

I will relate a simple analogy which, however trite, appears to me to be striking, if not necessarily well thought out. The state is an organism, formed of elementary organisms—of men. It cannot be denied that the whole state behaves on a grand scale, in a manner similar to individual man behaving on a small scale. The individual soldiers, craftsmen, civil workers (the muscle and nerve fibers) think many things which do not enter the consciousness of the government (the brain). On the other hand the elementary organs, which form the government, know many things in common of which the other members of the state discover only a part through commands, decrees, and the like. Every class has its skills, its traditions, of which only a small part comes to the consciousness of the government. Everything that the government receives notice of from its organs is already infected by traditions and the particular logic of these organs. The consciousness of every man is partly individual, partly a group consciousness. This latter part is little altered even when the individual persons of the group change. If one could separate this group consciousness, as it actually is sorted out and appears separately in public life, one would find that every level, just as in the government, has its own memory, its own logic, and its own self-consciousness, by virtue of which it remains the same in spite of changes in its personnel.

Don't object that this is trite, and a delay of the explanation. It is one thing to understand the state and another to understand the individual man. We cannot understand the state before we understand the man. Likewise, we will not understand the psychology of man before we understand the much simpler psychology of the ganglion cells. The similarity of this psychology with that of the whole man permits conjecture and may serve us as a guiding star. It may thus well be the main task of physiological psychology to solve these simple basic psychological processes in the ganglion cells, out of whose reciprocal actions arises the psychology of man.

Who would believe that the monarch himself would check the passports of foreigners on the border? Is it not equally absurd to assume that the brain itself is concerned with every single light ray incident on the retina?

Let us proceed with a more serious consideration. How might the retinal areas behave with respect to one another in order to lead to optic phenomena such as are actually observed? The behavior of the retinal points may be similar to that of the larger parts of the retina. Therefore, let us investigate this.

White of a lesser intensity appears gray next to a brighter white. On the other hand, with various levels of illumination (in the same surroundings) such as bright sunshine, overcast sky, candlelight, or in twilight, we are never in doubt that we have before us a gray or a white paper. We always have nearly the same sensation.

What is the cause of this? The pupil opens in weaker light, but a complete equalization of such different light intensities is not possible by this means alone. If there is on the whole retina, under otherwise equal conditions, a 2, 3, . . . , n-fold increase in light, so is the retinal image of a white paper 2, 3, . . . , n-fold brighter. The relationship of the quantity of light on the entire retina and of the image of the paper remains constant under otherwise equal circumstances. The whiteness of the paper appears to depend on the value of this relation.

One cannot represent this adequately other than by thinking of a process as being initiated in the retina at the location of the image of the paper whose intensity depends on the relation of the illumination of the image of the paper and that of the entire retina. One could also say that a part of the retina evaluates its illumination in terms of that on the rest of the retina. This would not alter the facts. The first interpretation would be a physical one, the second a psychological one. Both have their justification.

Indeed, one can still otherwise convince oneself that the total light which falls on the retina or the average light corresponding to a unit of retinal surface is not a mere arithmetic quantity but also has a *physiological* value.

The diameter of the pupil depends on this total light or average light —but only on the total—and is independent of the distribution of the light on the retina within a wide range.

In order to verify this, I have carried out a simple experiment. A large disc painted with black and white sectors is placed vertically and set in rapid rotation so that it appears uniformly gray. One then steps so close that the entire field of vision is filled by it. The rotating disc is now suddenly stopped, so that suddenly in place of the gray image a spotted black and white image of equal total light appears. There results not the slightest noticeable alteration of the observer's pupil diameter.

One can show this by direct observation of another observer's eye, or can easily observe it in his own eye.

I wear weak concave eye glasses. If, during the observation of the disc I stand in such a way that some light falls on my eye glasses from the back and from the side, I always find some strongly glittering dust particles on them which form large dispersion circles in my eye corresponding to the diameter of the pupil.

I see the dispersion circles become distinctly larger when I cover one eye or otherwise decrease the light intensity. There is, however, no change when the rotating disc is suddenly stopped.

If I look at this disc through a small opening in a metal plate I can make the edge of the iris congruent with the edge of the disc. If the rotation of the disc is stopped, the two borders remain equally well in coincidence.

Thus, there is a process—the contraction of the pupil—whose intensity depends on the total illumination of the retina. The brightness sensation of a circumscribed retinal image appears to be a similar process whose intensity depends on the total illumination of the retina and on that of the image in question.

It appears to me quite plausible to assume that every part of the retina behaves in a way quite similar to larger subdivisions of the retina. Psychologically speaking, each point on the retina would evaluate its illumination in terms of the average illumination of its immediate surroundings, or, physically speaking, in every retinal point a sensation

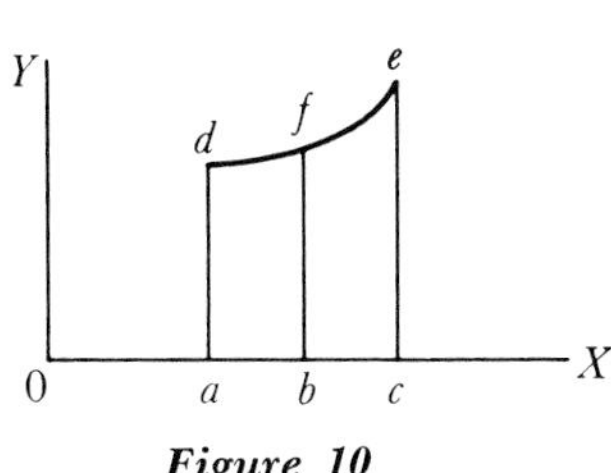

Figure 10

process would be initiated whose intensity corresponds to the relation of its illumination to the average illumination of its surroundings. The interrelation between the retinal points would naturally have to be regarded as becoming smaller the farther they are from one another.

In fact, all of the phenomena described here can be explained very well if one assumes that the *individual* retinal points already evaluate the light incident on them in terms of the average light on their surroundings.

Suppose that the light only varies in one direction on the retina, and that this variation is represented by the curve in Figure 10. If the curve *dfe* is convex with respect to the retina, then the intensity of illumination *bf* on the point *b* is less than the average illumination on the entire strip *ac*. The reverse would be true if the curve were concave.

Since our phenomena occur with colored light also, and if we make the same assumption for color sensation, one can easily convince oneself that all of the known phenomena of color contrast become special cases of our law.

A great range of phenomena of physiological optics might be explained by our assumption and brought into a single framework.

Our basic assumption, however, has in itself a high probability since it is nothing but an extension to the elementary sense organs of the so generally confirmed basic psychological law formulated by Fechner. It has been disputed whether this is a psychic, or a physical, or a psychophysical law. When I consider that it stands the sharpest tests in the realm of sound, where it obviously is based on the organization of the ear, it appears to me most plausible to accept the idea that it has its basis in the organization of the elementary sense organs. It operates wherever comparisons are made—that is, where several elementary organs cooperate. Is it not likely that it is because of the nature of the communication among these organs that the effects produced depend upon the relationships of the stimuli? A psychological, or, properly speaking, a psychophysical interpretation of the law would be less intelligible to me than the organic interpretation just given. Naturally, I regard this principle simply as an article of faith.

More rigorous analyses of the phenomena discussed here and the associated mathematical developments may be found in my papers in the Sitzungsberichten der Wiener Akademie (Vols. 52, 54).*

* Translator's note: Papers 1, 2, and 3 in this series.

ERNST MACH

6. *On the influence of spatially and temporally varying light stimuli on visual perception**

I. Forty years ago I observed phenomena on rotating discs, then in shadows, and on various other visual objects, the further investigation of which has led me to the hypothesis of a characteristic organic reciprocal interrelation of retinal points.† These phenomena may best be called contrast phenomena, insofar as the phenomena thus referred to, previous to that time, can be considered as special cases of those observed by me. If one puts aside all unwarranted and all preconceived notions, then the facts can be described as follows: The illumination of a retinal point will, in proportion to the difference between this illumination and the average of the illumination on neighboring points, appear

* Translated from: E. Mach, "Über den Einfluss räumlich und zeitlich variierender Lichtreize auf die Gesichtswahrnehmung," Sitzungsberichte der mathematisch-naturwissenschaftlichen Classe der kaiserlichen Akademie der Wissenschaften, 1906, 115/IIa, 633-648.

† The first page of the second paper contains an apparent *lapsus,* which, however, has had no effect on the following. [Translator's note: Mach is referring to the preceding papers in this series. See also Mach (1914) pages 215-220.]

brighter or darker, respectively, depending on whether the illumination of it is above or below that average. The weight of the retinal points in this average is to be thought of as rapidly decreasing with distance from the particular point considered. This relation, therefore, can be symbolically and approximately expressed by means of a formula.

Let us call the intensity of illumination u on a uniform mat plane where $u = f(x, y)$. Thus, the brightness sensation v of the corresponding retinal point is given by $u - m[d^2u/dx^2) + (d^2u/dy^2)]$, where m is a constant. If the expression in brackets is positive, then the sensation of brightness is reduced; in the opposite case, it is increased. Thus, v is not only influenced by u, but also by its second differential quotients. This formula can be regarded as a short summary of the phenomena, so long as the radii of the curvatures of the elements of the surface f (by reduction of the size of the retinal image x, y) are assumed to be large relative to the diameter of a retinal element. It is, however, not a standard formula; it is to be understood only that the brightness v increases and decreases with the value it gives. A proper measurement of the sensation of brightness is out of the question. Moreover, the retina is not a continuum to which a differential quotient alone can be applied exactly, but consists of elements of finite extent. If, for example, the surface, whose equation is $u = f(x, y)$, has flections, then the second differential quotients of u become infinite and the formula is useless. Naturally, in this case the eye does not see an infinitely great brightening and darkening, confined to mathematical lines, but, instead, prominent although washed-out brightenings or darkenings (i.e., lighter or darker stripes).

If we pay attention to the average brightness of the surroundings of a particular retinal point, we will never be disappointed in our expectations.

II. My reports have remained almost unknown or unnoticed for a long time, such that, indeed, the facts concerned were again discovered independently by observers more than 30 years later.* Since the interest of physiologists and physicists has now turned to this subject, I would like to add to my earlier description some explanations and improvements.

* See H. Seeliger, "Die scheinbare Vergrösserung des Erdschattens bei Mondfinsternissen." Abhandlungen der Münchener Akademie, 1896; H. Haga, and C. H. Wind, "Beugung der Röntgenstrahlen." Wiedemann's *Ann.*, **68** (1899), p. 866; C. H. Wind, "Zur Demonstration einer von E. Mach entdeckten optischen Täuschung," *Physik. Zeitschr. von Riecke and Simon,* **I**, 10; A. v. Obermayer, "Über die Säume um die Bilder dunkler Gegenstände auf hellem Hintergrunde." *Eder's Jahrbuch für Photographie,* 1900. [Translator's note: See also Sherrington (1897) and McDougall (1903).]

III. I will begin by describing the experiments which, at that time, I had to carry out by the most primitive means. If one lets the shadow of the edge of a house in sunlight fall on a piece of white paper, one notices, in accordance with the law mentioned above, a dark line *d* at the border of the umbra *K* and the penumbra *H*, and a bright line *h* at the boundary between the penumbra *H* and the fully illuminated space *V*, even though the transitions at both boundaries are continuous and there are neither maxima nor minima. One can also make the same observation of one's own shadow if it falls on a fairly uniform ground or even while walking on a sandy road. In these cases the phenomenon is weakened by the scattered daylight, just as are analogous observations in a bright room. The phenomenon appears very nicely, however, if one fits the large objective of a telescope in a heliostat opening of the window shutter in a dark room, and, with the ocular removed, lets the image of the sun fall on a transparent plate of frosted glass or celluloid. This provides a light source with sufficiently uniform radiation from all parts which one can give any desired form and size by covering it with an opaque template with various openings. If one wants a larger source and if a lesser intensity is satisfactory, then a short tube in the heliostat opening, closed with a frosted plate, suffices. The sunlight then simply falls on the frosted plate without the aid of a lens and one sets a diaphragm *D*, of the chosen form and size, in the aperture. The shadow of the edge *R* of an opaque screen, cast on a white paper screen *P*, by means of the illuminated plate bounded by *D*, shows the phenomena in full clearness and intensity. Between *K* and *H* there appears the significantly darker line *d*, between *H* and *V*, however, the brighter line *h* appears. It is even more suitable to cast the shadow of *R* on a rotating white paper disc, instead of on a stationary paper screen. If the shadow falls on printed or on otherwise unequally bright paper, one does not see the phenomenon. It immediately appears, however, by a kind of abstraction, if one moves the paper in its own plane perpendicular to the lines *d* or *h*. These lines can, even under the most favorable circumstances, completely escape the attention for a short time. One then notices instead another remarkable phenomenon. Let us assume that, for the observer, *K* is situated on the left and *V* to the right. To the observer, positioned with his back toward the light, the stripe between *d* and *h* will then appear either as a convex elevation lighted from the right or as a concave depression illuminated from the left. We will return to this plastic phenomenon later.

IV. The procedure described above, unlike the use of rotating discs with painted sectors, offers many advantages and conveniences, and permits by slight modifications the production of very manifold distributions of brightness. Let x be the horizontal midline of a diaphragm opening D on the frosted plate. Perpendicular to x the ordinate y, corresponding to the edge of the opening, is equal above and below the midline and is so chosen that $y = f(x)$. If one now places a screen S with a longer, vertical narrow slit s, parallel to y, and behind it a paper screen P, one obtains on the latter a brightness distribution which, in a section through the horizontal plane x (and not too far from it), corresponds very nearly to the form $u = kf(x)$ where k is a constant factor. By choice of the distance of P from D, and by similar suitable positions of S on the line DP one can prescribe the size of the image on P. Moreover, the width of the slit s has an influence on the brightness and sharpness of the image. Naturally, one chooses a narrow slit, but not one so narrow as to decrease the brightness too much and to permit diffraction to exert a detrimental influence on the sharpness of the image. It is advantageous to use a rotating celluloid disc (frosted on both sides) instead of using a stationary disc of the same material in front of the diaphragm.

V. In order to obtain greater brightness of the image one can make the slit s several centimeters broad and place in it a cylindrical lens with the axis of the cylinder parallel to y. One must, of course, take care that SD and SP are conjugate focal distances. We will make use of these arrangements and will not, however, describe them individually any more but will refer to the above remarks.

VI. We cast a shadow of a straight vertical edge R on an opaque screen by means of a brightly illuminated frosted plate. The diaphragm opening we will choose as quadratic with the side vertical, then circular, and again quadratic with the diagonal vertical. The upper halves of the openings, whose greatest horizontal dimensions are made equal to the diameter of the circle, are represented in Figure 1 by Q, C, and P. Assume that the total light energy transmitted through all the apertures is equal. Accordingly, the strengths of illumination on a unit of surface are respectively in the ratio 1 to $4/\pi$ to 2. One observes in the first case that d between K and H is darkest and h between H and V is brightest; both are still quite distinct in the second case, but they are much weaker in the third case. If we again let u represent the strength of illumination in the penumbra and x represent the abscissa of the midline measured from the border of the umbra, then the ordinates of the curves Q, C, and P illustrate directly the course of (du/dx) in the penumbra space. One must think of them, however, only as enlarged respectively in the relation 1, $4/\pi$, and 2. The course of the strength of illumination u in the penumbra which is given by integration of (du/dx) is represented

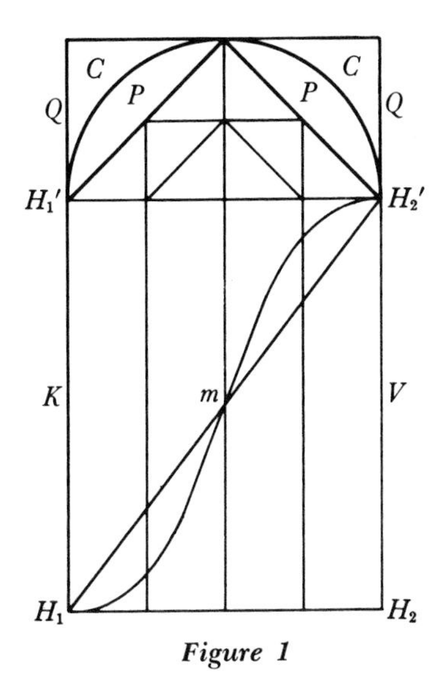

Figure 1

by the curves in the field $H_1H_2H_1'H_2'$. As a glance at the figure shows immediately, to Q there corresponds a completely uniform increase of u, a straight line which at H_1 and H_2' bends to the horizontal. For P the connection between the horizontals forms two congruent parabolas centered symmetrically which join the vertical lines from the horizontal at H_1 and H_2' and pass through m. The curve of u for C lies between the two previous curves, and has in common with them the points H_1, H_2' and m.* One sees at once that the deviation from the mean line connecting H_1 and H_2' is the greatest for Q and the least for P, which is in agreement with the results of the experiment.

VII. The experiments with the intensity of illumination varying in only one direction are easily feasible in different ways. However, if one wants to view a surface whose intensity of illumination varies in two directions, then one is somewhat restricted in the choice of method. The most convenient way to combine illumination varying in two directions is in the form $\varphi(x) + \psi(y)$ or in a second form $\varphi(x) \cdot \psi(y)$. The first occurs where two independent illuminations superimposed on one another are

* This curve, not shown in the figure, may be obtained, if one diagrams as abscissae $r(1 - \cos \alpha)$ and as ordinate $r^2/2$ $(\arcsin \alpha - \sin \alpha \cos \alpha)$ either by a simple integration or by an elementary geometric consideration. The initial values for the computation are:

$$\left(\frac{du}{dx}\right)_{x=0} = 0, \quad \left(\frac{d^2u}{dx^2}\right)_{x=0} = \infty.$$

summed,* whereby, however, the effect of one is dulled by the other. The gradations of the brightness remain stronger and do not lose their character in the second method. When a surface has the material property to appear unequally bright in different places when illuminated uniformly with the intensity i, and to radiate according to the law $i\varphi(x)$, then with illumination $\psi(y)$ the light distribution will be $\varphi(x)\cdot\psi(y)$. The latter occurs, for example, when, in a dark room, one lets the shadow of the edge of a vertical screen, whose brightness varies in a horizontal direction according to the law $\psi(y)$, fall on a rotating disc, painted with black and white sectors whose brightness varies along the direction of a (vertical) radius according to the law $\varphi(x)$. Where x and y cross perpendicularly one has a distribution of light corresponding to the second form. If, instead of the white sectors, the same areas are cut out of an opaque rotating disc and the shadow of an edge is cast through these openings on the rotating disc, then one can obtain the same light distribution on a stationary screen. The star-disc of Figure 2, combined with the shadow of an edge shows two intersecting sets of lines of the type d and h described above.

VIII. With the aid of the methods described in paragraphs III-VII one can obtain, in many ways, brightnesses varying in one direction and project them on rotating discs or cylinders whose brightness (diffusibility, albedo) varies in a direction perpendicular to the first. One can thus show that strong curvatures in the surface corresponding to the equation $u = \varphi(x)\cdot\psi(y)$ have effects optically similar to, if weaker than, those of flections. I carried out somewhat similar experiments forty years ago by superimposing and crossing transparent photographic plates taken of rotating discs and cylinders. The fine collodion plates were better suited to this purpose than are the now-common dry plates with their coarser grain.†

IX. In general, our visual system serves to perceive surfaces, lines, and points, and, therefore, boundaries of three dimensional visual objects. But we all know that under special conditions we can also see a luminous solid space with its entire contents. Consider, for example, a number of congruent rectangles of white cardboard, which intersect one another at approximately the same angles in the same relative places around a common axis of symmetry. If we then rotate this system of "wings" rapidly

* One can superimpose two images projected on a screen or optically combine the image of one rotating disc with a second by reflection from an unsilvered plane glass.

† It does not lead to a useful result to observe or to illuminate a rotating disc with painted sectors through the cut-out sectors of a second disc, because two combined rotations produce spoke-curves.

Figure 2

about this axis we see a cylinder filled with a white fog which becomes thicker nearer the axis of rotation—a cylinder which is luminous throughout its entire space, which we can distinguish quite well from a transparent cylindrical shell enclosing empty space. If we make the surface of these rectangles red, however, and place in the homologous positions small congruent green squares so that their paths of rotation perfectly coincide, then we see a translucent red cylinder, in which a translucent green four-edged ring floats. The edges, the surfaces, and the solidity are quite distinct. Any chosen spot which we place on the surface of the wings thus appears solid immediately upon rotation. Through variation of the experiments it was found, however, that this effect is certain only under favorable stereoscopic relations, sufficient differences in the two monocular images, head movements, etc. The smaller deviations of brightness from the average of the surroundings, as discussed in the law in section I, cannot generally be perceived in translucent spaces, since the lights at different depths overlap and stifle one another and do not permit any significant stereoscopic effects to appear. For example, if one allows the shadow of an edge—as described in section III—to fall on a cylindrical space obtained by rotation of wings of white cardboard as just described, then one obtains, using the previous notation, a full-shadow space K and a half-shadow space H, which are differentiated from one another by darker plane d, while H itself is separated from the space V by a brighter plane h. However, one sees d and h only when one is nearly in the plane d or h.

X. The sums of the two second differential quotients, whose optical significance is pointed out in section I, will remind physicists of the corresponding trinomial expression of the Laplacian–Poissonian equations which play such an important role in all areas of physics. Also, we are not dealing here with a mere outward resemblance, as the simplest example shows. Let us consider the shadow of a vertical edge of a screen which is cast on a vertical white sheet by an illuminated square with vertical sides. The strength of illumination increases in H from K toward V exactly in the same manner as the potential between two infinite plane parallel Franklin plates of which the first, corresponding to d, is grounded and the second, corresponding to h, is positively charged. Indeed, one sees that the charge represents a deviation from the average potential, the negative charge at d represents a darkening, and the positive charge at h represents a brightening. More of these examples can easily be found. If one considers the Laplace–Poisson equation as an expression of the deviation of a point from the mean of an infinitely small surrounding with regard to any one property, then one can easily arrive at an extension of it to the case of finite surroundings.*

XI. It must be striking to every unbiased observer that the second differential quotients of the strength of illumination have such a significant influence on the sensation of brightness, while the first differential quotients have little effect. The constant increase of the strength of illumination of a surface in one direction is hardly noticed. On the contrary, special arrangements are necessary in order to convince oneself of the great difference in the strength of illumination of points nearby one another under these circumstances. The first differential quotients, taken along one direction, appear to determine the perception of brightness to a lesser degree than that of relief. Everyone who experiments with rotating discs or cylinders provided with sectors of various forms knows the beautiful phenomena of plasticity which they show. If one uses Figure 3 as the surface of a cylinder where ab remains parallel to the

Figure 3

* Compare *Prinzipien der Wärmelehre,* 2nd edition, 1900, p. 118.

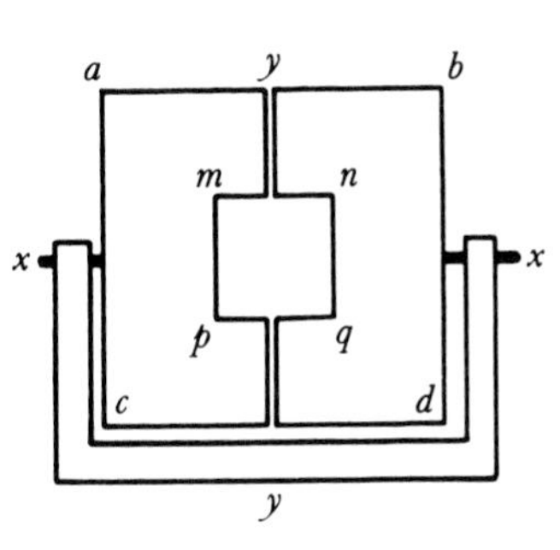

Figure 4

horizontal axis of rotation, then one sees either vertical troughs illuminated from the right or vertical bulges illuminated from the left on the rotating cylinder. The practiced observer can easily choose between or change the two impressions as soon as his back is turned toward the light incident from behind. As soon as the light is really incident from the right or from the left and the translucent sclera of the eyes are not artificially protected from this light, there is a strong compulsion to see the first or second image respectively. The light penetrating the sclera of the eyes appears to play a co-determining role, as in Fechner's "lateral-candle and window experiment." In order to encompass these phenomena in a general symbolic expression, let us think of a convex or concave cylinder surface with a circular horizontal plane directrix and a vertical generatrix, the light, however, falling horizontally from the left or right (perpendicular to the median plane of the observer). The direction from right to left, or the reverse, we call x, that from front to rear or vice versa, we call τ. With the value of the first differential quotient of the strength of illumination on the surface element (du/dx), the value of the second differential quotient $(d^2\tau/dx^2)$ and the depth τ of the illuminated element increase and decrease in the same direction x.*

XII. The plastic effects caused by illumination stand out especially vividly when the illumination is varied in time. The following experiment is very simple. One takes a rectangular cardboard screen *abcd* (Fig. 4) which can be rotated about the horizontal axis x, but which is large enough that with a considerable inclination to the vertical it still covers the whole luminous frosted plate. Then one cuts the window *mnpq* and, with a vertical cut *yy*, divides the whole screen in two parts which can be twisted to a fixed angle with respect to one another on the axis *xx*. Now one turns the entire screen back and forth about the axis *xx* in front of the luminous plate so that alternately the right and

* Translator's note: Compare Mach (1914) pages 215-220.

then the left half of the luminous plate is larger. The image of the plate, projected on a screen through a vertical slit or cylindrical lens (compare section V), appears falsely as a sheet of paper, with a fold along a vertical line, which executes rotations about this line as an axis as the two halves become alternately brighter and darker.

XIII. The following experiment is astonishing. The illuminated celluloid plate surface is limited by a diaphragm (Fig. 5) which consists of movable sectors. These sectors, *s*, turn about pins, *p*, which are firmly countersunk in the celluloid diffusing material, *z*, and are fastened with rivets, *q*, to a bar, *V*, which can turn them collectively in a corresponding way, so that initially all of the left borders of the sectors are vertical, but after their displacement the right borders are vertical. When now the diffusing surface thus framed is imaged on a screen by means of a vertical slit or a cylindrical lens one sees a number of vertical grooves, which are separated from one another by protruding edges. By changing the position of the bar, each edge changes into a small bulge which becomes broader until the whole groove is consumed so that, finally, only shrinking edges separating the bulges remain. Since the perception of the image is ambiguous, the same displacement can just as well show the conversion of bulges into grooves.

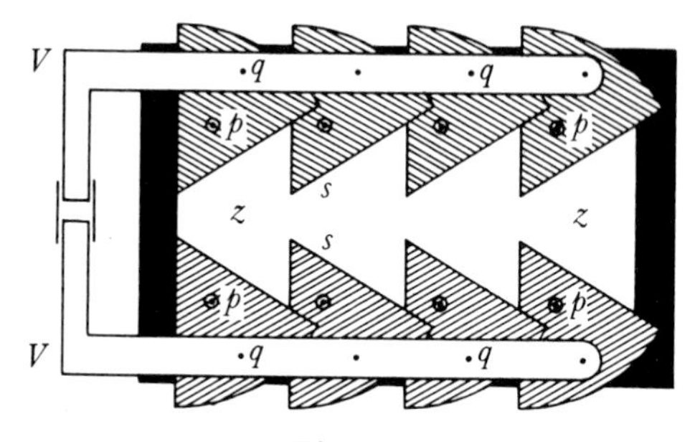

Figure 5

XIV. The course of the described phenomenon can be seen, in all details, in the diagrams Figure 6(a) and (b). The intensity of illumination on the projection screen is represented on the abscissae *xx* by the zig-zag line. It moves linearly back and forth between 0 and 1. An observer at I would see such a linear distribution as in Figure 6(a) if the light would fall from the left on a series of quadrants of circular cylinders lying next to each other with axes vertical * such that each of the left-hand borders of the quadrants in the sketch would be grazed by the incident light

* Compare the third of the papers in this series.

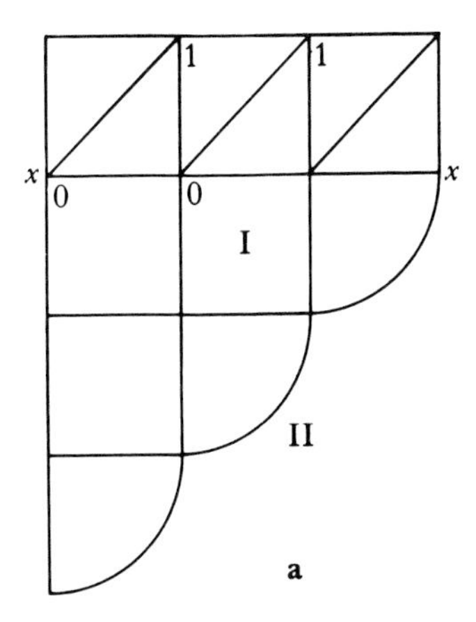

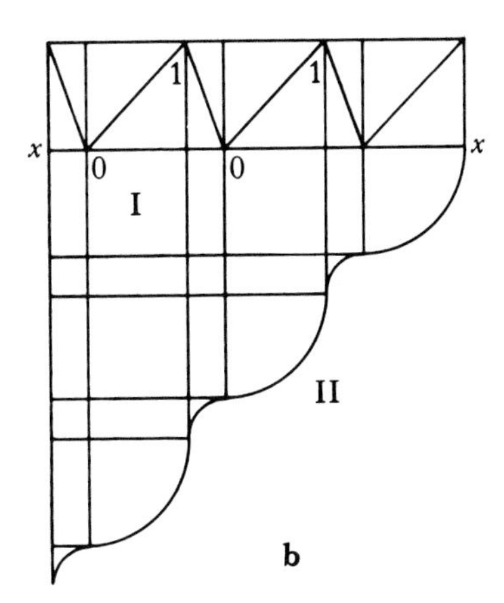

Figure 6

while the illumination would be normal to the right-hand borders of the quadrants. An observer at II would have the same view if the light came from the right. If the light distribution is altered somewhat as in Figure 6(b) so that the same variations from 0 to 1 are unequal and form different-sized striae, then alternating cylinder quadrants of unequal radii and alternating concave and convex forms are necessary to realize this light distribution.

XV. It is hardly necessary to point out that the structure of the retina is not everywhere uniform and equally fine. Accordingly, the influence of the second differential quotients diminishes in the peripheral parts of the retina. When I rotate a cylinder with black and white inflected sectors, I see the light and dark stripes very distinctly upon fixating the corresponding places. If, however, I place myself about 150 cm from the rotating cylinder and bring next to it a movable mark on which I fixate, by measuring the distance in millimeters of the mark from the position of the stripes, I can easily demonstrate that those stripes already disappear when the fixation point is about three degrees to one side of them. To be sure, I must carefully attend to the suppression of involuntary eye movements which may be caused by the merest suggestion of the stripes lying to one side.

XVI. In order to obtain a conception of approximately how far from the fixated place retinal elements are located which still can be said to have a noticeable effect on that place, I proceeded in the following way. The brightly illuminated frosted plate was covered with a diaphragm *D* whose opening had the form and orientation of Figure 7. Through a cylindrical lens *C*, fitted into a screen with the axis of the cylinder verti-

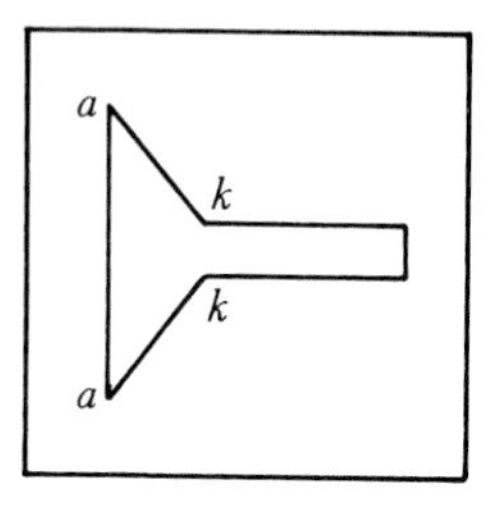

Figure 7

cal and with a focal length of 60 cm, this luminous object projected onto a frosted celluloid plate *Z* a sharp image *B* of nearly rectangular form, which showed a beautiful dark vertical stripe *ss* at the points corresponding to the flection points *kk* of the diaphragm opening. All vertical lines of this image appeared equally bright nearly to the upper and lower ends. I then sat behind the translucent celluloid plate *Z*, on which I observed the transmitted image *B* with my eye 1 meter distant from the image and so that *DCB* and my eye which was fixating the stripe *ss* almost formed a straight line. Now all points receiving, from the rectangular part of the diaphragm opening, the same amount of light as the points *ss* have no modifying influence on the sensation at the retinal points *ss* which are below the average brightness of the surroundings; the value of the mean, however, increases because of the points which are illuminated by the *V*-shaped part of the diaphragm. When now my assistant* slowly moved a screen with edge parallel to *aa* on the *V*-shaped part of the diaphragm toward *kk*, the stria *ss* was unchanged until the screen edge was within 7 mm of *kk*; it became indistinct when the screen was moved to within 5 mm and disappeared with a further decrease of the distance to 3 mm. Reduced to the size of image *B*, these distances corresponded to 4.9, 3.5, and 2.1 mm, respectively. The corresponding visual angles are 16′, 11′, and 7′, respectively. One may conclude from this experiment that the darkening of the fixated point by contrast is no longer significantly affected by retinal points at a visual angle greater than 16′ from the point fixated. When the stripe is diminished by the process described, it is not only less dark, but also thinner. Finally, one has the impression that the uniformly bright field, formed by the rectangular part of the diaphragm opening, borders on a uniformly brighter very narrow strip, which however no longer appears to be separated from it by a contour.

* All of the experiments described here I have carried out in good sunlight in the years 1903 to 1906, with the assistance of my son Dr. Ludwig Mach.

Bibliography

Adrian, E. D., and R. Matthews. 1928: "The Action of Light on the Eye. Part III. The Interaction of Retinal Neurones." *J. Physiol.,* **65,** 273-298.

———, and D. W. Bronk. 1928: "The Discharge of Impulses in Motor Nerve Fibers," *J. Physiol.,* **66,** 81-101.

Alpern, M., and H. David. 1959: "The Additivity of Contrast in the Human Eye," *J. Genl. Physiol.,* **43,** 109-126.

Anonymous. 1954: "Ernst Mach," *The Scientific Monthly,* **79,** 252.

Baines, H. 1958: *The Science of Photography,* London, Fountain Press.

Barlow, H. B. 1953: "Summation and Inhibition in the Frog's Retina," *J. Physiol.,* **119,** 69-88.

———, R. FitzHugh, and S. W. Kuffler. 1957: "Dark Adaptation, Absolute Threshold and Purkinje Shift in Single Units of the Cat's Retina," *J. Physiol.,* **137,** 327-337.

———, and R. M. Hill 1963: "Selective Sensitivity to Direction of Movement in Ganglion Cells of the Rabbit Retina," *Science,* **139,** 412-414.

———, R. M. Hill, and W. R. Levick, 1964: "Retinal Ganglion Cells Responding Selectively to Direction and Speed of Image Motion in the Rabbit," *J. Physiol.,* **173,** 377-407.

———, and W. R. Levick. 1965: "The Mechanism of Directionally Selective Units in the Rabbit's Retina," *J. Physiol.,* **178,** in press.

Baumgartner, G. 1961a: "Kontrastlichteffekte an retinalen Ganglienzellen: Ableitungen vom Tractus opticus der Katze," in *Neurophysiologie und Psychophysik des visuellen Systems,* R. Jung and H. Kornhuber, eds., Berlin, Springer-Verlag, 45-53.

———. 1961b: "Die Reaktionen der Neurone des zentralen visuellen Systems der Katze im simultanen Helligkeitskontrast," in *Neurophysiologie und Psychophysik des visuellen Systems,* R. Jung and H. Kornhuber, eds., Berlin, Springer-Verlag, 298-311.

———. 1965: "Neuronale Mechanism des Kontrast- und Bewegungssehens," *Berichte der deutschen Gesellschaft für Ophthalmologie,* **66,** 111-125, Munich, J. F. Bergmann.

Beitel, R. J. 1936: "Inhibition of Threshold Excitation in the Human Eye," *J. Genl. Psychol.,* **14,** 31-61.

Békésy, G. von. 1928: "Zur Theorie des Hörens: Die Schwingungsform der Basilarmembrane," *Physik. Z.,* **29,** 793-810.

———. 1947: "A New Audiometer," *Acta oto-laryngol.,* **35,** 411-422.

———. 1958: "Funneling in the Nervous System and Its Role in Loudness and Sensation Intensity on the Skin," *J. Acoust. Soc. Am.,* **30,** 399-412.

———. 1959a: "Similarities between Hearing and Skin Sensations," *Psychol. Rev.,* **66,** 1-22.

———. 1959b: "Neural Funneling along the Skin and between the Inner and Outer Hair Cells of the Cochlea," *J. Acoust. Soc. Am.,* **31,** 1236-1249.

———. 1960a: *Experiments in Hearing,* New York, McGraw-Hill Book Co.

———. 1960b: "Neural Inhibitory Units of the Eye and Skin. Quantitative Description of Contrast Phenomena," *J. Opt. Soc. Am.,* **50,** 1060-1070.

Bernhard, C. G. 1942: "Isolation of Retinal and Optic Ganglion Response in the Eye of *Dystiscus,*" *J. Neurophysiol.* **5,** 32-48.

———, and C. R. Skoglund. 1941: "Selective Suppression with Ethylalcohol of Inhibition in the Optic Nerve and of the Negative Component PIII of the Electroretinogram," *Acta physiol. scand.,* **2,** 10-21.

Bittini, M., A. M. Ercoles, A. Fiorentini, L. Ronchi, and G. Toraldo di Francia. 1960: "Enhanced Contrast of an Indefinitely Contoured Object by Movement or Intermittent Illumination," *Atti Fond. Giorgio Ronchi,* **15,** 62-84.

Bliss, J. C., and W. B. Macurdy. 1961: "Linear Models for Contrast Phenomena," *J. Opt. Soc. Am.,* **51,** 1373-1379.

Blough, D. S. 1961: "Experiments in Animal Psychophysics," *Scientific American,* **205,** 113-122.

Boring, E. G. 1929: *A History of Experimental Psychology,* New York–London, D. Appleton-Century Company, Inc.

———. 1942: *Sensation and Perception in the History of Experimental Psychology,* New York and London, D. Appleton-Century Company, Inc.

Bracewell, R. N. 1955: "Simple Graphical Method of Correcting for Instrumental Broadening," *J. Opt. Soc. Am.,* **45,** 873-876.

Brindley, G. S. 1960: *Physiology of the Retina and the Visual Pathway,* London, Edward Arnold.

Brooks, V. B., and V. J. Wilson. 1959: "Recurrent Inhibition in the Cat's Spinal Cord," *J. Physiol.,* **146,** 380-391.

Brown, K. T., and K. Tasaki. 1961: "Localization of Electrical Activity in the Cat Retina by an Electrode Marking Method," *J. Physiol.,* **158,** 281-295.

Bryngdahl, O. 1964a: "Visual transfer characteristics from Mach Band Measurements," *Kybernetik,* **2,** 71-77.

———. 1964b: "Eine neue Methode zur Bestimmung der Übertragungseigenschaften des Gesichtssinnes," *Die Naturwissenschaften,* **51,** 177-180.

———. 1964c: "Characteristics of the Visual System: Psychophysical Measurements of the Response to Spatial Sine-wave Stimuli in the Mesopic Region," *J. Opt. Soc. Am.,* **54,** 1152-1160.

———. 1964d: "Linear Relationship between Visual Response and Sinusoidally Varying Spatial Stimuli in the Mesopic Region," *J. Opt. Soc. Am.* 54, 1398.

———, and L. Riseberg. 1964: "New Phenomena in the Visual Response to Sinusoidally Varying Spatial Stimuli," *Optica Acta,* **2,** 117-130.

Burnham, R. W., and J. E. Jackson. 1955: "Mach Rings Verified by Numerical Differentiation," *Science,* **122,** 951-953.

Campbell, F. W., and J. G. Robson. 1964: "Application of Fourier Analysis to the Modulation Response of the Eye," *J. Opt. Soc. Am.,* **54,** 581.

Carus, P. 1911: "Professor Mach and His Work," *The Monist,* **21,** 19-42.

Charman, W. N., and B. M. Watrasiewicz. 1964: "Mach Effect Associated with Microscope Images," *J. Opt. Soc. Am.,* **54,** 791-795.

Chevreul, M. E. 1890: *The Principles of Harmony and Contrast of Colours,* London, George Bell and Sons, Bohn's Library, translated by Charles Martel.

Cornsweet, T. N. 1956: "The Determination of the Stimuli for Involuntary Drifts and Saccadic Eye Movements," *J. Opt. Soc. Am.,* **46,** 987-993.

———. 1962: "A Stabilized Image Requiring no Attachments to the Eye," *Am. J. Psychol.,* **75,** 653-656.

Courant, R., and K. O. Friedrichs. 1948: *Supersonic Flow and Shock Waves,* New York, Interscience Publishers, Inc., Ltd.

Craik, K. J. W., and M. D. Vernon. 1941: "The Nature of Dark Adaptation. Part I. Evidence as to the Locus of the Process," *Brit. J. Psychol.,* **32,** 62-81.

Crawford, B. H. 1947: "Visual Adaptation in Relation to Brief Conditioning Stimuli," *Proc. Roy. Soc.* (London). B, **134,** 283-302.

Dallos, P. J., and R. W. Jones. 1963: "Learning Behavior of the Eye Fixation Control System," *IEEE Trans. on Automatic Control,* **AC-8,** 218-227.

Dessauer, J. H., G. R. Mott, and H. Bogdonoff. 1955: "Xerography Today," *Photographic Engineering,* **6,** 250-269.

DeValois, R. L., G. H. Jacobs, and I. Abramov. 1964: "Responses of Single Cells in Visual Systems to Shifts in the Wavelength of Light," *Science,* **146,** 1184-1186.

Dicke, R. H. 1959a: "Gravitation—An Enigma," *American Scientist,* **47,** 25-40.

———. 1959b: "New Research on Old Gravitation (Are the observed physical constants independent of the position, epoch, and velocity of the laboratory?)," *Science,* **129,** 621-625.

———. 1962: "The Earth and Cosmology," *Science,* **138,** 653-664.

———, and P. A. M. Dirac. 1961: "Dirac's Cosmology and Mach's Principle," *Nature,* **192,** 440-441.

Dingler, H. 1924: *Die Grundgedanken der Machschen Philosophie,* Leipzig, Johann Ambrosius Barth.

Ditchburn, R. W., D. H. Fender, and S. Mayne. 1959: "Vision with Controlled Movements of the Retinal Image," *J. Physiol.,* **145,** 98-108.

Ditchburn, R. W., and B. L. Ginsborg. 1952: "Vision with a Stabilized Retinal Image," *Nature,* **170,** 36.

Dodge, R. 1907: "An Experimental Study of Visual Fixation," *Psychol. Rev., Monogr. Suppl.,* **8,** 1-95.

Dodt, E., and E. Heerd. 1962: Mode of Action of Pineal Nerve Fibers in Frogs," *J. Neurophysiol.,* **25,** 405-429.

Duffieux, P. M. 1946: *L'integrale de Fourier et ses applications a l'optique,* Rennes, Société anonyme Oberthur.

Eccles, J. C. 1964: *The Physiology of Synapses,* New York, Academic Press, Berlin, Springer-Verlag.

Einstein, A. 1916: "Ernst Mach," *Physik. Z.* **17,** 101-104, Leipzig, S. Hirzel Verlag.

Einstein, A. 1951: "Autobiographical Notes," in *Albert Einstein: Philosopher-Scientist,* P. A. Schilpp, ed., New York, Tudor Publishing Company.

Ercoles, A. M. 1957: "Visione di campi con distribuzione complessa di luminanza," *Atti Fond. Giorgio Ronchi,* **XII**, 187.

Ercoles-Guzzoni, A. M., and A. Fiorentini. 1958: "Simultaneous Contrast Effect Produced by Non-Uniform Coloured Fields," *Atti Fond. Giorgio Ronchi,* **XIII**, 135-144.

Ercoles, A. M., and A. Fiorentini. 1959: "Visibility of the Mach Bands as a Function of Field Luminance," *Atti Fond. Giorgio Ronchi,* **XIV**, 230-235.

Fatehchand, R., G. Svaetichin, G. Mitarai, and J. Villegas. 1961: "Location of the Non-Linearity in Horizontal Cell Response to Retinal Illumination," *Nature,* **189**, 463-464.

Fechner, G. T. 1965: *Elements of Psychophysics,* E. G. Boring and D. H. Howes, eds., translated by H. Adler, New York, Holt, Rinehart & Winston.

Fender, D. H., and P. W. Nye. 1961: "An Investigation of the Mechanisms of Eye Movement Control," *Kybernetik,* **1**, 81-88.

Fiorentini, A. 1956: "Influence d'un gradient d'éclairement rétinien et de ses variations sur la sensation subjective de brilliance," in *Proc. Florence Meeting on Problems in Contemporary Optics,* Florence, Istituto Nazionale di Ottica.

———. 1957: "Foveal and Extrafoveal Contrast Threshold at a Point of a Non-Uniform Field," *Atti Fond. Giorgio Ronchi,* **XII**, 180-186.

———. 1958: "Effet de contraste dans la vision d'un champ avec un bord flou fixé ou mobile," *Optica Acta,* **5**, 71-76.

———. 1961: *Progress in Optics,* E. Wolf, ed., Amsterdam, North-Holland Publishing Company.

———, and A. M. Ercoles. 1957: "Vision of Oscillating Non-uniform Fields," *Optica Acta,* **4**, 150-157.

———, M. Jeanne, and G. Toraldo di Francia. 1955a: "Measurements of differential threshold in the presence of spatial illumination gradient," *Atti Fond. Giorgio Ronchi,* **X**, 371-379.

———, M. Jeanne, and G. Toraldo di Francia. 1955b: "Mesures photometriques visuelles sur un champ a gradient d'eclairement variable," *Optica Acta,* **1**, 192-193.

———, and T. Radici. 1957: Binocular Measurements of Brightness on a Field Presenting a Luminance Gradient," *Atti Fond. Giorgio Ronchi,* **XII**, 453-461.

———, and T. Radici. 1958: "Brightness, Width and Position of Mach Bands as a Function of the Rate of Variation of the Luminance Gradient," *Atti Fond. Giorgio Ronchi,* **XIII,** 145-155.

Florey, E., ed. 1961: *Nervous Inhibition,* Proceedings of an International Symposium, New York, Pergamon Press.

Fomm, L. 1896: "The Wavelength of Roentgen-rays," *Annalen der Physik,* **59,** 350-353.

Frank, P. 1949: *Modern Science and Its Philosophy,* Cambridge, Mass., Harvard Univ. Press.

———. 1951: "Einstein, Mach, and Logical Positivism," in *Albert Einstein: Philosopher-Scientist,* P. A. Schilpp, ed., New York, Tudor Publishing Company.

Fry, G. A. 1948: "Mechanisms Subserving Simultaneous Brightness Contrast," *Am. J. Optom. and Arch. Am. Acad. Optom.,* **25,** 162-178.

———. 1963: "Retinal Image Formation: Review, Summary and Discussion," *J. Opt. Soc. Am.,* **53,** 94-97.

Fuortes, M. G. F. 1959: "Initiation of Impulses in Visual Cells of *Limulus,*" *J. Physiol.,* **148,** 14-28.

Galambos, R., and H. Davis. 1944: "Inhibition of Activity in Single Auditory Nerve Fibers by Acoustic Stimulation," *J. Neurophysiol.,* **7,** 287-304.

Gouras, P. 1960: "Graded Potentials of Bream Retina," *J. Physiol.,* **152,** 487-505.

Granit, R. 1933: "The Components of the Retinal Action Potential and their Relation to the Discharge in the Optic Nerve," *J. Physiol.,* **77,** 207-240.

———. 1946: "The Distribution of Excitation and Inhibition in Single-Fiber Responses from a Polarized Retina," *J. Physiol.,* **105,** 45-53.

———. 1947: *Sensory Mechanisms of the Retina,* London, Oxford University Press.

———. 1948: "The Off/On Ratio of the Isolated On-Off Elements in the Mammalian Eye," *Brit. J. of Ophthal.,* **32,** 550.

———. 1955: *Receptors and Sensory Perception,* New Haven, Yale University Press.

———, J. E. Pascoe, and G. Steg. 1957: "The Behavior of Tonic α and γ Motoneurones During Stimulation of Recurrent Collaterals," *J. Physiol.,* **138,** 381-400.

———, and P. O. Therman. 1935: "Excitation and Inhibition in the Retina and in the Optic Nerve," *J. Physiol.,* **83,** 359-381.

Greene, P. H. 1957: "Factors in Visual Acuity: I. Neural Inhibition and the Visual Perception of Contours," *Bull. Math. Biophys.,* **19,** 147-156.

Grüsser–Cornehls, U., O. J. Grüsser, T. H. Bullock. 1963: "Unit Responses in the Frog's Tectum to Moving and Nonmoving Visual Stimuli," *Science,* **141,** 820-822.

Guilford, J. P. 1936: *Psychometric Methods,* New York and London, McGraw-Hill Book Company, Inc.

Haga, H., and C. H. Wind. 1889: "Beugung der Röntgenstrahlen," *Wiedemann's Annalen,* **68,** 866.

———. 1899: "Die Beugung der Röntgenstrahlen," *Ann. Physik und Chem.,* **68,** 884-895.

Hake, H. W., and E. Averbach. 1956: "Spatial Effects in Foveal Brightness Discrimination," *J. Opt. Soc. Am.,* **46,** 274-277.

Harmon, L. D. 1962: "Neural Analogs," *Spring Joint Computer Conference,* San Francisco, Proceedings, **21,** 153-158 (The National Press, Palo Alto, Calif.).

———. 1964: "Neuromimes: Action of a Reciprocally Inhibitory Pair," *Science,* **146,** 1323-1325.

Hartline, H. K. 1938a: "The Discharge of Impulses in the Optic Nerve of Pecten in Response to Illumination of the Eye," *J. Cellular Comp. Physiol.,* **11,** 465-478.

———. 1938b: "The Response of Single Optic Nerve Fibers of the Vertebrate Eye to Illumination of the Retina," *Am. J. Physiol.,* **121,** 400-415.

———. 1939: "Excitation and Inhibition of the "Off" Response in Vertebrate Optic Nerve Fibers," *Proc. Am. Physiol. Soc., Am. J. Physiol.,* **126,** 527.

———. 1940: "The Receptive Fields of Optic Nerve Fibers," *Am. J. Physiol.,* **130,** 690-699.

———. 1941-1942: "The Neural Mechanisms of Vision," *The Harvey Lectures,* XXXVII, 39-68.

———. 1949: "Inhibition of Activity of Visual Receptors by Illuminating Nearby Retinal Elements in the *Limulus* Eye." *Fed. Proc.,* **8,** 69.

———, and C. H. Graham. 1932: "Nerve Impulses from Single Receptors in the Eye," *J. Cellular and Comp. Physiol.,* **1,** 277-295.

———, and F. Ratliff. 1954: "Spatial Summation of Inhibitory Influences in the Eye of *Limulus,*" *Science,* **120,** 781.

———, and F. Ratliff. 1957: "Inhibitory Interaction of Receptor Units in the Eye of *Limulus,*" *J. Genl. Physiol.,* **40,** 357-376.

———, and F. Ratliff. 1958: "Spatial Summation of Inhibitory Influences in the Eye of *Limulus,* and the Mutual Interaction of Receptor Units," *J. Genl. Physiol.,* **41,** 1049-1066.

———, F. Ratliff, and W. H. Miller. 1961: "Inhibitory Interaction in the Retina and Its Significance in Vision," in *Nervous Inhibition,* E. Florey, ed., New York, Pergamon Press, 241-284.

———, H. G. Wagner, and E. F. MacNichol, Jr. 1952: "The Peripheral Origin of Nervous Activity in the Visual System," *Cold Spring Harbor Symposia on Quantitative Biology,* **17,** 125-141.

———, H. G. Wagner, and F. Ratliff. 1956: "Inhibition in the Eye of *Limulus,*" *J. Genl. Physiol.,* **39,** 651-673.

Hartmann, J. 1891: "Die Vergrösserung des Erdschattens bei Mondfinsternissen," *Abhandlungen der Mathematisch-Physikalischen Classe der Königlich Sächsischen Gesellschaft der Wissenschaften,"* **XVII,** 363-553.

Hartwig, E. 1958: "Modelluntersuchungen zur quantitativen Erfassung von physiologischen Kontrastfehlern," *Optik,* **15,** 414-421.

Heinemann, E. G. 1955: "Simultaneous Brightness Induction as a Function of Inducing and Test-field Luminances," *J. Exp. Psychol.* **50,** 89-96.

Helmholtz, H. von. 1962: *Helmholtz's Treatise on Physiological Optics,* James P. C. Southall, ed., New York, Dover Publications (translated from the third German edition of *Handbuch der Physiologischen Optik*).

Henning, H. 1915: *Ernst Mach als Philosoph, Physiker und Psycholog,* Leipzig, Johann Ambrosius Barth.

Hering, E. 1964: *Outlines of a Theory of the Light Sense,* translated by Leo M. Hurvich and Dorothea Jameson, Cambridge, Mass., Harvard University Press.

Herneck, Friedrich. 1956/1957: "Über eine unveröffentliche Selbstbiographie Ernst Machs," *Wissenschaftliche Zeitschrift der Humboldt Universität Berlin, mathematisch-naturwissenschaftliche Reihe,* **6,** 209-220.

Hiwatashi, K., A. Watanabe, T. Mori, and S. Nagata. 1964: "Spatial Sinewave Response Function in the Human Vision," *Technical Journal of Japan Broadcasting Corporation,* **16,** 38-60.

Homer, W. I. 1964: *Seurat and the Science of Painting,* Cambridge, Mass., M.I.T. Press.

Hubel, D. H., and T. N. Wiesel. 1959: "Receptive Fields of Single Neurons in the Cat's Striate Cortex," *J. Physiol.,* **148,** 574-591.

———. 1962: "Receptive Fields, Binocular Interaction and Functional Architecture in the Cat's Visual Cortex," *J. Physiol.,* **160,** 106-154.

Huggins, W. H., and J. C. R. Licklider. 1951: "Place Mechanisms of Auditory Frequency Analysis," *J. Acoust. Soc. Am.,* **23,** 290-299.

Hurvich, L. M., and D. Jameson. 1960: "Perceived Color, Induction Effects, and Opponent-Response Mechanisms," *J. Genl. Physiol.,* **43,** 63-80.

Jennison, R. C. 1961: *Fourier Transforms and Convolutions for the Experimentalist,* New York, Pergamon Press.

Jung, R. 1961: "Korrelationen von Neuronentätigkeit und Sehen," in *Neurophysiologie und Psychophysik des visuellen Systems,* R. Jung and H. Kornhuber, eds., Berlin, Springer-Verlag, 410-434.

Katsuki, Y., T. Watanabe, and N. Suga. 1959: "Interaction of Auditory Neurons in Response to Two Sound Stimuli in Cat," *J. Neurophysiol.,* **22,** 603-624.

Kirschfeld, K., and W. Reichardt. 1964: "Die Verarbeitung stationärer optischer Nachrichten im Komplexauge von Limulus," *Kybernetik,* **2,** 43-61.

Koffka, K., and M. R. Harrower. 1931: "Colour and Organization, Part I." *Psychologische Forschung,* **15,** 146-192.

Krauskopf, J. 1957: "Effect of Retinal Motion on Contrast Thresholds for Maintained Vision," *J. Opt. Soc. Am.,* **47,** 740-744.

———. 1962: "Light Distribution in Human Retinal Images," *J. Opt. Soc. Am.,* **52,** 1046-1050.

Kuffler, S. W. 1953: "Discharge Patterns and Functional Organization of Mammalian Retina," *J. Neurophysiol.,* **16,** 37-68.

Kühl, A. 1928: "Über den Einfluss des Grenzkontrastes auf Präzisionsmessungen," *Physik. Zeit.,* **29,** 1-34.

———. 1951: "Die Fortschritte der photographischen Optik vor der Kritik des Auges," *Feinwerktechnik,* **55,** 1-7.

Lange, G. D. 1965: *Dynamics of Inhibitory Interactions in the Eye of Limulus: Experimental and Theoretical Studies,* thesis, Rockefeller Institute.

LeGrand, Y. 1957: *Light, Colour, and Vision,* New York, John Wiley and Sons, Inc.

Lenin, V. I. 1927: *Materialism and Empirio-Criticism,* New York, International Publishers. (First Russian edition, 1909.)

Lettvin, J. Y., H. R. Maturana, W. S. McCulloch, and W. H. Pitts. 1959: "What the Frog's Eye Tells the Frog's Brain," *Proc. IRE,* **47,** 1940-1951.

Lipetz, L. E. 1961: "A Mechanism of Light Adaptation," *Science,* **133,** 639-640.

———. 1962: "A Neural Mechanism of the Purkinje Shift," *Am. J. Optom-Arch. Am. Acad. Optom.,* **299,** 1-8.

Lovejoy, A. O. 1930: *The Revolt Against Dualism,* LaSalle, Ill., The Open Court Publishing Company. (Second Edition 1960.)

Lowry, E. M., and J. J. DePalma. 1961: "Sine-Wave Response of the Visual System, I. The Mach Phenomenon," *J. Opt. Soc. Am.,* **51,** 740-746.

Ludvigh, E. 1953a: "The Perception of Contour. I. Introduction." *Joint Project Report Number 4,* U.S. Naval School of Aviation Medicine, Pensacola, Fla.

———. 1953b: "The Perception of Contour. II. Effect of Rate of Change of Retinal Intensity Gradient." *Joint Project Report Number 5,* U.S. Naval School of Aviation Medicine, Pensacola, Fla.

Mach, E. 1865: "Über die Wirkung der räumlichen Vertheilung des Lichtreizes auf die Netzhaut, I," *Sitzungsberichte der mathematisch-naturwissenschaftlichen Classe der kaiserlichen Akademie der Wissenschaften,* **52,** 303-322.

———. 1866: "Über den physiologischen Effect räumlich vertheilter Lichtreize, II," *Sitzungsberichte der mathematisch-naturwissenschaftlichen Classe der kaiserlichen Akademie der Wissenschaften,* **54,** 131-144.

———. 1866: "Über die physiologische Wirkung räumlich vertheilter Lichtreize, III," *Sitzungsberichte der mathematisch-naturwissenschaftlichen Classe der kaiserlichen Akademie der Wissenschaften,* **54,** 393-408.

———. 1868: "Über die physiologische Wirkung räumlich vertheilter Lichtreize, IV," *Sitzungsberichte der mathematisch-naturwissenschaftlichen Classe der kaiserlichen Akademie der Wissenschaften,* **57,** 11-19.

———. 1868: "Über die Abhängigkeit der Netzhautstellen von einander," *Vierteljahresschrift für Psychiatrie in ihren Beziehungen zur Morphologie und Pathologie des Centralen Nervensystems,* **2,** 38-51.

———. 1872: *Die Geschichte und die Wurzel des Satzes von der Erhaltung der Arbeit,* Prague, J. A. Barth Verlag.

———. 1875: *Grundlinien der Lehre von den Bewegungsempfindungen,* Leipzig, Wilhelm Engelmann.

———. 1882: "Über Herrn Guebhards Darstellung der Aequipotentialkurven," *Wiedemann's Annalen,* **XVII,** 864.

———. 1890: "The Analysis of the Sensations," *The Monist,* **1,** 48-68.

———. 1896a: *Die Principien der Wärmelehre,* Leipzig, Johann Ambrosius Barth Verlag.

———. 1896b: "On the stereoscopic application of Roentgen rays," *The Monist,* **VI,** 321-323.

———. 1897: *Contributions to the Analysis of Sensations,* C. M. Williams, trans., Chicago, The Open Court Publishing Company, 98-99.

———. 1905: *Erkenntnis und Irrtum. Skizzen zur Psychologie der Forschung,* Leipzig, J. A. Barth.

———. 1906: "Über den Einfluss räumlich und zeitlich variirender Lichtreize auf die Gesichtswahrnehmung," *Sitzungsberichte der mathematisch-naturwissenschaftlichen Classe der kaiserlichen Akademie der Wissenschaften,* **115,** 633-648.

———. 1910a: "Die Leitgedanken meiner naturwissenschaftlichen Erkenntnislehre und ihre Aufnahme durch die Zeitgenossen," *Scientia,* **VII,** 225-240.

———. 1910b: *Popular Scientific Lectures,* T. J. McCormack, trans., Chicago, The Open Court Publishing Company.

———. 1911: *History and Root of the Principle of the Conservation of Energy,* P. E. B. Jourdain, trans., Chicago, The Open Court Publishing Company.

———. 1914: *The Analysis of Sensation and the Relation of the Physical to the Psychical,* C. M. Williams, trans., revised by Sidney Waterlow, Chicago and London, The Open Court Publishing Company.

———. 1915: *Kultur und Mechanik,* Stuttgart, W. Spemann Verlag.

———. 1926: *The Principles of Physical Optics* (Originally published 1921, Leipzig, Johann Ambrosius Barth), John S. Anderson and A. F. A. Young, trans., London, Methuen & Co., Ltd., (See also Dover Publications, Inc., 1953.)

———. 1942: *The Science of Mechanics,* T. J. McCormack, trans., La Salle, Illinois and London, The Open Court Publishing Company, 5th ed. See also 6th edition, 1960, with new introduction by Karl Menger.

———, and L. Mach. 1889: "Weitere ballistisch-photographische Versuche," *Sitzungsberichte der mathematisch-naturwissenschaftlichen Classe der kaiserlichen Akademie der Wissenschaften,* V. **XCVIII,** part II, 1-7.

Mackavey, W. R., S. H. Bartley, and C. Casella. 1962: "Disinhibition in the Human Visual System," *J. Opt. Soc. Am.,* **52,** 85-88.

MacLeod, R. B. 1947: "The Effect of 'Artificial Penumbrae' on the Brightness of Included Areas," in *Miscellanea psychologica Albert Michotte,* Paris, Librairie philosophique, 138-154.

MacNichol, E. F., Jr. 1956: "Visual Receptors as Biological Transducers"; in Molecular Structure and Functional Activity of Nerve Cells, *Publ. No. 1 Am. Inst. Biol. Sci.,* 34-53.

———, and R. Benolken, 1956: "Blocking Effect of Ethyl Alcohol on Inhibitory Synapses in the Eye of *Limulus,*" *Science,* **124,** 681-682.

———, and H. K. Hartline. 1948: "Responses to Small Changes of Light Intensity by the Light-adapted Photoreceptor," *Fed. Proc.,* **7,** 76.

———, and W. E. Love. 1960: "Electrical Responses of the Retinal Nerve and Optic Ganglion of the Squid," *Science,* **132,** 737-738.

———, L. Macpherson, and G. Svaetichin. 1957: "Studies on Spectral Response Curves from the Fish Retina," *Paper 39, Symposium on Visual Problems of Colour,* Teddington, Middlesex, England, National Physical Laboratory.

———, and G. Svaetichin. 1958: "Electric Responses from the Isolated Retinas of Fishes," *Am. J. Ophthal.* **46,** 26-40.

Marimont, R. B. 1963: "Linearity and the Mach Phenomenon," *J. Opt. Soc. Am.,* **53,** 400-401.

Maturana, H. R., and S. Frenk. 1963: "Directional Movement and Horizontal Edge Detectors in the Pigeon Retina," *Science,* **142,** 977-979.

McCollough, C. 1955: "The Variation in Width and Position of Mach Bands as a Function of Luminance," *J. Exp. Psychol.,* **49,** 141-152.

McDougall, W. 1903: "Intensification of Visual Sensation by Smoothly Graded Contrast," *Proc. Physiol. Soc.,* **1,** 19-21.

Mees, C. E. 1954: *The Theory of the Photographic Process,* New York, The Macmillan Company.

Melzak, Z. A. 1962: "On a Uniqueness Theorem and Its Application to a Neurophysiological Control Mechanism, *Information and Control,* **5,** 163-172.

Menzel, E. 1959: "Der Gesichtssinn als linearer Übertragungskanal und die Machschen Streifen," *Die Naturwissenschaften,* **46,** 316-317.

Miller, W. H. 1957: "Morphology of the Ommatidia of the Compound Eye of *Limulus,*" *J. Biophys. Biochem. Cytol.,* **3,** 421-428.

———. 1958: "Derivatives of Cilia in the Distal Sense Cells of the Retina of *Pecten,*" *J. Biophys. Biochem. Cytol.,* **4,** 227-228.

———, and M. L. Wolbarsht. 1962: "Neural Activity in the Parietal Eye of a Lizard," *Science,* **135,** 316-317.

Mises, R. von. 1956: *Positivism, A Study In Human Understanding,* New York, George Braziller, Inc.

Mitarai, G. 1958: "The Origin of the So-called Cone Potential," *Proc. Japanese Acad.,* **34,** 299.

———. 1960: "Determination of Ultramicroelectrode Tip Position in the Retina in Relation to S-Potential," *J. Genl. Physiol.,* **43,** 95-99.

Motokawa, K., T. Oikawa, K. Tasaki, and T. Ogawa. 1959: "The Spatial Distribution of Electric Responses to Focal Illumination of the Carp's Retina," *Tohoku J. Exp. Med.,* **70,** 151-164.

———, E. Yamashita, and T. Ogawa. 1961: "The Physiological Basis of Simultaneous Contrast in the Retina," in *The Visual System: Neurophysiology and Psychophysics,* R. Jung and H. Kornhuber, eds., Berlin, Springer Verlag, 32-43.

Mountcastle, V. B., and P. S. Powell. 1959: "Neural Mechanisms subserving Cutaneous Sensibility, with Special Reference to the Role of Afferent Inhibition in Sensory Perception and Discrimination," *Bull. Johns Hopkins Hosp.,* **105,** 201-232.

Naka, K., S. Inoma, Y. Kosugi, and S. Tong. 1960: "Recording of Action Potentials from the Single Cells in the Frog Retina," *Japanese J. Physiol.,* **4,** 436.

O'Brien, V. 1958: "Contour Perception, Illusion and Reality," *J. Opt. Soc. Am.,* **48,** 112-119.

Oikawa, I., T. Ogawa, and K. Motokawa. 1959: "Origin of So-called Cone Action Potential," *J. Neurophysiol.,* **22,** 102-112.

Oomura, Y., and H. A. Kuriyama. 1952/53: "On the Action of the Optic Lobe of *Limulus Longspina,*" *Japanese J. Physiol.,* **3,** 165-169.

Ooue, S. 1959: "Response Function of the Eye," *Journal of Applied Physics,* Japan, **28,** 531-534.

Planck, M. 1909: *Die Einheit des physikalischen Weltbildes,* Leipzig, S. Hirzel Verlag. (English translation in *A Survey of Physical Theory,* M. Planck, ed., New York, Dover Publications, 1960.)

Polyak, S. 1941: *The Retina,* Chicago, University of Chicago Press.

Popper, K. R. 1953: "A Note on Berkeley as Precursor of Mach," *Brit. J. Philosoph. Sci.,* **4,** 26-36.

Purple, R. L. 1964: *The Integration of Excitatory and Inhibitory Influences in the Eccentric Cell of the Eye of Limulus,* thesis, The Rockefeller Institute.

Raab, D. H. 1963: "Backward Masking," *Psychol. Bull.,* **60,** 118-129.

Ratliff, F. 1958: "A Stationary Retinal Image Requiring no Attachments to the Eye," *J. Opt. Soc. Am.,* **48,** 274-275.

———. 1961: "Inhibitory Interaction and the Detection and Enhancement of Contours," in *Sensory Communication,* W. A. Rosenblith, ed., Cambridge, Mass., M.I.T. Press, and New York, John Wiley & Sons, 183-203.

———. 1962: "Some Interrelations Among Physics, Physiology, and Psychology in the Study of Vision," in *Psychology: A Study of a Science,* S. Koch, ed., New York, McGraw-Hill, 417-482.

———, and D. S. Blough. 1954: "Behavioral Studies of Visual Processes in The Pigeon," *USN;ONR, Technical Report,* (Contract N5 ori-07663, Project NR 140-072).

———, and H. K. Hartline. 1956: "Inhibitory Interaction in the Eye of *Limulus*," *Fed. Proc.*, **15** (Abstract).

———, and H. K. Hartline. 1959: "The Response of *Limulus* Optic Nerve Fibers to Patterns of Illumination on the Receptor Mosaic," *J. Genl. Physiol.*, **42**, 1241-1255.

———, H. K. Hartline, and W. H. Miller. 1963: "Spatial and Temporal Aspects of Retinal Inhibitory Interaction," *J. Opt. Soc. Am.*, **53**, 110-120.

———, W. H. Miller, and H. K. Hartline. 1958: "Neural interaction in the eye and the integration of receptor activity," *Annals of the New York Academy of Sciences*, **74**, 210-222.

———, and C. G. Mueller. 1957: "Synthesis of 'On-Off' and 'Off' Responses in a Visual-Neural System," *Science*, **126**, 840-841.

———, and L. A. Riggs. 1950: "Involuntary Motions of the Eye During Monocular Fixation," *J. Exp. Psychol.*, **40**, 687-701.

Reichardt, W. 1961: "Über das optische Auflösungsvermögen der Facettenaugen von Limulus," *Kybernetik*, **1**, 57-69.

———. 1962: "Nervous Integration in the Facet Eye," *Biophys. J.*, **2**, 121-144.

———, and G. MacGinitie. 1962: "Zur Theorie der lateralen Inhibition," *Kybernetik*, **1**, 155-165.

Reiss, R. F. 1962: "A Theory and Simulation of Rhythmic Behavior Due to Reciprocal Inhibition in Small Nerve Nets," *Spring Joint Computer Conference*, San Francisco, Proceedings, **21**, 171-194 (The National Press, Palo Alto, Calif.).

Rewald, J. 1954: *Seurat* (1859-1891), Paris, Braun et Cie.

Riggs, L. A., J. C. Armington, and F. Ratliff. 1954: "Motions of the Retinal Image During Fixation," *J. Opt. Soc. Am.*, **44**, 315-321.

———, F. Ratliff, J. C. Cornsweet, and T. N. Cornsweet. 1953: "The Disappearance of Steadily Fixated Test Objects," *J. Opt. Soc. Am.*, **43**, 495-501.

———, F. Ratliff, and U. T. Keesey. 1961: "Appearance of Mach Bands with a Motionless Retinal Image," *J. Opt. Soc. Am.*, **51**, 702-703.

Ronchi, L., and G. Toraldo di Francia. 1957: "On the Response of the Human Eye to Light Stimuli Presenting a Spatial or Temporal Gradient of Luminance," *J. Opt. Soc. Am.*, **47**, 639-642.

Rose, A., P. K. Weimer, and H. B. Law. 1946: "The Image Orthicon, A Sensitive Television Pickup Tube," *Proc. IRE*, **34**, 424.

Schade, O. H. 1956: "Optical and Photoelectric Analog of the Eye," *J. Opt. Soc. Am.*, **46**, 721-739.

Sciama, D. W. 1959: *The Unity of the Universe,* New York, Doubleday & Co., Inc.

Seeliger, H. 1899: "Die scheinbare Vergrösserung des Erdschattens bei Mondfinsternissen," *Abhandlungen der mathematisch-physikalischen Classe der königlich bayerischen Akademie der Wissenschaften,* **19,** 385-499.

Sherrington, C. S. 1897: "On Reciprocal Action in the Retina as Studied by Means of Some Rotating Discs," *J. Physiol.,* **21,** 33-54.

Stevens, C. F. 1964: *A Quantitative Theory of Neural Interactions: Theoretical and Experimental Investigations,* thesis, The Rockefeller Institute.

Svaetichin, G. 1953: "The Cone Action Potential," *Acta physiol. scand.,* **29,** Suppl. 106, 565-600.

———. 1956: "Spectral Response Curves from Single Cones," *Acta physiol. scand.,* **39,** Suppl. 134, 17-46.

Taylor, W. K. 1956: "Electrical Simulation of Some Nervous System Functional Activities," in *Information Theory,* Colin Cherry, ed., New York, Academic Press.

———. 1958: "Visual Organization," *Nature,* **182,** 29-31.

Thouless, R. H. 1922-3: "Some Observations on Contrast Effects in Graded Discs," *Brit. J. Psychol.,* **13,** 301-307.

Tomita, T. 1957: "A Study on the Origin of Intra-Retinal Action Potential of the Cyprinid Fish by Means of Pencil-type Microelectrodes," *Japanese J. Physiol.,* **7,** 80-85.

———. 1958: "Mechanism of Lateral Inhibition in the Eye of *Limulus,*" *J. Neurophysiol.,* **21,** 419-429.

———. 1963: "Electrical Activity in the Vertebrate Retina," *J. Opt. Soc. Am.,* **53,** 49-57.

———, M. Murakami, Y. Sato, and Y. Hashimoto. 1959: "Further Study on the Origin of the So-called Cone Action Potential (S-potential). Its Histological Determination," *Japanese J. Physiol.,* **9,** 63-68.

———, M. Murakami, Y. Hashimoto, and Y. Sasaki. 1961: "Electrical Activity of Single Neurons in the Frog's Retina," in *The Visual System: Neurophysiology and Psychophysics,* R. Jung and H. Kornhuber, eds., Berlin, Springer-Verlag, 24-30.

Varju, D. 1962: "Vergleich zweier Modelle für laterale Inhibition," *Kybernetik,* **1,** 200-208.

Verheijen, F. J. 1961: "A Simple After Image Method Demonstrating the Involuntary Multi-directional Eye Movements during Fixation," *Optica Acta,* **8,** 309-311.

———. 1963: "Apparent Relative Movement of 'Unsharp' and 'Sharp' Visual Patterns," *Nature,* **199,** 160-161.

Wagner, H. G., E. F. MacNichol, Jr., and M. L. Wolbarsht. 1960: "The Response Properties of Single Ganglion Cells in the Goldfish Retina," *J. Genl. Physiol.,* **43,** 45-62.

———, E. F. MacNichol, Jr., and M. L. Wolbarsht. 1963: "Functional Basis for 'On'-Center and 'Off'-Center Receptive Fields in the Retina," *J. Opt. Soc. Am.,* **53,** 66-70.

Waterman, T. H. 1954: "Directional Sensitivity of Single Ommatidia in the Compound Eye of *Limulus,*" *Proc. Nat. Acad. Sci.,* **40,** 252-257.

———, and C. A. G. Wiersma. 1954: "The Functional Relation between Retinal Cells and Optic Nerve in *Limulus,*" *J. Exp. Zoology,* **126,** 59-86.

Watrasiewicz, B. M. 1963: "Measurements of the Mach Effect in Microscopy," *Optica Acta,* **10,** 209-216.

Westheimer, G. 1963: "Optical and Motor Factors in the Formation of the Retinal Image," *J. Opt. Soc. Am.,* **53,** 86-93.

———, and F. W. Campbell. 1962: "Light Distribution in the Image Formed by the Living Human Eye," *J. Opt. Soc. Am.,* **52,** 1040-1045.

Whittaker, E. T. 1899: "Report on the Progress of the Solution of the Problem of Three Bodies," *Brit. Ass. Rep.,* p. 121.

———. 1959: *A Treatise on the Analytical Dynamics of Particles and Rigid Bodies,* Cambridge University Press.

Wiesel, T. N. 1959: "Recording Inhibition and Excitation in the Cat's Retinal Ganglion Cells with Intracellular Electrodes," *Nature,* **183,** 264-265.

Willmer, E. N. 1950: Interaction Between Lights of Different Wavelengths in the Central Fovea, *J. Physiol.,* **111,** 69-80.

———. 1955: "A Physiological Basis for Human Colour Vision in the Central Fovea," *Doc. Ophthal.,* **9,** 235-313.

Wilska, A., and H. K. Hartline. 1941: "The Origin of 'Off-Responses' in the Optic Pathway," *Am. J. Physiol.,* **133,** 491.

Wilson, V. J., and P. R. Burgess. 1961: "Changes in the Membrane During Recurrent Disinhibition of Spinal Motoneurons," *Nature,* **191,** 918-919.

Wilson, V. J., F. P. Diecke, and W. H. Talbot. 1960: "Action of Tetanus Toxin on Conditioning of Spinal Motoneurons," *J. Neurophysiol.,* **23,** 659-666.

Wind, C. H. 1899-1900: "Zur Demonstration einer von E. Mach entdeckten optischen Täuschung," *Physik. Zeit.,* **1,** 112-113.

Wittgenstein, L. 1922: *Tractatus Logico-Philosophicus,* London, Kegan Paul, Trench, Trubner & Co.

Zworykin, V. K., G. A. Morton, and L. E. Flory. 1937: "Theory and Performance of the Iconoscope," *Proceedings of the Institute of Radio Engineers,* **25**, 1071-1092.

———, and E. G. Ramberg. 1949: *Photoelectricity,* New York, John Wiley & Sons, and London, Chapman & Hall, Ltd.

Name Index

Subject Index

This book is set entirely in Baskerville, with Baskerville bold, using Linotype and Monotype fonts in various sizes. The book was designed by Jean Swift, and the composition was done by Colonial Press. It was printed by Halliday Lithograph Corporation on Warren's Patina. It was bound by Colonial Press.